Contents

Join the conversation

- openhouselondon
- #openhouselondon, @openhouselondon
- openhouselondon

Revealing...
London's changing shape

Welcome to the 2015 edition of London's greatest showcase of architecture, engineering and landscape design.

London faces many challenges in the coming years, including the increasing demand for housing, the pressure on our green and open spaces, and the need for more transport infrastructure. The city is expanding into previously underused areas, increasing density in others, and creating whole new residential and business districts. To make these places sustainable and liveable means that we need high-quality design more than ever before.

Open House London is your chance to discover and explore the inspiring schemes that today's architects, engineers and landscape designers are producing to respond to these challenges.

Open House London is just one part of the work of Open-City in championing the value of well-designed places and spaces in making a liveable and vibrant city, and the role everyone plays within it. Overleaf you can find out more about what we develop and deliver as London's leading architecture education charity.

This year, as every year, we invite everyone to explore and understand the value of a well-designed built environment over 48 hours in September.

Be inspired and tell us about your Open House London this year by joining us on Facebook, Twitter and Instagram.
#openhouselondon

Victoria Thornton OBE HonFRIBA
Founding Director, Open-City

Open-City is a registered charity no. 1072104

KU-246-553

Five things you might not know about

① ②

Open House London, London's largest festival of architecture and urban design, is just one part of the year-round work of Open-City. This charity was set up 23 years ago with a passion to open eyes and minds to the power of good design.

People of all ages and backgrounds want to influence the shape of their neighbourhoods. We provide training opportunities for communities and local decision-makers to advocate for good design throughout the city. We offer opportunities to share knowledge and skills, and platforms for debate on all issues green. We also encourage people to discover how their city is designed and built every year through Open House London and our regular architecture tours.

We have found that the best way to nurture enthusiasm and launch a journey of discovery into architecture is to work with children and young people through challenging building explorations and creative workshops.

With our professional partners, we also provide role models, practical support and hands-on experience to enable young people to develop the inspiration and confidence to enter the built environment professions.
Find out more at **open-city.org.uk**.
Follow us **@opencityorg**

We champion the value of design in making a liveable and vibrant city, and the role that everyone plays within it.

The quality of our urban environment is essential to the success of our society, culture, health and wellbeing ... but we never learn about it formally.

"How would I describe Open-City? In one word: inspirational."
Norman Foster, Lord Foster of Thames Bank, Chairman, Foster and Partners

We are at the centre of creating better places for people.

We don't just argue the case for design. We enable thousands of people of all ages to develop the skills and confidence to do this themselves.

"Open-City's bespoke training with easy tools and materials makes learning fun, and its ability to allow people to take ownership is outstanding."
Theresa Coyle MBE, CEO of Finsbury Park Community Hub

Sculpture in the City Education Programme

Advocacy and Enabling Programme

Open–City...

③

④

⑤

We inspire young people to have their say about their city.

It proves that when young people take the lead in improving the built environment, their peers will be inspired to do so too.

"Getting young people enthused in terms of long-term planning in their area is crucial to their communities."
Stephen Kelly, Assistant Director Planning, London Borough of Haringey

We foster civic pride, ownership of and interest in local places.

Providing free and open access enables everyone to challenge existing ideas about the city, and raises expectations of what is possible.

"I take infrastructure for granted; it's not until I stop and look during Open House London that the real quality and utility become obvious."
Open House London visitor

We are committed to showing how London can become a greener and healthier city.

Our programme of innovative green design and associated public debates asks how we can improve London's environment.

"Open-City's programmes are really important industry events that help put sustainability topics firmly on the agenda of professionals and the wider community."
Lesley Treacy, Greengage Environmental LLP

My City Too! Youth Participation

Open House London Weekend

Green Sky Thinking Week

The Shape of Future London:
Join the Debate

#myfutureLDN

London is undergoing a scale and speed of change that have never been seen before in its history. Major redevelopment, regeneration and infrastructure projects are needed to provide for the expected boom in the capital's population by 2050.

Demand for public transport is forecast to increase by 50 per cent, and that for electricity supplies is set to more than double. To meet the demand for housing around 42,000 new homes a year must be provided.

Demand for water is expected to exceed supply by 10% in 2025, rising to 21% by 2040. The prospects for transport are similar, with a 50% increase in public transport capacity required by 2050 to keep the city moving.

What will our future city look and feel like? How will the future shape of London respond to and reflect these challenges, and how do we ensure that good design remains at the top of the citymaking agenda?

THE SHAPE OF YOUR FUTURE LONDON

Finding out what Londoners think about their city has always been one of Open-City's priorities.

We give a voice to your opinions and ideas by carrying out and publishing regular polls, surveys and research into the major issues that affect London's built environment, such as sustainability, housing design and the use of public space.

This year we want to hear what you think is important for the future shape of London, and also your views on the buildings and spaces in your local area. In the run-up to London's mayoral elections in 2016, we will use your answers to our online survey at **open-city.org. uk/futurelondon** to question candidates on how they will help to make a better London for everyone.

Here's a snapshot of your views so far:

HOUSING

What is the most important factor to you for the design of new *housing* in your local area?

"That it fits in with the environment and is a practical building to use and not be just a small box that looks fancy."

"That it involves as much light and green as possible. This leads to people feeling inspired, refreshed and relaxed which is important in the busy pace of London."

HIGH STREETS

Do you think the design of your local *high street* can be improved?

"Wider pavements, more road crossing points, frequent cycle stands and co-ordinated street furniture are all important."

"High streets need a cohesive 'look' rather than often a random collection of mismatching shop fronts or buildings without a sense of community space."

INFRASTRUCTURE

What developments/initiatives do you see as preventing London's transport *infrastructure* from grinding to a halt?

"Only when new urban developments (mixed use) are totally planned around transport infrastructure and sprawl and car use are prevented will London develop properly!"

GREEN LIVING

Research indicates that people act in more *environmentally friendly* ways at home than in the workplace. Do you agree?

"It's all about being responsible for your actions. The office offers a non-personal environment where no one is responsible."

"The way the majority of people still have to commute and work in large buildings which are ever more energy intensive (both in construction and use) all militate against them being able to work in more sustainable ways."

Tell us what you think about the buildings and spaces in your local area. What should the priorities be for the future shape of your capital?

Join the debate now at open-city.org.uk/ futurelondon

#myfutureLDN

Support Open-City

Each year thousands of people, like yourselves, are given the opportunity to learn about their built environment through participating in Open House London. It is key to our philosophy that everyone can access and learn about London's inspiring architecture, free of charge. Our initiatives are only made possible through the generosity of donors and supporters.

Through a portfolio of education and skills initiatives we enable everyone to understand how their city is created and used. We aim to create a legacy for learning providing new skills, confidence and knowledge that can be applied in daily life, helping young people especially to reach their full potential. Our vision is that every young person in London has the opportunity to learn through architecture.

"Children enjoyed the practical approach to maths and design, and the great experience of working with design professionals."
Sarah Smith, Henry Maynard Primary School 2015

Our annual Architecture in Schools – broadens core knowledge: over 1000 primary and secondary pupils take part each year

Youth Engagement initiatives – develop life skills: over 3000 young people have been trained to contribute to decision making about London's public spaces

Archikids – opens up horizons: annual festival for children, giving 4000 young children and their families a unique opportunity to enjoy and explore the City of London though workshops and fun filled activities

Accelerate mentoring initiative – widens access: for 45 young people each year from economically and culturally disadvantaged backgrounds to higher education

Engaging Places – providing new sources of inspiration: the leading UK online hub to support, develop and enhance built environment education

"The space was amazing and the view was incredible! We learnt about how triangles help structure."
Asia and Mia, aged 12 – Archikids Festival 2014

There are lots of ways to support Open-City to keep on enabling, educating and engaging.

Make a donation:
Text **CITY23 £3** to 70070

Join our **Benefactor Scheme** –
for those who share our passion
open-city.org.uk/ getinvolved/giving.html

Revealing...
Open House London 2015

Revealing: spaces to live in

"How are architects rising to the challenge of designing more and better housing in London?"

We all have ideas about what makes a good home in terms of its design.

Demand for housing has always been one of the capital's most pressing issues. With London's current population of 8 million projected to age and expand in the next 20 years, we need design solutions for homes that meet the long-term needs of their occupants.

Open House London shows first hand how architects are turning the constraints of limited space, reuse of existing structures and restricted budgets to create outstanding and sustainable homes. More than ever before the creativity of the architect is key to finding the best solutions to suit our individual and collective needs. Take a look at the following designs for living:

Contemporary insertions:

— **St Mary of Eton Church Mixed Use Development** – new housing surrounding a refurbished Grade II* listed church with new community facilities (p37)

— **Darbishire Place** – a new block of 13 homes which completes an ensemble of six housing blocks surrounding an internal courtyard. The facade complements the existing Victorian buildings (p64)

Shared spaces for living:

— **17–21 Wenlock Road** – housing with four courtyards giving direct visual connections to the city whilst also fostering an intimate community experience (p35)

— **The Arcade** – a development of affordable rental and shared ownership homes surrounding a communal garden, built in vertical modules to encourage ownership and interaction (p67)

Using 'leftover' spaces:

— **Spiral House** – a single-storey house conceived as one wall, which wraps the boundary and spirals into the centre of the site (p69)

— **Tin House** – making efficient use of an irregular site, this house is made up of interconnecting pavilions around a quiet private courtyard (p38)

— **Courtyard House** – a timber-frame house designed around four courtyards. A black clad exterior gives way to a light open-plan interior with flexible living space (p55)

Refurbishing our existing homes:

— **Nightingale Lane** – dramatic refurbishment of a typical 1930s semi. A carefully selected palette of materials is used throughout (p68)

— **Trevelyan House** – a contemporary re-design of a maisonette located in a classic 1950s Grade II listed Brutalist building designed by Denys Lasdun (p66)

— **Raw House** – refurbishment and extension of an existing Victorian terrace to create a light-filled home of industrial elegance (p62)

New housing models & structures:

— **Hackney's Timber Buildings** – a cluster of three of the most significant timber buildings in the world just a short walk apart, including Stadthaus, at 9 storeys the world's tallest timber apartment block (p37)

— **Courtyard Housing** – a housing typology developed to suit the needs of the over 55s community, derived from distilling the key elements of traditional almshouses (p19)

Revealing: how the city works

"What are the infrastructure solutions to cope with London's growth?"

ice
Institution of Civil Engineers

High-quality, robust and forward-thinking engineering is fundamental to the growth and functioning of London, as it touches almost every aspect of our lives: water, waste, energy, transport and infrastructure.

The Institution of Civil Engineers (ICE) and its members work to shape the world we live in. Its partnership with Open House London helps to highlight just how important civil engineering is to London and its future.

Look for the orange dot ● for engineering exemplars and the ICE logo **ice** in the listings for some of ICE London's award-winning projects. Here are just a few of the places to experience and learn about civil engineering. See also **openhouselondon.org.uk/engineering**

Upgrading our transport system:
— **Crossrail – Pudding Mill Lane** – Crossrail reaches the surface at Pudding Lane, so a new station was needed. The station has been designed to accommodate future increases in passenger demand as well as to incorporate escalators at a later date (p55)
— **St Pancras International** – renowned for its Victorian architecture, St Pancras Station was opened in 1868 and is a Grade I listed building. A new terminal was constructed for Eurostar services to continental Europe (p25)

Training:
— **University of Greenwich, Stockwell Street** – the new library and academic building is located along an approach from Greenwich Town to Greenwich Park within Maritime Greenwich, the UNESCO World Heritage Site (p34)
— **City Heights E-ACT Academy** – this exciting new secondary school will provide 900 places for pupils aged 11–16 and a further 200 places for young people aged 16–18 (p49)

Mitigating flood risk:
— **Thames Barrier & Information Centre** – in operation since 1982, this is one of the world's largest moveable flood barriers (p34)

Ground-breaking structural achievements:
— **The Coca-Cola London Eye** – the world's tallest cantilevered observation wheel, now a much-loved symbol of modern Britain (p50)
— **Emirates Air Line** – the first urban cable car in the UK. It crosses the river between North Greenwich and Silvertown (p33)

Special ICE events and tours:
One Great George Street – Institution of Civil Engineers
Grade II* listed HQ of the world's premier engineering institution, the first of its kind, and a fine example of Edwardian architecture (p74)

Boat Tours – London's Engineering Heritage
Live commentary from London's leading engineers on aspects including Bazalgette's legacy, flood risk management, current and future engineering landmarks and London's historical structures (p51)

Engineering Highlights Cycle Tour of the Queen Elizabeth Olympic Park
Join leading engineer Andrew Weir, Director, Expedition Engineering, and architect Kay Hughes, Director, Khaa, to explore the Olympic Park's enabling works and the construction of the venues, through to the utilities and their supporting infrastructure (p55)

Revealing: a greener city

"What does a sustainable city look like?"

SKANSKA

London is the greenest city of its size in the world. It leads the way with innovative environmental design solutions, green infrastructure and energy performance. Yet the city continues to face environmental challenges such as air quality, overheating and flooding.

Our Green Exemplar strand highlights projects that are making significant steps in creating sustainable places for us to work and live in. Take a look this year at how designers are making a cleaner and greener place for Londoners.

Look for the Green Exemplar dot ● in the programme listings for green projects. See also **openhouselondon.org.uk/green** for more sustainable related events. Here are just a few examples:

Healthy living and working:
— **Ewart House** – winner of the Mayor of London / RTPI award for 'Best New Place to Live in London' (p41)
— **Hermitage Community Moorings** – a model for river dwelling with floating community centre (p64)

Home retrofit:
— **24 St John's Church Road** – gracefully refurbished Victorian terrace introducing the UK's first heated clay ceiling system (p35)
— **54 Cambria Road** – Self-build conversion of a C19 terrace using reclaimed materials, natural insulation and biofuel heating (p49)

Practice what you teach:
— **London School of Economics: Saw Swee Hock Student Centre** – shortlisted for the Stirling Prize 2014 (p72)
— **Ravensbourne** – an inspirational new learning and teaching environment with BREEAM Excellent status (p33)

New build:
— **Sulgrave Gardens Passivhaus** – the capital's largest mixed tenure development built using a Passivhaus approach (p38)
— **The Pavilion** – an uncompromisingly modern house in the Blackheath Conservation Area built to Code Level 5 (p53)
— **5 Pancras Square** – LB Camden leads the way with one of the greenest buildings in London (p22)

Open Debate 2015

'Polluting the City'
Our annual live debate for Londoners is now in its third year.

As a citizen, is making London a more sustainable place to live important to you? What aspects do you think should take priority? Open-City want to know your thoughts on the pressing issues. See **openhouselondon.org.uk/opendebate** for further details and how to apply for a place at this year's debate.

Revealing: places and spaces of the city

"How can we make a London landscape that endures?"

Landscape Institute
Inspiring great places

As citizens we are moving away from thinking about our public spaces and green areas as unconnected patches of squares and gardens.

These days, with land use under increasing pressure, green infrastructure – the network of green spaces that nourishes a city – is as significant for the future of a functional London as major infrastructure projects such as Crossrail and HS2.

Landscape highlights for this year's Open House London programme show that successful projects work with what is already there.

Public realm schemes such as Connected Croydon (p30), Clapham Old Town and Venn Street (p51), High Street Harrow (p41) and King's Cross (p24) all make the most of local character. At King's Cross original cobbles have been re-laid and the gasholder, a landmark pulled down in 2000, has been restored and put to a new use as a park.

Similarly, Dalston Eastern Curve (p37), a garden created on an abandoned piece of railway land, and the Peckham Coal Line (p62), a linear garden proposed for disused coal sidings, show how by working with the infrastructure of our industrial past we can create successful green and social landscapes for today.

Take a look at some of the projects with landscape at their heart in our long-term partnership with the Landscape Institute. Look for the yellow dot ● in the programme listings for landscape/public realm projects.

See **openhouselondon.org.uk/landscape** for more on landscape-related events. For more details on landscapes in London see **landscapeinstitute.org/openhouse**

Interventions:

— **Ladywell Fields** – tour of a river restoration project within an existing park with new river channels, backwaters, pools and greatly improved habitats. An enhanced footpath network with new lighting, boardwalks and park furniture provides new links to surrounding areas connecting the local community to the parkland (p53)
— **Many Ways to Sit: the Social Dynamics of Gordon Square** – a tour and talk looking at the problems and potential of seating in public places, focusing on Gordon Square, Woolwich (p34)

Large-scale transformations:

— **King's Cross Public Realm** – a guided walk by Dominic Cole exploring the regeneration and landscape design of King's Cross Regent's Quarter, Kings Place, canal, Central St Martin's and St Pancras Old Church (p24)
— **Walk in the Olympic Park: Function and Beauty in Landscape** – walk the Queen Elizabeth Olympic Park looking at the design approaches which have shaped this new park for London. Exploring the South Park and its post-Games landscape with new approaches to green space design, key to making cities healthy and liveable for the future (p56)

Revealing: revitalising the city

"What will a 21st-century Thamesmead look like?"

PEABODY

London's changing shape includes the regeneration of existing areas, improving neighbourhoods for established communities and creating new opportunities in the capital. One such place is Thamesmead in south-east London.

Thamesmead was originally conceived as a 'new town' and completed in 1968 to address the housing crisis after the Second World War. Spanning the same distance as Bond Street to Shoreditch, and with over 100 acres of developable land, it can make a significant contribution to tackling London's 21st-century housing crisis.

With the arrival of Crossrail at Abbey Wood in 2018 the area will be just 11 minutes away from Canary Wharf and 17 minutes from the City of London.

Peabody is one of London's oldest and largest housing associations, building homes and communities for over 150 years. It is passionate about the potential for positive change in Thamesmead's neighbourhoods.

Peabody is making major investment in the area and has supported the London Borough of Bexley and the Royal Borough of Greenwich to secure funding from the GLA to create complementary Housing Zones in the two boroughs. The plan is to deliver nearly 3,000 new homes to rent and buy as well as creating thousands of jobs.

With plenty of green open spaces, miles of waterways and river frontage, good schools, superb community and leisure facilities and improving transport links, the town has the potential to be one of London's most desirable places to live, work and visit.

To find out more visit
www.peabody.org.uk/thamesmead

Visit Thamesmead

The Link Thamesmead
Belvedere Road, Off Harrow Manor Way, Thamesmead
SE28 9BS
Saturday 19 & Sunday 20 9am – 6.30pm
A stunning, state-of-the-art community hub made up of nine arches located under the Harrow Manor Way flyover. During Open House weekend you'll be able to find out more about the regeneration plans for the area. There will be people on hand there to give information and tours around the buildings and facilities.
Station: Abbey Wood, Buses: 177, 229, 244, 401 601, 602, 669
thelinkthamesmead.co.uk

Sporting Club Thamesmead
Bayliss Avenue, Thamesmead SE28 8NJ
Saturday 19 & Sunday 20 9am – 9pm
Cutting edge facilities to enjoy sports and fitness

activities along with social and community events at affordable prices. There will be people on hand there to give information and tours around the buildings and facilities.
Station: Abbey Wood, Buses: 177, 229, 244, 401 601, 602, 669
sportingclubthamesmead.co.uk

Tump 53 Nature Reserve
Thamesmead SE28 8AS
Saturday 19 & Sunday 20 10am – 4pm
A former munitions testing site which has been reclaimed for nature. The site now contains mixed woodland, a glade, and a pond, and is surrounded by a reed-fringed moat. Volunteers will be on hand to explain about the Tump & its history and show off the nature. Come and enjoy the space and bring a picnic.

Revealing: connecting communities

"What is happening in your local area?"

The challenges of development in London include the creation of new public and community buildings – the vitality of the city is very much about places and spaces where people can meet.

Permanent and temporary community led and community focused schemes can provide a new lease of life to buildings and areas. But of course there are also much loved and locally significant buildings that have a timeless appeal.

The weekend provides opportunities to see examples of the above and hear about some future development plans and proposals, including a few still in construction – revealing more about the future of London at a local level.

Community focused:

— **Regeneration at Heart of Community – Camberwell Residential** – reconstruction of a building derelict for more than 40 years, transformed into a modern residential property over a community restaurant/bar (p62)
— **Crystal Palace Subway** – subway under Crystal Palace Parade resembling a vaulted crypt. The subway once connected the former High Level Station to the Crystal Palace (p60)
— **Pop Brixton** – ad-hoc and quick-thinking design on a large scale, recycling and repurposing components providing a temporary platform for community events and fledgling businesses (p49)
— **Impact Hub King's Cross** – innovative workspace for social entrepreneurs with recycled fittings and furniture (p46)

Fitzrovia Chapel – located within the Fitzroy Place development on the site of the former Middlesex Hospital, the chapel was preserved as part of a development agreement for the wider project, and has been the subject of a £2m restoration by Fitzroy Place's developers Exemplar and Aviva. The Fitzrovia Chapel Foundation, a charitable organisation, has been created to ensure a strong future for the Grade II* listed chapel. Designed in 1891 by celebrated architect John Loughborough Pearson, the chapel was completed in 1929 by his son Frank (p71)

Bringing people together for learning, culture and entertainment:

— **The Library at Willesden Green** – new 4-storey building incorporating the Victorian library, creating a new cultural landmark in Brent (p21)
— **New Wimbledon Theatre** – a striking Edwardian theatre with main auditorium seating 1,600+ and which has recently been refurbished (p54)
— **New Horizon Youth Centre** – an institutional building invested with the flexibility and generosity of a welcoming settled house through an innovative design approach (p24)
— **Thrive, Battersea Park** – training building and garden for charity teaching gardening and life skills to local residents with disabilities (p69)

Places in development:

— **V&A FuturePlan** – introducing the rich and varied architecture of the V&A Museum, allowing access to some areas usually closed to the public and the latest gallery projects (p48)
— **Barking Town Centre Tour** – this area has seen significant new development over recent years. Now designated one of London's Housing Zones, meaning further development over the next decade. See a number of award-winning schemes and plans for the next 5 years (p19)

Revealing: explore your city

"Open House is one of my favourite weekends of the year – totally inspiring!"

With more than 700 buildings, walks, talks and tours, here are some of the ways to get ahead and make the most of your weekend:

1. FIRST, CHOOSE YOUR BUILDINGS AND PLAN YOUR WEEKEND ...

All buildings and events taking part this year are listed in the directory section of this guide from p19. For updates see **openhouselondon.org.uk/search**

Get the app! The invaluable tool for your weekend, the Open House London app contains the all-important map on the day, 'store your favourites' and 'buildings nearby me', as well as complete listings. August early-birds can download for only 69p until 1 September (thereafter £2.99).

2. DIG DEEPER ...

Find background information on most Open House buildings through free 'archifacts' sheets available at **openhouselondon.org.uk/search** If you want to dig deeper here are some ideas ... and visit **openhouselondon.org.uk/resources**

Buy the book ... Get a copy of Victoria Thornton's book *Open House London 2012* for an overview of 100 of some of the most architecturally inspiring buildings that have featured in the past 20+ years of Open House. Available with 15% discount by quoting the code OPENHOUSE at checkout from **open-city.org.uk/shop**

AJ Buildings Library: View architectural photography, drawings and details of Open House London projects in the AJ Buildings Library. For more information, see online listings and the OHL app, and entries marked with the red AJ symbol ⓐ in this guide. The AJ Buildings Library, which contains 2,100 exemplar British schemes, is free to OpenHousers in September. **AJBuildingsLibrary.co.uk**

Buildings Library

An Extra Dimension: the Burton House (p23) is among London's most significant architect-designed homes. This book, with specially commissioned photographs, tells the story of how it came about. **open-city.org.uk/shop**

Robert Elms
BBC London and Open House

Robert Elms Show Monday to Fridays 12-3pm and Saturdays 10am-1pm BBC London 94.9FM

"When Open House throws open the portals of so many otherwise inaccessible London buildings, it also opens our eyes to the surprising variety of architectural wonders in our midst and our minds to infinite possibilities of the built environment. For years now we have covered this staggeringly successful cultural event with relish on my daily show on BBC London 94.9. Every year we receive an avalanche of calls and e-mails from people eager to know more about the opportunities afforded by this unique extravaganza of the edifice. They are hungry to see behind the façades, to learn the tales and the techniques that all buildings have to tell. So yet again in nearly every London borough, Londoners will learn a little more about the city we all share, and BBC London 94.9 will of course be with them."
Robert Elms

BBC LONDON 94.9 FM

3. CHOOSE A HUB ...

Temple Inns of Court and Temple Church

In some places you can step from one building straight to another, and the Temple Inns of Court and Temple Church is just one of those hubs. To mark the anniversary of the sealing of the 1215 Magna Carta, Inner Temple, Middle Temple and Temple Church have a whole host of activities and tours taking place over the weekend at this unique site, including a self-guided family quiz around the grounds and a Children's Court taking place at the Royal Courts of Justice on Sunday. You might also want to grab some refreshments at their street food market or have a brief picnic before further continuing on your Open House weekend journey (pp28-9).

4. CHOOSE A NEW ROUTE ...

Join the Summer of Cycling! ...

Santander Cycles has joined with Open House London giving lucky winners exclusive access to selected sites participating across London, including Lambeth Palace. You'll have the chance to see some of London's most fascinating and great landmarks from the comfort of your Santander Cycle. See santander.co.uk/cycles for further details. #SantanderCycles

The keys to the city...
yours for one night only !

Come with us as we head out into the night, discovering cultural, architectural and artistic delights in London, whilst raising as much as we can to support people living with cancer and their family and friends. Working in partnership with Open House London, Maggie's Culture Crawl is part 15 mile night-walk, part cultural adventure, curated by former Director of the National Portrait Gallery, and writer, Sandy Nairne.

From the Foreign Office to The Royal Academy of Arts by way of Foster + Partners, you'll get access to all these buildings and many others. You'll encounter talented performers including the world renowned Royal Ballet and enjoy delicious food and drink along the way. So come out walking with us on Friday 18 September to help people with cancer. Places are limited – so sign up today and visit maggiescentres.org/culturecrawllondon or call 0300 123 1801.

Get active! ... Walking or cycling is the perfect way to keep fit while taking in some great architecture. With Transport for London's Legible London initiative we've created some handy London mapguides to help you plan a walking route between buildings. Download at openhouselondon.org.uk/legiblelondon

Go on a road trip with Arriva ... This year the Arriva bus tour for Open House will be taking a radically different – and greener – route through London. In collaboration with the Landscape Institute, our 1960s Routemaster Bus will take a route from Central to East London, exploring the historic relationship between landscape and inhabitation within the city itself. The tour will be led by Paul Lincoln of the Landscape Institute and Joe Kerr of the Royal College of Art/Arriva Heritage Fleet. 40 places available by ballot. See p17 for how to enter. theheritagefleet.com

5. LEARN FROM THE EXPERTS ...

Meet the architect ... Hundreds of architects and landscape architects will be giving talks and tours of buildings they've designed. This is your unique opportunity to meet them in person and quiz them about their work. Look out for listings marked 'A'. This year includes the architect of the Unicorn Theatre, Keith Williams

...and the engineer Structural engineers will also be on site explaining their role where listings have the code 'E'. Among these are The Sutton Life Centre (p63) engineered by **Elliott Wood**. Other Elliott Wood projects: 3floor-in2 Apartment (p47), Jerwood Space (p61), ORTUS (p61) and Elliott Wood's own offices (p54). www.elliottwood.co.uk

See openhouselondon.org.uk/special for a list of experts on site

6. GET THE KIDS INVOLVED!

Open House Junior for families ... Your kids can become architectives by joining in the exciting family activities taking place throughout the weekend. Inspiring the next generation of Londoners aged 5 to 12, the programme is full of fun and free activities. Come and join us to design, draw and build London's cityscape! Highlights include:

City of a Thousand Architects
City Hall in the London Living Room (p60).
Structurally Found
Photo Treasure Hunt challenging you to track down London's engineering for a chance to win prizes. **structurallyfound.org.uk**
Build a View Shaper!
Part of the City of London's Sculpture in the City programme.
Scale Up the City!
Make small-scale replicas of key London buildings with Open-City and architects (p73).
Design your own city
Be inspired by RIBA's collection and spectacular views across London to design your own cityscape, and make your own London skyline hat and button badge! (p73)
City Children's Trail with three carefully chosen, kid-friendly, self-guided routes – perfect for short legged walkers! Available from the City of London Information Centre, EC4M 8BX.
For full details and more great activities, check out **openhouselondon.org.uk/junior**

Audio Described Tours... Blind and partially sighted people can enjoy VocalEyes audio-described tours of four of London's iconic buildings: the London School of Economics: Saw Swee Hock Centre (p72); The Temple Church (p29); 10 New Burlington Street (p70); and Drapers' Hall (p27). Tours are led by VocalEyes describers with building representatives or designers. Find out more and book at **vocaleyes.co.uk** or email **enquiries@vocaleyes.co.uk**. Collaboration between **VocalEyes**, the national charity providing access to the arts and Open House London, kindly supported by the Greater London Fund for the Blind and The Sir Jules Thorn Trust.

7. BID FOR YOUR OWN MINI OPEN HOUSE

This year Open House London has teamed up with Skyline Chess to produce an exclusive chess set depicting iconic buildings taking part over the weekend.

The new set includes BT Tower, marking its 50th anniversary. The chess set is based on an original Staunton chess set, designed by architect Nathan Cook in 1849, which is based on elements taken from neoclassical architecture.

The set is available in an **online auction**, the proceeds of which will go towards ensuring Open House London and Open House Junior will remain free next year.
See **openhouselondon.org.uk/special**

8. HAVE A SAY ...

The Open Debate 'Polluting the City' Our annual debate for Londoners is now in its third year. See **openhouselondon.org.uk/opendebate** for further details.

9. SHARE YOUR ARCHITECTURE ADVENTURE

Keep up to date and share your Open House experience on Facebook, Twitter and Instagram' **@openhouselondon**. Tell us which buildings you liked best. **#openhouselondon**

10. HELP TO KEEP OPEN HOUSE ALIVE!

Open House London was started in 1992 by a small charity (now called Open-City). Giving everyone the chance to explore London's great buildings helps us all to make more informed judgements on the places and spaces we use every day. The concept is so successful it has been taken up by communities in more than 30 cities around the world.
openhouseworldwide.org

The event is delivered by its community. Open House London is only possible with the support of hundreds of property and building owners, architects and engineers and others who give a huge amount of time and resources for **free** in putting on events and opening buildings. Without them, and the 6000 volunteers over the weekend, the event simply would not happen.

Open-City has to raise funding every year to deliver Open House London.
We can only continue with your support.

Part of the
Open House Worldwide Family
openhouseworldwide.org

Please help keep Open House weekend free for all Text CITY23 £3 to 70070

How to use this guide

This guide gives you details of all the buildings, walks, tours and special events taking part in Open House London over the weekend of 19 and 20 September. Use this guide to help you plan your visits and route.

— Get the most up-to-date listings on our website **openhouselondon.org.uk**
— Get the iPhone or android app to store your **favourites and use the map on the day**
— Keep up to date and share over the weekend on **Facebook, Twitter and Instagram @openhouselondon #openhouselondon**

How does the event work?
The Open House London annual event is fully inclusive and admission is free to all, in line with the Open-City charity ethos of increasing wider understanding about the importance of good design.

How can I find the building(s) I'm interested in seeing?
Buildings and related events are listed geographically by borough to reflect the support of our local authority partners, and then alphabetically by name within each borough. The index (p75) also lists buildings by type.

You can also use our online search facility at **openhouselondon.org.uk/search** and **our app** (69p until 1 September, thereafter £2.99) to find the building(s) you want. Search by building name but also by date, type, architect and area. Use the map interface to plan your route between buildings and events.

What information is given in each listing?
In this guide and on the website each listing has:
— building name
— address including postcode
— opening days and hours
— visitor access
— pre-booking details where relevant
— amenities
— nearest transport (with bus numbers at the end)

Which days are the buildings open?
Each building decides which day(s) and times it can open. Use the following key to plan your visit:
- Open Saturday only
- Open Sunday only
- Open BOTH Saturday and Sunday

Key to the listings
Facilities on site, access information, special events, tours by architects and engineers, and highlight buildings have the following codes and icons:

A Architect on site
B Bookshop
C Children's activities
d Some disabled access
D Full wheelchair access
E Engineer on site
G Green Features
N Normally open to public
P Parking
Q Long queues envisaged
R Refreshments
T Toilets

AJ AJ Library Building
   Green Exemplar
   Landscape / Public realm
   Infrastructure/ Engineering

How do I get entry to a building?
Buildings taking part in Open House London are generally on a **first come basis**, in line with our mission to make architecture accessible to all. Therefore you DON'T need to book except in a number of cases.

Each building selects its own method of opening, and for various reasons some decide to operate a booking system. Details can be found in each listing.

In the very few cases where bookings are required, use the contact details in these listings to book on or after 14 August ONLY – **DO NOT** try to book earlier than this as your request will not be accepted.

Terms of entry
Open House London is a free event inviting everyone to take part. Each building's opening, security arrangements and terms of entry are controlled by individual owners, and entry to each building is on terms and at times specified, on 19 & 20 September 2015. Participation in events is at your own risk. Information in this guide is provided by contributors. Open-City has taken all reasonable care to verify the information provided and cannot accept responsibility for any variation from the details published here. Please do respect building owners and their privacy, and be mindful when taking photos.
Important: see disclaimer see p 78

BALLOTS
Ballots are operated for the following buildings and events ONLY:

10 Downing Street (p70)
Arriva archibus mystery tour (p15)
The Coca-Cola London Eye (p50)

The ballots will close on **5 September**. Go to **openhouselondon.org.uk/ballots** to enter. PLEASE NOTE ONLY successful applicants will be notified.

What will I find on the weekend?
Thousands of Open House volunteer expert guides and stewards will be showing you around and answering your questions over the weekend. Both professionals and amateur enthusiasts give their time and knowledge. In recognition of their support, their volunteer badge gives them priority access to buildings (apart from those that are pre-booking only). Email **volunteers@open-city.org.uk** if you want to find out how to become a future Open House volunteer.

More copies of the guide for your friends ...
Buy from: Foyles, RIBA Bookshop, AA Bookshop, Tate Britain, Tate Modern, V&A Museum Bookshop.

Keep in touch!
Keep up to date with all of Open-City's programmes by signing up to our regular **enewsletter** at **open-city.org.uk**

Please help keep Open House weekend free for all Text CITY23 £3 to 70070

Revealing: London!

"What can I see near me?"

Buildings By Area – Contents

The programme listings on the following pages are ordered by borough area. In each borough section buildings are listed first, with walks and tours at the end. This map shows you where the boroughs are located. **You have 48 hours to discover this city's places and spaces!**

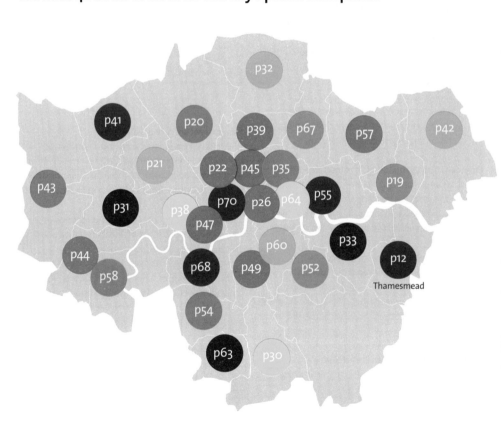

Barking & Dagenham

See openhouselondon.org.uk/barking
to find out more about this area

Courtyard Housing

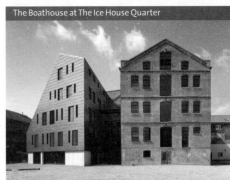
The Boathouse at The Ice House Quarter

Barking Abbey with St Margaret's Church
The Broadway, North Street, Barking IG11 8AS
■ Sat 10am–3pm. N D R T P
Grade I listed St Margaret's Church (1215 onwards) has interesting monuments, art and impressive stained glass. Includes Arts & Crafts work by George Jack and Walker Organ (1914). Captain Cook married here. Abbey dates from 666AD and includes ruins, Curfew Tower and Chapel of Holy Rood with C12 Rood Stone. Bell tower also open. Ronald Wylde Associates (restoration) 2005.
Tube/Rail: Barking; 5,62,EL1,287,366,387,EL2

Barking Riverside Development – Rivergate Centre and Buzzard Mouth ●
Entry to Exhibition in Rivergate Centre on Minter Road, Barking IG11 0FJ
■ Sat 10am–3pm. Tours 11am, 1pm. Last entry 2.30pm. D T C G P R
A new sustainable neighbourhood being created alongside two kilometres of Thames river frontage at Barking Riverside – 10,800 homes to house 26,000 people, and a London Overground station. Stage 1 of Phase 1 is complete with high quality examples of shared community building, incorporating primary school, nursery, church, café and community facilities. van Heyningen and Haward Architects 2011.
Tube/Rail: Barking; 387,EL1

Courtyard Housing ●
Courtyard Housing, Wood Lane, Dagenham RM8 1JX
■ Sun 10am–1pm. Regular architect-led tours. A
A housing typology developed to particularly suit the needs of the over 55's community, Courtyard Housing was derived from studying the rich tradition of housing for the elderly and the English Almshouse. The housing is of an intimate scale and surrounds a communal landscaped garden that forms the heart of the site. Patel Taylor 2014.
Tube: Romford; Rail: Chadwell Heath

Dagenham Library
1 Church Elm Lane, Dagenham RM10 9QS
■ Sat 10am–5pm. N D T
A contemporary flagship building situated on a newly-created 'Gateway Square' (part of the Mayor's designated 100 spaces), the library is a shared 2-storey public building with a Council 'One Stop Shop'. A striking glazed façade with 82 residential units above the library featuring coloured balcony panels. ArchitecturePLB 2010. Entry: public areas.
Tube: Dagenham Heathway; 145,173,174,175,364

Eastbury Manor House
Eastbury Square, Barking IG11 9SN
■ Sat 12noon–4pm. Regular tours with architects of recent refurbishment, first come basis. Last tour 3pm. R T B C A P d
Architecturally distinguished and well-preserved, brick-built, Grade I listed manor house, originally the residence of a wealthy Tudor gentleman. Contains C17 wall-paintings, wood panelling and a fine Tudor turret. Many original features have been restored, including east turret. Charming walled garden. Unknown C16/Richard Griffiths Architects (restoration) 2003/2008-09. Entry: house, gardens, café, shop.
Tube: Upney; Tube/Rail: Barking; 62,287,368

Goresbrook Village
Goresbrook Road, Dagenham RM9 4YG
■ Sat 10am–5pm. Hourly tours, first come basis. Duration 45mins. D R A P
Reintroduction of traditional streets of mixed tenure homes to replace three unpopular tower blocks. Simple, repeatable houses within a masterplan that maximises family homes with gardens. Stitch 2015.
Tube: Upney, Becontree; Tube/Rail: Barking; 173,287,62,368

Technical Skills Academy ●
1 Short Blue Place, Barking IG11 8FJ
■ Sat 10am–3pm. D T
Highest quality education and vocational training for young people, focusing on hospitality and food, hair and beauty, construction trades. Commissioned by London Borough of Barking & Dagenham and run by Barking & Dagenham College, a key part of the civic regeneration of Barking. BREEAM rated Excellent. Sustainable features include combined heat and power heating system. Rick Mather Architects 2012.
Tube/Rail: Barking; 5,62,287,EL1,387

The Broadway
Broadway, Barking IG11 7LS
■ Sat/Sun 10am–1pm. Regular tours, pre-book ONLY via 020 8507 5607. N D R T
Original theatre modernised with striking but sympathetic new double-height foyer space, preserving the original façade which now forms part of interior. H Jackson and R Edmonds 1930/Tim Foster Architects (refurb) 2004. Entry: foyers, auditorium, studios, offices.
Tube/Rail: Barking; 5,62,366,387,EL1

The Boathouse at The Ice House Quarter
80 Abbey Road, Barking IG11 7BT
■ Sat 10am–1pm. Access via river terrace. D T P
The Boathouse consists of space within a restored 5-storey Victorian Granary and Malthouse on the River Roding, within contemporary bronze-clad extension, featuring a low-tech approach to viable sustainability. The Malthouse is the home of the Ice House Quarter, an arts/creative centre. Schmidt Hammer Lassen/Pollard Thomas Edwards 2012. Entry: Granary and Malthouse terrace.
Tube/Rail: Barking
www.icehousequarter.co.uk

The Millennium Centre
The Chase, Dagenham Road, Rush Green, Romford RM7 0SS
■ Sat/Sun 10am–5pm. N D T G P
Steel structure, timber-clad exterior and interior, and sweeping south-facing roof designed to house solar panels. Eco-friendly building using recycled materials throughout, including car windscreens and newspapers. Penoyre & Prasad 1997.
Tube: Dagenham East; Rail: Romford; 174

The Mobile Museum
Sat: Valence House Museum, Becontree Avenue, Dagenham RM8 3HT; Sun: venue TBC via www.openhouselondon.org.uk
■ Sat 10am–4pm/Sun 10am–6pm. R T B C A
Multi-strand art project by Verity-Jane Keefe touring 12 housing estates within the Borough, making a new collection in response to the built environment and contemporary landscape via a programme of making, digging and collecting workshops. Entry: Mobile Museum, Lending Library
Tube: Becontree, Dagenham Heathway; Rail: Chadwell Heath; 62,128,150

Valence House
Becontree Avenue, Dagenham RM8 3HT
■ Sat 10am–4pm. Regular tours. N D R T B P
Grade II* listed C15 manor house with medieval moat. Recently discovered late C16 wall painting and impressive oak panelling. Reopened 2010 with new museum galleries, visitor centre, and archive and local studies centre with new 'passive' collection strongrooms. Unknown C15/Feilden Clegg Bradley (refurb) 2010. Entry: museum, café, giftshop, archives centre.
Tube: Becontree; Rail: Chadwell Heath; 150,62,128,368

WALKS/TOURS

Barking Town Centre Tour
■ Meet: Sun 10am, 12noon, 2pm, 4pm outside Barking Town Hall, Clockhouse Avenue, Barking IG11 7LU
Duration 2 hours. Pre-book ONLY via keeley.gourlay@lbbd.gov.uk. N G d
Barking Town Centre has seen significant new development over recent years and the announcement that it is one of London's Housing Zones will mean further development over the next decade. These guided walking tours will visit a number of award winning schemes, including Barking Central, William Street Quarter, Short Blue Place/Technical Skills Academy, the Ice House Quarter/Roding Riverside, as well as showcasing plans for the next 5 years.
Tube/Rail: Barking

Supported by

London Borough of
Barking & Dagenham
lbbd.gov.uk

●AJ Library Building ●Green Exemplar ■Landscape/Public realm ●Infrastructure/Engineering
■Open Saturday ■Open Sunday ■Open Saturday and Sunday

Barnet

Friends Meeting House
North Square NW11 7AD
■ Sun 2pm-5pm. Max 40 at one time. R T B P
Delightful brick and tile building inspired by the famous 1688 Meeting House at Jordans in Buckinghamshire. A simple building in a tranquil setting, reflecting the Quakers' beliefs and which recently celebrated its centenary. Fred Rowntree 1913.
Tube: Golders Green; H2

Golders Green Unitarians
31-and-a-half Hoop Lane NW11 8BS
■ Sat 10am-5pm/Sun 1pm-5pm. D R T
Grade II listed small interwar building with Arts & Crafts pulpit and mural by Ivon Hitchens in the tradition of Morris & Co. Reginald Farrow 1925. Entry: church, gardens.
Tube: Golders Green; H2,82,102,210,460

Hampstead Garden Suburb Free Church
Central Square NW11 7AG
■ Sat 10am-6pm/Sun 12noon-6pm. Last entry 5.45pm. D R T P
Grade I listed Nonconformist church, set in the suburb's integrally planned Central Square to balance St Jude's Church nearby, but with a low concrete dome. Distinctive interior with large Tuscan columns on high brick plinths. Sir Edwin Lutyens 1911.
Tube: Golders Green then H2 bus

Middlesex University – Hendon Campus
The Burroughs, Hendon NW4 4BT
■ Sat 11am-4pm. Half-hourly architect-led tours, first come basis. Last tour 3.30pm. Max 40 per tour. D R T A P
The College Building: an innovative glass and steel roof was added to the original 1930s quadrangle creating one of London's largest covered spaces. The project included the complete refurbishment of all teaching facilities. The Grove: £80million purpose-built arts building. One of the largest in the UK, the centre includes TV studios, workshops and photography studios. Sustainable features include sedum roof and beehives, BREEAM Excellent rating. H W Burchett 1939/ BPR Architects 2006/2011.
Tube: Hendon Central; Rail: Hendon; 113,143,183
www.mdx.ac.uk

Phoenix Cinema
52 High Road N2 9PJ
■ Sun tours at 10.30am, 11.15am, 12noon, 12.45pm. Film screening at 1.30pm. Pre-book ONLY via 020 8444 6789. Max 10 per tour. N D R T
The Phoenix is one of the oldest cinemas in the country with 1910 barrel-vaulted ceiling and Art Deco wall reliefs by Mollo and Egan. Grade II listed. Birwood 1910/Howes & Jackman 1938/Pyle Boyd Architects 2002/HMDW Architects 2010. Entry: auditorium, projection room, public and private areas.
Tube: East Finchley; 102,143,234,263
www.phoenixcinema.co.uk/

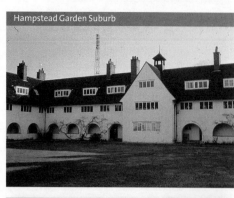
Middlesex University - Hendon Campus

St Jude on the Hill
Central Square NW11 7AH
■ Sat 10am-5pm/Sun 12noon-5pm. Guided talk on the Walter Starmer murals at 3pm. N R T B P d
Eccentric and magnificent Edwardian church by Sir Edwin Lutyens, Grade I listed. Described in Simon Jenkins' Thousand Best Churches as 'one of Lutyens' most distinctive creations'. England's most extensive C20 wall-painting scheme by Walter Starmer, memorial to horses killed in WWI, and local archives display. Sir Edwin Lutyens 1911. Entry: nave, choir and chapels.
Tube: Golders Green then H2 bus to Heathgate

Waterlow Court
Heath Close NW11 7DT
■ Sat/Sun 10am-5pm. Guided tours, first come basis. Last entry 4.30pm. d P R
Communal low cost housing built for professional women as part of early Hampstead Garden Suburb; now private homes. Mackay Hugh Baillie Scott 1909. Entry: one flat, cloister, garden.
Tube: Golders Green; 82,13,260,226,328

Wrotham Park
Wrotham Park, Barnet EN5 4SB
■ Sun 10am-5pm. Tours on the hour except 1pm. Pre-book ONLY via 020 8275 1425. No children under 16. Last tour 4pm. Max 20 per tour. T P
A privately-owned Grade II listed Palladian mansion with grand interiors restored in 1883, set in 300 acres of parkland in the midst of 2500 acres. Built for Admiral The Hon. John Byng. Isaac Ware 1754/Thomas Cubitt 1883. Entry: entrance hall, dining room, drawing room, saloon, staircase hall.
Tube: High Barnet; Rail: Potters Bar; then 84 from either to main gates
http://www.wrothampark.com/

WALKS/TOURS

Hampstead Garden Suburb Artisans' Quarter Walk ●
■ Meet: Sun 2pm and 4.30pm. Register inside St Jude on the Hill, Central Square NW11 7AH. First come basis. Max 20 per tour.
Guided walks of 'the most nearly perfect example of the C20 Garden Suburb' (Pevsner). Informally laid out terraces and

Hampstead Garden Suburb

Phoenix Cinema

picturesque Arts & Crafts vernacular cottages. Additionally, material for self-guided walks will be available at all the Hampstead Garden Suburb Open House sites throughout the weekend. Unwin & Parker, Lutyens, Bunney, Baillie Scott and others.
Tube: Golders Green; then 82 or 102 bus (direction North Finchley) to Hampstead Way

Gratefully supported by:

Golders Green Unitarians

Hampstead Garden Suburb Residents Association

Phoenix Cinema 1910-2010

WROTHAM PARK

HAMPSTEAD · GARDEN · SUBURB · TRUST

Middlesex University London

Key. A Architect on site **B** Bookshop **C** Childrens' activities **d** Some disabled access **D** Full wheelchair access **E** Engineer on site **G** Green Features **N** Normally open to the public **P** Parking **Q** Long queues envisaged **R** Refreshments **T** Toilets

Brent

See **openhouselondon.org.uk/brent** to find out more about this area

Wembley Park

BAPS Shri Swaminarayan Mandir
·105-119 Brentfield Road, Neasden NW10 8LD
- Sat/Sun 9am-4pm. Regular guided tours. Last entry 3.30pm. Max 30 per tour. N D T B P

Masterpiece of traditional Hindu design and exquisite workmanship that rises serenely amid London's iconic skyline. Using 5000 tonnes of Italian Carrara and Indian Ambaji marble and the finest Bulgarian limestone, it was hand-carved in India before being assembled in London. Entry: all areas except monks' quarters, admin block, kitchen, gym. NB. Respectful dress please: no shorts, short skirts, sleeveless tops.
Tube: Harlesden then 224 bus, Wembley Park then 206 bus

Brent Civic Centre ◉
Engineers Way, Wembley HA9 0FJ
- Sat 10am-5pm. Regular architect-led tours. A D T

Located next to Wembley Stadium and The SSE Arena, the Civic Centre streamlines all aspects of Brent Council's activities. The spaces are arranged around a soaring, naturally-lit foyer and atrium housing a large public amphitheatre and staircase. A circular drum clad in timber fins features prominently, housing a multi-purpose community hall, library, customer services and civic chamber. BREEAM Outstanding – the first project in its category to have achieved this and the most sustainable local authority building in the UK. Multiple awards, including RIBA National Award 2014. Hopkins Architects 2013.
Tube: Wembley Park; Rail: Wembley Stadium; 83,92,182,206, 297

Christchurch with St Laurence
Willesden Lane, Brondesbury NW6 7BG
- Sat/Sun 10am-5pm. Informal guided tours. N D R T P

Victorian Gothic church (1866) converted in the 1980s to house 20 flats with one-third of church retained.
Tube: Kilburn; Rail Brondesbury Park; 98,206

Doyle Gardens
86 Doyle Gardens, Kensal Rise NW10 3SR
- Sun 1pm-5pm. First come basis. Last entry 4.45pm.

Renovation and extension of a 1930s semi-detached house which involved opening up of ground floor, preservation of existing finishes and construction of timber extension to connect living spaces with the south-facing garden. Jonathan Tuckey Design 2014. Entry: ground floor only.
Tube/Rail: Kensal Green; Rail: Kensal Rise;187,18,206,226,52

Fawood Children's Centre
35 Fawood Avenue, Harlesden NW10 8DX
- Sat 10am-1pm. General access with regular tours, first come basis. Last entry 12.30pm. Max 6 per tour. T G P

'Cage' or 'shed' structure of steel mesh with elliptical coloured acrylic 'lozenges' encasing the whole and sheltering the play areas. Rooms are brightly coloured/decorated recycled sea containers. The centre provides education, care, family support and health services. RIBA Award Winner 2005. Alsop Design Ltd 2004. Entry: all ground floor areas and upper walkways.
Tube/Rail: Harlesden;18,206,224

London Designer Outlet
Meet: Next to TGI Fridays, Wembley Park Boulevard HA9 0QL
- Sat tours 11am, 12noon, 1pm. Max 15 per tour. P A T D N

A retail and leisure development at the heart of the Wembley Park masterplan. The scheme brings together outlet shopping, food and beverage and a cinema. Leslie Jones Architecture/ Mcfarlane Associates 2013.
Tube: Wembley Park; Rail: Wembley Stadium; 83,92,182,206,297

The Library at Willesden Green
95 High Road NW10 2SF
- Sat 9am-5pm/Sun 11am-5pm. Guided tours Sat only, 10am-1pm on the hour, first come basis. N D R T A

A new 4-storey building incorporating the much-loved Victorian library, creating a new cultural landmark in Brent. The distinctive patterned brickwork samples colours from surrounding buildings, and a dramatic central atrium provides natural ventilation and daylight throughout. Allford Hall Monaghan Morris 2015.
Tube: Willesden Green; 52,98,460,266,260

The Tin Tabernacle/Cambridge Hall
12-16 Cambridge Avenue NW6 5BA
- Sat/Sun 1pm-5pm. Half-hourly tours, first come basis. Last tour 4pm. Last entry 4.30pm. Max 15 per tour. N R T d

1860s corrugated iron chapel. Inside transformed after the last war into a ship by local people, complete with decks, portholes, bridge and even a Bofors gun. Entry: chapel, roperoom, classroom, wardroom.
Tube: Kilburn Park; Rail: Kilburn High Road; 31,328,316,32,206

Underground Bunker, Neasden
Brook Road NW2 7DZ
- Sat 9am-5pm. Pre-book ONLY via katy.bajina@networkhg. org.uk. Sensible footwear and clothing required. Max 25 at one time. T d

Underground 1940s bunker used during WWII by Winston Churchill and the Cabinet. Purpose-built of reinforced concrete, bomb-proof subterranean war citadel 40ft below ground, with Map Room, Cabinet Room and offices, housed within a sub-basement protected by 5ft thick concrete roof.
Tube: Neasden, Dollis Hill; 182,232,226

WALKS/TOURS

London Underground – Bakerloo Tour
Meet: Queens Park Station NW6 6NL
- Sun tours 10am, 11.30am, 1pm. Pre-book ONLY via http://www.cvent.com/d/3rqdlq. Duration 1.5 hours. Min age 10 years. Max 10 per tour.

This tour will highlight the stations on the Bakerloo line, including some which will be celebrating their centenary in 2015. Groups will be taken along the Bakerloo line southbound, stopping at Kilburn Park, Maida Vale, Warwick Avenue and Paddington stations, highlighting architectural features as well as providing an insight into current Underground operations. Stanley Heaps 1915.
Tube: Queens Park

Roe Green Village
- Meet: Sun 11am and 2.30pm at Village Green, Roe Lane NW9, opposite entrance to Roe End. Tours of village with historian Peter Cormack FSA. N D W

Built to provide workers' housing for employees of AirCo, Roe Green was designed in the garden village idiom by Sir Frank Baines, principal architect at HM Office of Works. The 250 dwellings clearly show the influence of the Arts & Crafts movement. Sir Frank Baines 1918-19.
Tube: Kingsbury, Colindale; Tube/Rail: Kenton; 204,302,305,324,183

Wembley Park Masterplan
Meet: The Yellow Pavilion, off Olympic Way, Wembley HA9 0FA
- Sat tours 10.30am, 11.30am, 12.30pm, 1.30pm. Max 15 per tour. N D T A P

Drawing on an iconic heritage setting, Wembley Park's 85-acre mixed-use, residential, retail, leisure and commercial district is at a fascinating stage. Take a tour with the creative team from Quintain, Flanagan Lawrence and LDA Design.
Tube: Wembley Park; Rail: Wembley Stadium; 83,92,182,206, 297
www.wembleypark.com

Supported by

Camden

See **openhouselondon.org.uk/camden**
to find out more about this area

33 Heath Hurst Road

2 [point] 88
10 Regal Lane NW1 7TH
■ Sat 10am-5pm. Half-hourly tours. Pre-book ONLY via mail@
studio-gil.com. Last entry 4.30pm. Max 5 per tour. A T d
The extension and remodelling of a 1960s property originally
designed by the modernist architect John Winter. The interior
is clad and furnished with Russian birch plywood panels, steel
and exposed concrete. John Winter 1960s/Studio Gil 2015.
Tube: Camden Town; Tube/Rail: Kentish Town; 274,214,C2,393,29
www.studio-gil.com

2 Willow Road
2 Willow Road NW3 1TH
■ Sat/Sun 11am-5pm. Entry via limited timed tickets only (one
per person) available from house on day, first come basis. 15
people every 20 mins. Includes NT members. No tours, self-
guided viewing only. Last entry 4.20pm. Q
Goldfinger's unique Modernist home, largely in original
condition. The house is designed for flexibility, efficient use
of space and good day-lighting. Complete with fittings and
furniture designed by Goldfinger and an impressive modern
art collection including works by Marcel Duchamp, Max Ernst,
Henry Moore and Bridget Riley. Ernö Goldfinger 1939.
Tube: Hampstead; Rail: Hampstead Heath; 24,46,168,268,C11

5 Pancras Square ●
5 Pancras Square N1C 4AG
■ Sat/Sun 1pm-5pm. Tours 1pm, 2pm, 3pm, 4pm, first come
basis. Duration 45 mins. D R T G
One of the greenest buildings in London after achieving a
BREEAM Outstanding rating for sustainable design, Camden's
new 13-storey building combines two swimming pools, a
state-of-the-art fitness gym, café, relocated modern library,
customer access centre and office accommodation. Bennetts
Associates Architects 2014.
Tube/Rail: King's Cross St Pancras; 10,30,59,205,390
www.bennettsassociates.com

8 Stoneleigh Terrace (Highgate New Town, Stage 1)
8 Stoneleigh Terrace N19 5TY
■ Sun 10am-5pm. Hourly tours, first come basis. Last tour
4pm. NB closed 1pm-2pm. Max 25 per tour. T
Built during the golden era of Camden public housing by an
architect who studied with Ernö Goldfinger and worked with
Denys Lasdun. Peter Tábori, Camden Architect's Department
1972-9. Entry: whole flat plus tour of estate.
Tube: Archway; 4,C11

8a Belsize Court Garages ●
8a Belsize Court Garages NW3 5AJ
■ Sat/Sun 10am-1pm. Architect-led tours every 45 mins, first
come basis. Last entry 12.15pm. Max 10 per tour. A G d
Originally a late C19 coachman's living quarters and stable,
this mews house combines an award-winning architect's
studio and spacious light-filled maisonette after a 2-phase
retrofit. Sanya Polescuk Architects 2012.
Tube: Belsize Park, Swiss Cottage; 168,268,24,46,113

33 Heath Hurst Road
33 Heath Hurst Road, Hampstead NW3 2RU
■ Sat/Sun 10am-5pm. Pre-book ONLY via daniel@
studio1architects.co.uk quoting Open House as subject. A d
3000ft² of Hampstead high and splendour. Large
contemporary kitchen/dining area with sequence of seamless
windows/skylights that wrap up the walls and across the
ceiling. 6m-high ceilings and floating mezzanine in second
reception room. Period embellishments and creative
contemporary design throughout. Studio 1 Architects 2015.
Tube: Belsize Park; Rail: Hampstead Heath; 24,46,168,C11

39-47 Gordon Square (Birkbeck School of Arts)
43 Gordon Square WC1H 0PD
■ Sat/Sun 10am-5pm. Tours on the hour. Also tours of 'The
Wider Gordon Square'. Last tour 4pm. Max 15 per tour. R T A d
Georgian terrace, centre of the Bloomsbury Group activities.
Grade II listed. Includes recent radical interior intervention at
basement and ground floor levels. RIBA Award Winner 2008.
Thomas Cubitt 1820s/Surface Architects 2007. Entry: cinema,
Keynes Library.
Tube/Rail: Euston, King's Cross St Pancras; 168,59,68,91

58a Gondar Gardens
58a Gondar Gardens NW6 1HG
■ Sat 1pm-5pm. Regular tours, first come basis. Last entry
4.50pm. Max 4 per tour. A d
Garden flat designed to transport the client from London to St
Ives. An internal courtyard gives views of the stunning garden
from both master bedroom and living room. Studio McLeod
2012. Entry: ground floor flat, garden.
Tube: Kilburn; C11,328,332,189,16

73 Chester Road ●
73 Chester Road N19 5DH
■ Sat tours 10am, 11am, 12noon, 2pm, 3pm, 4pm. First come
basis. Max 10 per tour. G P
Victorian house refurbished to reduce carbon emissions
by 85%. Sustainable features include: solid wall insulation;
double/triple glazing; solar hot water and PV panels; wood-
burning stove. Sarah Harrison 2006.
Tube: Archway; C11,C2,214

Adaptable House
6 Doughty Mews WC1N 2PG
■ Sun 12noon-5pm. First come basis, queuing if necessary.
Max 20 at one time. A G
Self-build conversion followed by 30-year occupation,
from party house to office to family home for 6. Ash Sakula
Architects 1983 onwards.
*Tube: Russell Square; Tube/Rail: King's Cross St Pancras,
Farringdon; 19,38,17,45,55*

Alexandra Road ●
13b Rowley Way, Abbey Road NW8 0SF
■ Sat 10am-5pm. First come basis, queuing if necessary.
Regular tours. Last entry 4.30pm. Max 4 at one time. Q
The last large social housing complex in London – a low-rise,
high-density enclave. Terraced housing reinterpreted. Listed
Grade II* in 1993. Flat virtually as originally designed. Neave
Brown 1968-79. Entry: whole flat.
Tube: Swiss Cottage; Rail: South Hampstead; 189,139

Alexandra Road Park and Tenants Hall ● ●
Langtry Walk/Rowley Way NW8 0SW
■ Sat 10am-5pm. Hourly tours departing Tenants Hall, with
lead landscape architect. Max 25 per tour. A T R N d
Unique modernist sculpted linear park, integral to the iconic
Alexandra Road housing estate. The innovative landscape
design with series of outdoor 'rooms' has now been restored.
Original Tenants Hall overlooking park also open. Janet Jack/
Neave Brown 1979/J&L Gibbons/Erect Architecture 2015.
*Tube: Swiss Cottage; Tube/Rail: West Hampstead; Rail: South
Hampstead; 139,189,31,46,13*

Archive – Philip Hughes Studio
62 Rochester Place NW1 9JX
■ Sat 10am-5pm. First come basis. Max 12 at one time. A d
Private gallery and art archive. Mews workshop converted
to artist's studio/summerhouse. Uses mirrors and glazed
surfaces to produce theatrical distortion of spaces. Mezzanine
studio carpeted in red, double-height garden room, wedge-
shaped glazing. Rear connects to garden with spa. Hughes
Meyer Studio/Sanei Hopkins Architects 2004.
Tube: Camden Town; Rail: Camden Road; C2,29,134

Key. A Architect on site **B** Bookshop **C** Childrens' activities **d** Some disabled access **D** Full wheelchair access **E** Engineer on site **G** Green Features
N Normally open to the public **P** Parking **Q** Long queues envisaged **R** Refreshments **T** Toilets

Bertram Street Low Energy Victorian Terrace ●
8 Bertram Street N19 5DQ
- ■ Sat 10am-4pm. Hourly tours, first come basis. NB residents have a dog. No under 16s please. Last tour 3pm. Max 10 per tour. G

Low-carbon retrofit to a 3-storey Victorian terraced house in a conservation area to reduce emissions by 77%. Includes pioneering method of fitting internal wall insulation while the residents continued to live in the property. Sustainable features include: vacuum glazing; MVHR; solar thermal and PV panels. United House with Sustainable Energy Academy/ Parity Projects/ LB Camden 2010. Entry: most living areas.
Tube: Archway, Tufnell Park; 4,143,C11

British Medical Association House
Tavistock Square WC1H 9JP
- ■ Sun 10am-5pm. Hourly tours. Last tour 4pm. Pre-book ONLY via 020 7383 6363. Max 20 at one time. T d

Designed by Lutyens in 1913 for the Theosophical Society and acquired by the BMA in 1923. Extended by Wontner Smith (1928/9) and Douglas Wood (1938/50 and 1959/60). Entry: council chamber, Princes room, Hastings room, library, garden.
Tube: Russell Square; Tube/Rail: Euston; 59,68,91,168

British Museum Underground Tour
Great Russell Street WC1B 3DG
- ■ Sat tours 11am, 12.30pm. Meet at the Information Desk in the Great Court 15 minutes before the tour. Photo ID required. Pre-book ONLY via www.britishmuseum.org or 020 7323 8181. Max 20 per tour. D R T B

An exploration of the British Museum's basement corridors, old and new, focusing on the area underneath the Great Court and highlighting the inner workings of the Museum, plus talk about the birth of the Clore Centre for Education and associated spaces. These tours mark the 15-year anniversary of the opening of the Great Court and related education facilities.
Sir Robert Smirke 1823-1850/Foster + Partners 2000.
Tube: Russell Square, Holborn

BT Tower
45 Maple Street W1T 4BG
- ■ Sat/Sun 9.30am-7.30pm. Access by ballot ONLY, see p17 for more details. NB. Airport security in place, visitors and bags searched. Photo ID required (valid EU identity card, passport or drivers licence). D R T

50 years since it was declared operational in 1965, the BT Tower is still very much alive and relaying broadcast, internet and telephone information around the world today. An enduring, distinctive feature of the London skyline for all that time, this is a rare opportunity for members of the public to visit the famous revolving floor, 158 metres above the capital. GR Yeats, Ministry of Public Buildings & Works 1965.
Tube: Warren Street, Great Portland Street, Euston Square; Tube/Rail: Euston; 29,73,18,24

Burgh House
New End Square NW3 1LT
- ■ Sun 10am-5pm. Last entry 4.30pm. N R T B d

Grade I listed Queen Anne house (1704) retaining original panelling and staircase with a modern gallery set in a small terrace garden. Entry: café, period rooms, art gallery, shop, kids' corner, Museum of Hampstead. Exhibition of postcards.
Tube: Hampstead; Rail: Hampstead Heath; 46,24,268,168,C11

Burton House ●
1b Lady Margaret Road (big round gate) NW5 2NE
- ■ Sat 10am-5pm/Sun 10am-1pm. Last entry 15 minutes before close. Max 40 at 30 minute intervals. N B A G P

A family complex inserted into a C19 area, part self-built on a brownfield site with planted roofs and a retained plane tree with new planting. A passive and active solar, highly insulated example of green architecture in a city, using about half the energy per msq of a normal house. Timber structure, aluminium cladding and brick. Richard Burton (ABK) 1987-2002. Entry: house, studio, annex.
Tube/Rail: Kentish Town; C2,134,214,393

Fenton House
Hampstead Grove NW3 6SP
- ■ Sat/Sun 11am-5pm. Entry to house via limited timed tickets only available on the day, first come basis. Includes NT members. Last entry 4.30pm. T Q d

Beautiful town house retaining original features and housing important decorative arts collections. William Eades 1686.
Tube: Hampstead; Rail: Hampstead Heath; 46,210,268

Friends House
173-177 Euston Road NW1 2BJ
- ■ Sat 9am-4pm. Regular tours (max 10), first come basis, last tour 3.10pm. Architect-led tours 9.30am, 10.30am, 11.30am (max 15), pre-book ONLY via http://goo.gl/eCmmda. N R T B A

Grade II listed home of the Religious Society of Friends (Quakers) in Britain. Described by Architectural Review in 1927 as '...eminently Quakerly, uniting common sense with just so much relief from absolute plainness as gives pleasure'. RIBA Bronze Medal, 1927. Recent refurbishment transforms the Large Meeting House into a versatile, accessible and sustainable space. Moveable raked seating allows a range of configurations, and a dramatic rooflight fills the space with daylight. Winner RIBA Regional Award 2015. Hubert Lidbetter 1926/John McAslan + Partners (refurb) 2014.
Tube: Euston Square; Tube/Rail: Euston, King's Cross St Pancras; 10,18,30,73,91,68,205,253
http://www.mcaslan.co.uk

Garden Court Chambers
57-60 Lincoln's Inn Fields WC2A 3LJ
- ■ Sat 10am-4pm/Sun 10am-1pm. Hourly tours. Last tour Sat 4pm, Sun 1pm. Max 25 per tour. T Q d

Inigo Jones' design at no. 59-60 intended as model for Lincoln's Inn Fields development, copied by no.57-58, with portico and elliptical staircase added by Soane. Sympathetically refurbished by current occupiers, a barrister's chambers. Retains many original features, staircases, fireplaces, mouldings and historical associations. Display of historical photography and architectural drawings and recent restoration works. Inigo Jones 1640s /Sir John Soane 1700s. Entry: reception, staircases, meeting and conference rooms.
Tube: Holborn; Tube/Rail: Charing Cross; 1,59,68,91,168,171,188,243

German Historical Institute
17 Bloomsbury Square WC1A 2NJ
- ■ Sat 10am-2pm. Half-hourly tours, first come basis. D R T C

Originally constructed in the later C17, this Grade II* listed building was remodelled by John Nash c1777-8. Highlights include an Adam-style ceiling on the 1st floor and a beautiful staircase with wrought-iron balustrade. Once home to the Pharmaceutical Society of Great Britain, it now houses an historical research institute. 1660s/John Nash (altered) 1777. Entry: ground and first floors.
Tube: Holborn, Russell Square, Tottenham Court Road; 19,38,55,59,68,98

Gibbs Building, Wellcome Trust
215 Euston Road NW1 2BE
- ■ Sat 10am-5pm. Last entry 4.45pm. Max 600 at one time. D R T B C

BT Tower

HQ of the Wellcome Trust, a global charitable foundation dedicated to achieving improvements in health by supporting the brightest minds. Vast open plan design around a light-filled atrium featuring spectacular artwork. RIBA Award Winner 2005. Entry: ground floor atrium, 5th floor viewing gallery and art works. Talks on Thomas Heatherwick sculpture. Activities for families including create your own London skyline. Hopkins Architects 2004.
Tube: Euston Square, Warren Street; Tube/Rail: Euston, King's Cross St Pancras; 18,24,29,30,253

Government Art Collection
Queen's Yard, 179a Tottenham Court Road W1T 7PA
- ■ Sat/Sun 10am-5pm. Hourly tours. Duration 45 mins. Pre-book ONLY via 020 7211 2425 or www.gac.culture.gov.uk/ openhouse2015.html. Last tour 4pm. Max 25 per tour. T

Guided tour of premises and behind-the-scenes look at how this major collection of British art operates. Entry: all areas except office accommodation.
Tube: Goodge Street, Warren Street, Euston Square; Tube/Rail: Euston; 10,14,24,29,73,134,390

Gray's Inn
Gray's Inn WC1R 5ET
- ■ Sun tours 10.30am, 12noon, 2pm. Pre-book ONLY via graysinnopenhouse.eventbrite.co.uk. Duration 1 hour. Must enter via entrance in High Holborn next to Cittie of York. Max 30 per tour. T

700 year old legal collegiate institution. Hall includes C16 screen. Much of Inn redesigned in neo-Georgian style by Sir Edward Maufe after 1941 bombing. 1560/1800/1950. Entry: hall, large pension room, small pension room, chapel and the walks.
Tube: Chancery Lane, Holborn; Tube/Rail: King's Cross St Pancras, Blackfriars; 8,19,25,38,45,55,242,341

Hampstead Friends Meeting House

120 Heath Street NW3 1DR

■ Sun 1pm-5pm. Regular tours. N R T d

Listed Arts & Crafts freestyle building with plain interior and many charming original features, sympathetically modernised in 1991. Entrance via listed gateway. Frederick Rowntree 1907. Entry: ground floor, 1st floor library.
Tube: Hampstead; Rail: Hampstead Heath; 268

Jestico + Whiles

1 Cobourg Street NW1 2HP

■ Sat 10am-4pm. Half-hourly tours, first come basis. Last entry 4pm. Max 20 at one time. N A G

Modernist conversion of former Victorian stable block to provide radical mix of lofts and workspace. Sustainable features include natural ventilation, fast-reacting warm air and ventilation system. Exhibition on display. Jestico + Whiles (conversion) 1998.
Tube: Euston Square; Tube/Rail: Euston, King's Cross St. Pancras; 10,27,29,30,73,88,134

JW3-Jewish Community Centre London ●

341-351 Finchley Road NW3 6ET

■ Sun 10am-10pm. Self-guided tours of the main spaces until 10pm. Guided tours of the nursery until 6pm. Children's activities: 'crafternoon' 2pm-5pm, building with marshmallow geodesic shapes; behind the scenes building explorer tours, 2pm, 3pm, 4pm (pre-book via https://goo.gl/JfjAgJ). N D R T C A G

Award winning Jewish arts, community and cultural centre. Designed to host a wide range of activities: dance, cinema, restaurant, theatre, art, cooking, classes and courses for adults and children. Lifschutz Davidson Sandilands 2013. Entry: varies throughout the day, access to nursery and roof garden usually closed to the public.
Tube: Finchley Road; Tube/Rail: West Hampstead; Rail: Finchley Road & Frognal; 13,82,113,187,268
www.jw3.org.uk

King's Cross Public Realm ● ●

Western Transit Shed, 11 Stable Street N1C 4AB

■ Sat/Sun 10am-4pm. Regular site tours starting at King's Cross Visitor Centre, pre-book ONLY via http://tours.kingscross.co.uk. Max 20 per tour. N E D R T A G

The King's Cross Partnership is currently regenerating a 67 acre site previously known as the 'railway lands', This will contain 20 heritage industrial buildings and structures as well as 50 new buildings including homes, shops, offices, bars, restaurants, Central St Martins, a school and public realm areas such as Granary Square, Cubitt Park and Square, public art installation KX Pond and Skip Garden, home of Global Generation. Townshend Landscape Architects/Stanton Williams/Allies & Morrison/Porphyrios Associates 2012.
Tube/Rail: King's Cross St Pancras; 10,46,73,214,390

London Mathematical Society

De Morgan House, 57-58 Russell Square WC1B 4HS

■ Sun 10am-5pm. Half-hourly tours. Last tour 3.30pm. Max 10 per tour. R T d

Two Grade II listed buildings, 4-storey yellow stock brick with a rusticated stucco base. No.57 has a further attic level with a garden at the rear. Staircases are intact and each room still retains the high ceilings and ornamental fireplaces. James Burton 1803. Entry: lower ground floor, reception, room 14, members' room. Exhibition running.
Tube: Russell Square; Tube/Rail: Euston, King's Cross St Pancras; 188,91,168,7

London School of Hygiene & Tropical Medicine ●

Keppel Street WC1E 7HT

■ Sat 10am-5pm/Sun 10am-3pm. Hourly tours. Exhibition on history of building. School researchers available on Sun to showcase work and answer questions. Last tour one hour before closing. Max 20 per tour. D T G

Beautiful Grade II listed Art Deco building with highly decorated façade, period library, north courtyard extension and new south courtyard building. P Morley Horder & Verner O Rees 1929/Devereux Architects 2003/2009. Entry: entrance hall, library, north and south courtyard buildings.
Tube: Goodge Street; Tube/Rail: Euston, King's Cross St Pancras; 10,24,29,73,134

Loth House

1 Cliff Road NW1 9AJ

■ Sat/Sun 1pm-5pm. Regular architect-led tours, first come basis. Last entry 4.30pm. Max 30 at one time. N Q A G d

Architect's 1850s semi, reinvented and landscaped in an integrated modern design. Basement office faces waterfall, living room incorporates aluminium bas relief, top floor open to roof. Mediterranean, Japanese and American influences. Dale Loth refurb 1991-2012. Entry: all four floors and garden.
Tube: Caledonian Road; Tube/Rail: Kentish Town; Rail: Camden Road; 29,253,274,390,393

Lullaby Factory, Great Ormond Street Hospital for Children

Great Ormond Street WC1N 3JH

■ Sat 1pm-5pm. Tours 1pm, 2pm, 3pm, 4pm. Pre-book ONLY via gocreate@gosh.nhs.uk. Max 10 per tour. Duration 20 mins. D R T A

Studio Weave and Great Ormond Street Hospital have transformed an awkward exterior space landlocked by buildings into a secret world that cannot be seen except from inside the hospital and only heard from a few special listening pipes. Studio Weave 2012.
Tube: Holborn, Russell Square; 38,59,91,168,243

McCann London Offices

7-11 Herbrand Street WC1N 1EX

■ Sat 10am-5pm. Regular tours. Last entry 4.30pm. Max 15 per tour. T R

A 1930s Art Deco former Daimler Hire garage, now home to McCann London, an advertising agency. Wallis, Gilbert & Partners 1931.
Tube: Russell Square; Tube/Rail: Euston, King's Cross St Pancras; 59,68,91,98,168,188

Miranda House

58 Grafton Way W1T 5DL

■ Sat/Sun 1pm-5pm. Regular tours. R T

Former residence of Francisco de Miranda, a Venezuelan general with an international military career and an early advocate of independence from Spain. A rare survival of a Georgian town house (1792) which once welcomed Simon Bolivar. Venezuelan culture workshops. Boyd Auger (restoration) 1980s/Craig Downie (restoration) 2014. Entry: ground to third floor.
Tube: Warren Street, Euston Square; Tube/Rail: Euston; 29,134,30,73,18
www.mirandahouse.org

Montpelier Community Nursery ●

115 Brecknock Road N19 5AH

■ Sun 1pm-5pm. First come basis, queuing outside if necessary. Last entry 4.45pm. D T A G

New-build community nursery providing affordable childcare for 24 2-5 year olds. The energy efficient cross laminated timber building maximises daylight and has an excellent

Royal College of General Practitioners

relationship with the treescape of the secluded public gardens within which it is situated. RIBA National Award 2013 and Stephen Lawrence Prize Winner, Highly Commended in Camden Design Awards 2014. AY Architects 2012.
Tube: Tufnell Park; Tube/Rail: Kentish Town; 390,393,134,29

New Horizon Youth Centre

68 Chalton Street NW1 1JR

■ Sat/Sun 10.30am-4pm. Tours 11am, 11.30am, 12noon, 12.30pm, first come basis. Architects on site on Saturday. Last entry 12.30pm. Max 10 per tour. D R T

The architects' approach centred on the concept of home and how to invest an institutional building with the flexibility and generosity of a welcoming settled house. From outside the new Big Barn extension picks up the surrounding Arts & Crafts language of steeply pitched roofs and homely stability, but twists it to something fresh and surprising. RIBA Award winner 2010. LCC 1927/Adam Khan Architects 2010. Entry: drop-in, barn, balcony.
Tube/Rail: Euston, King's Cross St Pancras; 73,253,168,59,68

Paul McAneary Architects' Office

6 Flitcroft Street WC2H 8DJ

■ Sat/Sun 11am-6pm. Last entry 5.30pm. T G d

Architect's own studio designed and built by themselves over four years. Containing numerous innovative experimental and bespoke details designed using their trademark 'warm minimalism'. Mini architectural exhibition. Paul McAneary Architects 2015.
Tube: Tottenham Court Road; 24,29,134,176,242

Regent High School

Chalton Street, entrance opposite Cranleigh Street NW1 1RX

■ Sat 10am-3.30pm. Regular tours, first come basis. Accessible

Key. A Architect on site **B** Bookshop **C** Childrens' activities **d** Some disabled access **D** Full wheelchair access **E** Engineer on site **G** Green Features **N** Normally open to the public **P** Parking **Q** Long queues envisaged **R** Refreshments **T** Toilets

tours on request. Architect-led tour with Walters & Cohen 11am, duration 1 hour, max 20. 'I Spy' trail around the school for children. Last entry 3pm. D T C G A

New build and refurbishment. The new building features a triple-storey 'arcade' that links to the existing Victorian building, simplifies movement around the school and provides passive supervision. London School Board 1870s/Gollifer Langston Architects 2004/Walters & Cohen Architects 2014.
Tube: Mornington Crescent; Tube/Rail: Euston; 46,214,168,73,253

Royal College of General Practitioners ●
30 Euston Square NW1 2FB
■ Sat 10am-4pm/Sun 11am-4pm. Hourly tours, also architect-led tours describing restoration process. Pre-book ONLY via openhouse@rcgp.org.uk. Max 10 at one time. D R T A

Grade II* listed building recently restored to showcase magnificent Edwardian faience tile work, rust glass mosaic floor and other historic features in transformed modern surroundings that now provide the new headquarters of the Royal College of General Practitioners. Arthur Beresford Pite 1908/Harmsen Tilney Shane 2012. Entry: roof terrace, state of the art auditorium (Sun only) and boutique bedrooms.
Tube/Rail: Euston, Euston Square

Royal College of Physicians
11 St Andrew's Place, Regents Park NW1 4LE
■ Sun 11am-4pm. Regular architectural and garden tours bookable on the day. Lecture 'The Architecture of Sir Denys Lasdun' at 2.15pm given by Dr Barnabas Calder. Last entry 3.30pm. N D R T B C

Dramatic interior spaces and white mosaic exterior elevated on piloti. Grade I listed and one of London's most important post-war buildings. Sir Denys Lasdun 1964/1996. Entry: main hall, theatres, library, Osler Room, Censors' Room, council chamber, treasures, physic garden. Children's activities: family quiz and Lego building activities.
Tube: Warren Street, Great Portland Street, Regents Park; Tube/Rail: Euston, King's Cross St Pancras; C2,18,27,30,88,205,453
www.rcplondon.ac.uk/museum-garden

Senate House
University of London, Malet Street WC1E 7HU
■ Sat 10am-2pm. Informal tours. Max 250 at one time. D T Q G
London's tallest secular building when it opened in the 1930s as the administrative HQ of the University of London, this Grade II listed landmark Portland stone structure balances classicism and modernity beautifully. Handsome, lavishly-panelled interiors and original period features. Recently undergone extensive refurbishment, with some works ongoing. Charles Holden 1937/BDP (refurb) 2009.
Tube: Russell Square, Goodge Street, Euston Square; Tube/Rail: Euston, King's Cross St Pancras; 7,10,24,29,68,73,134,188

Sir John Soane's Museum
13 & 14 Lincoln's Inn Fields WC2A 3BP
■ Sat 10am-3pm. Half-hourly tours alternating between No.14 Lincoln's Inn Fields (max 15) and Soane's Drawing Office (max 6). First come basis. Last tour 2.30pm. T B Q d

No.14 Lincoln's Inn Fields, built by Sir John Soane in 1824 and let out in his lifetime as a private house, is a rare and beautiful example of the architect's late work with a number of fine interiors. Restored in 2006/7 by Julian Harrap Architects (RIBA Award Winner 2009). Soane's Drawing Office is a miracle of planning, a small pod-like space perched above the Colonnade at the heart of the Museum. Sir John Soane 1812 & 1824/Julian Harrap Architects (refurb) 2008. Entry: No.14 Lincoln's Inn Fields, Soane's Drawing Office. NB. No access to main museum.
Tube: Holborn; 1,8,19,25,38

St George's Bloomsbury
Bloomsbury Way WC1A 2SA
■ Sat 10am-5pm/Sun 12noon-5pm. Regular architect-led tours. Hawksmoor and Bloomsbury exhibition in Undercroft. N D T C

Last of Hawksmoor's six London churches and consecrated in 1730, St George's is regarded for its majestic portico and stepped tower with lion and unicorn sculptures. The nave is now graced with a magnificent late C17 chandelier, which once hung in the grand entrance of the V&A. The interior and exterior re-lighting scheme concludes the restoration project coordinated by World Monuments Fund Britain. Nicholas Hawksmoor 1720s.
Tube: Tottenham Court Road, Holborn, Russell Square; Tube/Rail: Euston; 8,19,25,38,55

St Pancras Chambers and Clock Tower ●
The Forecourt, St Pancras Station, Euston Road NW1 2AR
■ Sat/Sun 10am-5pm. Tours every 20 minutes. Pre-book ONLY via https://openhouselondon2015stpancras.eventbrite.co.uk.

Former Midland Grand Hotel, now St Pancras Renaissance Hotel and Chambers apartments. Includes hotel lobby and clock tower. George Gilbert Scott 1868-1873.
Tube/Rail: King's Cross St Pancras

St Pancras International ● ●
Meet at special assistance meeting point (next to Starbucks) Euston Road N1C 4QP
■ Sat/Sun 10am-5pm. Tours on the hour, pre-book ONLY via www.stpancras.com/events. Last tour 4pm. Max 20 per tour. N D R T

A unique Grade I listed Victorian railway station completed in 1868, with the original station hotel following in 1873. After a £800 million transformation, St Pancras International, home of HS1, has redefined railway stations for the twenty-first century and is a destination in its own right. The tour will include an architectural history of the iconic station. Barlow/Gilbert Scott 1868/Foster + Partners/Lansley 2007. Entry: grand terrace, arcade, circle.
Tube/Rail: King's Cross St Pancras; 10,30,59,205,390

Swiss Cottage Library
88 Avenue Road NW3 3HA
■ Sat 10am-5pm/Sun 11am-4pm. Regular tours focusing on the library's original architect Sir Basil Spence. N D R T

Grade II listed building by renowned Modernist, which has been refurbished and remodelled whilst protecting the building's landmark status. Sir Basil Spence 1963/John McAslan + Partners (refurb) 2003. Entry: public areas and basement reserve stock area.
Tube: Swiss Cottage; 31,C11,82,13,268,187,46

The Building Centre and the NLA
26 Store Street WC1E 7BT
■ Sat 10am-5pm/Sun 11am-4pm.

Displays include '41: A House for London', the world's first house made from Niobium steel shipping containers (tour and talk with designers Sat 12.30pm); NLA's interactive New London Model showing future plans for the city (Sat/Sun tours 1.30pm, 3pm); 'Drawn to the Future', an exhibition by The Building Centre exploring innovation in visualisation (curator-led talk Sat 12noon).
Tube: Goodge Street; Tube/Rail: Euston

The Coach House ●
2a Belsize Park Gardens NW3 4LA
■ Sat/Sun tours 10am, 11am, 12noon, 2pm, 3pm, 4pm, pre-book ONLY via http://www.superhomes.org.uk. Max 10 per tour. NB children over 12 only. G E

Victorian house retrofitted to save 70% carbon. High comfort internal and external insulation, high performance double glazing, heat recovery ventilation, LED low energy lights.
Tube: Belsize Park, Swiss Cottage, Finchley Road; 168,268,13,46,113

The Floating Cinema: Extra-Terrestrial Open Air Weekender, Humans in Space ●
Canalside Steps, Granary Square, King's Cross N1C 4AA
■ Sat 12noon-9.30pm/Sun 12noon-8.30pm. Pre-book only via www.floatingcinema.info/events. N d

UP Projects' extraordinary floating structure designed by Duggan Morris Architects, with a programme of open air film featuring sci-fi cult classics and rarities alongside talks and artist installations exploring life beyond Earth, visions of cosmic utopias and future intergalactic worlds. Duggan Morris Architects 2013.
Tube/Rail: King's Cross St Pancras

The Wiener Library
29 Russell Square WC1B 5DP
■ Sun 1pm-4pm. Half-hourly tours. Last entry 3.45pm. Max 10 per tour. N D R T

Sensitive yet bold refurbishment of historic Grade II listed townhouse for The Wiener Library including dramatic first floor reading room, new mezzanine and ground floor exhibition spaces. Barbara Weiss Architects (refurb) 2011. Entry: Wolfson Reading Room, exhibition, archive stores.
Tube: Russell Square; Rail: Euston; 59,68,168,188

Tottenham Court Road Station Upgrade ●
Crossrail Dean Street worksite W1D 3SY
■ Sat. See www.crossrail.co.uk/openhouse for booking details and meeting point. E

Crossrail is working alongside TfL on a £1bn transformation of Tottenham Court Road Station, the biggest transport investment in the West End for decades. Crossrail works include the construction of a secondary ticket hall in Dean Street, and the first new West End theatre in over a decade at the former Astoria. Hawkins\Brown due 2018.
Tube: Tottenham Court Road
www.crossrail.co.uk/openhouse

ZSL Library
Outer Circle, Regent's Park NW1 4RY
■ Sun tours 10am, 12noon, 2.30pm. Pre-book ONLY via library@zsl.org. Last entry 2.30pm Max 20 per tour. T N

The library of the Zoological Society of London, also contains ZSL Council Room and an interesting lift. Historical images and models will be on display. John James Joass 1910.
Tube: Camden Town; 274

WALKS/TOURS

King's Cross Area Guided Walk ●
■ Meet: Sat 11am on the corner of Pancras Road and King's Boulevard (pedestrianised) N1C 4TB. Pre-book ONLY via www.landscapeinstitute.org/events. Duration 1.5-2 hours. Max 20 per tour. A E

Walk and talk with landscape architect Dominic Cole exploring the regeneration and landscape design of King's Cross Regent's Quarter, Kings Place, canal, Central St Martin's, St Pancras Old Church and back.
Tube/Rail: King's Cross St Pancras

Supported by

● AJ Library Building　● Green Exemplar　● Landscape/Public realm　● Infrastructure/Engineering　■ Open Saturday　■ Open Sunday　■ Open Saturday and Sunday

openhouselondon.org.uk | **Camden** | 25

City of London

See **openhouselondon.org.uk/cityoflondon**
to find out more about this area

1 Finsbury Circus
1 Finsbury Circus EC2M 7EB
■ Sat/Sun 10am-1pm. Half-hourly tours led by renovation architect. Last tour 12.30pm. Max 20 per tour. D T A
This Lutyens Grade II listed building has been comprehensively redeveloped to provide a high quality contemporary interior, with a fully glazed spectacular atrium roof to maximize daylight and aspect. Edwin Lutyens 1925/Gaunt Francis (refurb) 2008. Entry: reception, listed staircase, atrium, 8th floor, basement, listed boardroom.
Tube/Rail: Liverpool Street; Tube: Moorgate; 43,76,100,141

4 Bayer House ⊙
Golden Lane Estate EC1Y 0RN
■ Sun 11am-5pm. Half-hourly tours, first come basis. Closed between 1pm and 2pm. Last tour 4.30pm. Max 10 per tour.
Part of Golden Lane Estate which was the first public housing to be listed. A maisonette with many of the original detailing and finishes. Chamberlin, Powell & Bon 1957. Entry: all rooms.
Tube: Barbican; Tube/Rail: Farringdon, Liverpool Street; 4,55,56,153,243

6 Bevis Marks
Entrance on Bury Court EC3A 7BA
■ Sun 10am-5pm. Hourly tours, first come basis, queuing outside if necessary. Last entry 4pm. Max 28 per tour. D T A G
This 16-storey building in the City provides a covered roof top garden with spectacular views. It also improves the public amenity spaces around the building with wider pavements and links to the plaza of 30 St Mary Axe (the Gherkin). Fletcher Priest Architects 2013. Entry: ground floor reception, levels 10, 11 and 16 terrace.
Tube: Aldgate, Moorgate; Tube/Rail: Liverpool Street; 47,78,100,135,205
www.fletcherpriest.com

10 Exchange Square – Rooftop
10 Exchange Square Appold Street EC2M 2QA
■ Sat 10.30am-3pm. 15-minute rooftop tours, first come basis. Max 6 per tour. G d
A relatively new addition to the Broadgate family designed by Skidmore, Owings, & Merrill. The roof gives a bird's eye view of Exchange Square and the rest of the development. Skidmore, Owings & Merrill 2004.
Tube/Rail: Liverpool Street; 8,11,26,35,42,47

30 St Mary Axe (The Gherkin) ⊙
30 St Mary Axe EC3A 8EP
■ Sun 8am-5pm. Groups of 30 people every 10 mins, strictly 20 mins duration in total, first come basis. High security with bag and body scans. Bring photo ID. Last tour 4.30pm. Open House volunteer access 5-6pm only. D T Q
30 St Mary Axe, affectionately known as the 'Gherkin', is a landmark curvilinear 40-storey office building in the heart of London's financial centre and is unlike any other ever conceived. With distinctive tapering form that minimises its footprint and effect on the London skyline and eco-friendly glazed skin with lightwells. Foster + Partners 2003. Entry: foyer, top of the building.
Tube: Aldgate; DLR/Tube: Bank; Tube/Rail: Liverpool Street; 4,8,25,100,149

88 Wood Street ⊙
88 Wood Street EC2V 7AJ
■ Sat 10am-5pm. First come basis, queuing if necessary. Last entry 4.30pm. Max 4 at one time. E D T Q
Office building arranged as 3 linked blocks that step up from 8 to 17 storeys, with fully glazed floors and roof terraces offering spectacular views across the City. Richard Rogers Partnership 1999. Entry: reception area, lift lobbies including 17th floor.
Tube: St Paul's; 100,4,56

100 Victoria Embankment – Unilever House
100 Victoria Embankment EC4Y 0DY
■ Sat 10am-5pm. First come basis, queuing outside if necessary. Last entry 4.30pm. Max 200 at one time. D T
Landmark curved Grade II listed building which has been transformed to give it a new lease of life. RIBA Award Winner 2009. James Lomax Simpson 1930/Kohn Pedersen Fox Associates 2007. Entry: lobby and ground floor atrium.
Tube/Rail: Blackfriars; 63,100,388,45

Apothecaries' Hall
Black Friars Lane EC4V 6EJ
■ Sun 10am-3pm. First come basis. Last entry 2.45pm. Max 100 at one time. Q
A courtyard building with some of the best-preserved C17 livery hall interiors, on the site of the Blackfriars Priory on which the original hall burnt down in 1666. Thomas Locke 1672. Entry: parlour, court room, great hall.
Tube: Monument; Tube/Rail: Blackfriars; 4,11,15,23,26,45,63,76,172

Armoury House
City Road EC1Y 2BQ
■ Sat 1pm-5pm. Last entry 4.30pm. T G d
The home of the Honourable Artillery Company, completed in 1735 to designs by Thomas Stibbs and financed in part by a gift of £500 from King George I. The building cost £1690 including the price of the furniture. West and East Wings built 1828.
Tube: Old Street, Moorgate; 43,141,21,76
www.hac.org.uk

Bank of England
Threadneedle Street EC2R 8AH
■ Sat/Sun 9.30am-4pm. Tours available on first come first serve basis, ending in museum. Many steps. Duration 30 mins. No priority for Open House volunteers. High security: bag and body scans. Last entry 4pm. Max 15 per tour (limited to 500 tour places per day). D T Q
Originally by George Sampson, Robert Taylor and John Soane, rebuilt by Herbert Baker in imperial classical style. Soanian remnants: screen walls and reconstruction of 1793 Stock Office in Museum. Sir Herbert Baker 1925-39. Entry: museum also open, with no access restrictions.
DLR/Tube: Bank; Tube/Rail: Liverpool Street; 8,11,26,43,76,133,242

Barbican Open Garden
Meet: Ticket Hall of Barbican Station EC1A 4JA
■ Sat/Sun tours 11am, 11.30am, 12noon, 1.30pm, 2pm, 2.30pm, 3pm. Pre-book ONLY, check Open House website entry for details. NB. Tour contains many stairs, not accessible for pushchairs or wheelchairs. Max 15 per tour.
This is the first community garden on the Underground, installed on a disused platform at Barbican. This project is a partnership between Friends of City Gardens and London Underground. The garden was designed by international architecture practice Gensler, and it fills the 100m long platform with flowers and herbs.
Tube: Barbican

6 Bevis Marks

Bells and Belfries at St Botolph Aldgate
Aldgate High Street EC3N 1AB
■ Sat/Sun 10am-5pm. Bell ringing demonstrations and limited belfry tours on Sat only (10am-12noon & 2pm-4pm). Max 20 in belfry. Last entry 3.30pm. N R T d
Rare opportunity to see the bells and belfry of this church by the architect of Mansion House. Inside is London's oldest organ. George Dance the Elder 1744.
Tube: Aldgate, Aldgate East; Rail: Liverpool Street, Fenchurch Street; 42,78,100,67,15

Billingsgate Roman House and Baths
101 Lower Thames Street EC3R 6DL
■ Sat/Sun 11am-4pm. Museum of London curators on site. T
Some of London's best Roman remains, comprising late C2 house with a C3 bath house built within its courtyard. First discovered in 1848.
Tube: Monument; Rail: Fenchurch Street, Blackfriars; 15,35,40,43,47,48,78

Bishopsgate Institute
230 Bishopsgate EC2M 4QH
■ Sat 10am-5pm. Tours on the hour, first come basis. Last tour 4pm. N R T B d
This beautifully restored historic Grade II* listed building combines elements of Arts & Crafts/Art Nouveau/Victorian architecture. Charles Harrison Townsend 1894/Sheppard Architects (restoration) 2011. Entry: library, great hall, boardroom (restricted access). Displays of original plans for Institute and images through time.
Tube/Rail: Liverpool Street; 8,26,35,42,47,48,78,149,242,344,388

City of London School
Queen Victoria Street (main entrance on river walkway near Millennium Bridge) EC4V 3AL
■ Sat 10am-6pm/Sun 10am-4pm. Last entry half hour before close. Special activity: Sun – children's author talks, including Caroline Lawrence, 11am, 2pm in the Winterflood Theatre (limited 150 seating). Please email tjo@clsb.org.uk to reserve tickets and for further information. D R T B
Founded in 1442, the new building was designed by the City architects' department on the site of the C15 Baynard Castle. Includes much Victorian art. Stuart Murphy & Tom Meddings

Key. A Architect on site **B** Bookshop **C** Childrens' activities **d** Some disabled access **D** Full wheelchair access **E** Engineer on site **G** Green Features **N** Normally open to the public **P** Parking **Q** Long queues envisaged **R** Refreshments **T** Toilets

1986. Entry: 'Public' rooms, new theatre, Great Hall with Walker organ and model railway room. Wheelchair access via public inclinator on Peter's Hill next to Millennium Bridge.
Tube: Mansion House, St Paul's; Tube/Rail: Blackfriars; 4,11,15,26,45,63,76,100,172

CityPoint (Simmons & Simmons' offices)
Ropemaker Street EC2Y 9SS
- ■ Sat tours 1.15pm, 2pm, 2.45pm, 3.30pm, 4.15pm, pre-book ONLY on http://tinyurl.com/m4jyqmg. Please arrive 15 mins before tour start. D T

Built in 1967 for BP, CityPoint was the first building in the City of London taller than St Paul's Cathedral. The building was refurbished in 2000, and its height increased to 127 metres. F Milton Cashmore and HNW Grosvenor 1967/Santiago Calatrava/Sheppard Robson 2000.
Tube: Barbican, Moorgate; Tube/DLR: Bank; Tube/Rail: Liverpool Street; 43,76,100,141,153

Crossrail – Liverpool Street ●
Crossrail Liverpool Street site, 1-14 Liverpool Street EC2M 7NH
- ■ Sat 10am-4pm. Hourly tours. Pre-book ONLY, see www.crossrail.co.uk/openhouse for details. Max 10 per tour. E

Crossrail's Liverpool Street station marks the deepest point on the Crossrail route, with infrastructure 50m beneath the City of London. It will link both Liverpool Street and Moorgate stations, increasing capacity, improving accessibility and upgrading existing interchanges. Mott MacDonald/Wilkinson Eyre/Urban Initiatives due 2018.
Tube: Moorgate; 21,100,43,76,141

Custom House
20 Lower Thames Street EC3R 6EE
- ■ Sat/Sun 9.30am-4pm. Last entry 3.50pm. Possible security bag checks. T d

Iconic elegant late-Georgian building partly rebuilt by Smirke after subsidence. The 58m neo-classical Long Room was the central reporting point for all London Customs business in the C19. David Laing 1813-17/Sir Robert Smirke 1825. Entry: west reception ground floor, main hall, Long Room, robing room, quay. Various displays and children's quiz. Detection dog displays 10.30am, 12noon, 1.30pm, 3pm.
Tube: Tower Hill, Monument; Rail: Fenchurch Street; 15,25

Drapers' Hall
Throgmorton Street EC2N 2DQ
- ■ Sun 10am-4pm. Last entry 3.30pm. T d

Livery hall first built in the 1530s, twice destroyed by fire and rebuilt (1666 & 1772). Late C19 facade and opulent Victorian interior. H Williams and Sir T G Jackson 1868. Entry: principal function rooms.
Tube: Moorgate; DLR/Tube: Bank; Tube/Rail: Cannon Street, Liverpool Street; 21,26,76,242,388

EXHIBIT at Golden Lane Estate ● ●
EXHIBIT Gallery, Golden Lane Estate, 20 Goswell Road EC1M 7AA
- ■ Sat tours 12noon, 2pm (duration 1 hour), pre-book ONLY by email: info@exhibit-goldenlane.com. Max 20 per tour.

Golden Lane is a Grade II listed estate, an early exemplar of British Modernist architecture. A tour of the previously abandoned Day Care Centre (now Sir Ralf Perring Club), an artist resident exhibition and a community allotment. Chamberlin, Powell & Bon 1957 onwards.
Tube: Barbican, St Paul's; Tube/Rail: Farringdon, Liverpool Street; 4,55,56,153

Explore Broadgate ●
Broadgate Welcome Centre, Finsbury Avenue Square, Broadgate EC2M 2PA
- ■ Sat 10am-4pm. E D T C

Broadgate is home to an outstanding series of buildings designed by renowned architects including Skidmore, Owings & Merrill, Arup and Make. It forms a unique environment in the city with public art, event spaces, shops, bars and restaurants. Recent developments include Broadgate Circle which opened in April 2015, and 5 Broadgate due for completion in 2016. Arup Associates and SOM 1984-90. Pick up a guide to Broadgate's architecture and see an interactive model of the campus in the Broadgate Welcome Centre before exploring receptions of 155 Bishopsgate, 201 Bishopsgate, Exchange House, 1&2 Broadgate, and Broadgate Tower.
Tube: Moorgate; Tube/DLR: Bank; Tube/Rail: Liverpool Street; 8,11,26,35,42,47
www.broadgate.co.uk

Fishmongers' Hall
London Bridge EC4R 9EL
- ■ Sat/Sun tours 10.30am, 12noon. Pre-book ONLY via http://fishhallopenhouse2015.eventbrite.co.uk. Max 30 per tour. Duration 1 hour. T d

Fishmongers' Hall is a rare example of a Greek Revival town building featuring an arcaded granite base and a riverside terrace. Designed by the architect Henry Roberts, a student of Sir Robert Smirke, the Hall's classical simplicity is contrasted by the magnificence of its interior rooms. Henry Roberts 1831-5.
Tube: Monument; Tube/Rail: London Bridge; 17,43,21,149

Gresham College – Barnard's Inn Hall
Barnard's Inn Hall, Holborn EC1N 2HH
- ■ Sat 11am-3pm. Talks at 11am, 12.30pm, 2.30pm. D T

Barnard's Inn dates back to at least the mid C13. Hall contains three wooden bays dating from C15 with later linenfold wood panelling added in the 1600s. The Mercers Company organised repairs in 1932. Roman fragments below medieval hall contain unique roof timber structure. Renovated in 1990 to become the home of Gresham College.
Tube: Chancery Lane; 8,17,25,45,46,242,341

Guildhall
Gresham Street EC2V 7HH
- ■ Sat/Sun 10am-5pm. Last entry 4.30pm. N B d

The City's seat of municipal government since C12. Grade I listed, rare example of Medieval civic architecture with post-war extensions and rebuilding. John Croxton 1440/George Dance the Younger 1789. Entry: Great Hall.
Tube: St Paul's, Mansion House, Moorgate; Tube/DLR: Bank; Tube/Rail: Liverpool Street; 8,76,100,133,242

Guildhall Art Gallery
Guildhall Yard EC2V 5AE
- ■ Sat/Sun 10am-5pm. Half-hourly tours 10.30am-4pm. N D T B

Purpose built art gallery housing the City of London's art collection, built over remains of London's C2 Roman amphitheatre. Front façade is sympathetic to the Grade I listed Guildhall neighbour and uses same traditional materials – Portland stone and Collyweston stone slates. Interior uses fine finishes of marble, American elm, damask and painted wall coverings. The new City of London Heritage Gallery displays some of the City's finest archival treasures, with its centrepiece during Open House being the City's 1297 Magna Carta – the last time the City's Magna Carta will be on public display for some time. Special Exhibition 'No Colour Bar: Black British Art in Action, 1960-1990' (10 Jul 2015 – 24 Jan 2016). Richard Gilbert Scott 1999. Entry: art gallery and Roman amphitheatre.
Tube: St Paul's, Mansion House, Moorgate; Tube/DLR: Bank; Tube/Rail: Liverpool Street; 8,100,133,21,149

Drapers' Hall

Guildhall – The Magna Carta Lights up the City of London
Guildhall Yard, Gresham Street, EC2V 5AE
- ■ Sat 8pm-9pm. First come basis.

To mark 800 years of the creation of the Magna Carta, Guildhall Library is lighting up the City of London Guildhall with a Magna Carta Son et Lumiere. The Guildhall School of Music and Dance have produced a composition of music and light inspired by the stories behind the Charter. This will be projected onto the fine Hindoo-Gothic architectural façade of the Guildhall. To find out more, please visit Guildhall Library's exhibition, which runs from 17-23 September.
Tube: St Paul's, Mansion House, Moorgate; Tube/DLR: Bank; Tube/Rail: Liverpool Street; 8,76,100,133,242

Guildhall Library
Aldermanbury EC2V 7HH
- ■ Sat 9.30am-5pm. T N d

Purpose built over 5 floors to house printed books and manuscripts. Features include old pneumatic tubes system and 56 listed translucent pyramid roof lights. Sir Giles Scott, Son + Partners 1974. Entry: library and basement stores.
Tube: St Paul's, Mansion House, Moorgate; Tube/DLR: Bank; Tube/Rail: Liverpool Street; 8,100,133,21

Guildhall School of Music & Drama, Milton Court
Milton Court, 1 Milton Street EC2Y 9BH
- ■ Sun 11am-6pm. Regular tours to front of house and backstage areas, first come basis. First tour 11.15am, last tour 5pm. Some performances taking place. D R T G

Milton Court is the Guildhall School's world-class new building, which opened in 2013. State-of-the-art facilities include a concert hall, two theatres (proscenium arch and studio), rehearsal spaces and a specially-commissioned artwork by Martin Creed. RIBA London Regional Award winner. RHWL Arts Team and David Walker Architects 2013.
Tube: Barbican, Moorgate; Tube/DLR: Bank; Tube/Rail: Liverpool Street; 4,43,76,100,153

Haberdashers' Hall ●
18 West Smithfield (opposite Barts Hospital by traffic barrier under flagpole) EC1A 9HQ
- ■ Sat 10am-4pm. Last entry 3.30pm. Max 350 at one time. D B A

Opened by the Queen in 2002 as one of the first new livery halls in the Square Mile for nearly 40 years, this is a brick building with traditional lime mortar and handsome lead roof, standing around a peaceful courtyard. American oak panelling and old artefacts and pictures provide internal finishes. Hopkins Architects 2002. Exhibition on display.
Tube: Barbican, St Paul's; Tube/Rail: Farringdon; 8,25,56,242

King's College London, The Maughan Library

Chancery Lane WC2A 1LR

■ Sat/Sun 1.30pm-5pm. Last entry 4.30pm. D T

London's first fireproof building, built to house records of the Court of Chancery. Now renovated to house a fine university library. J Pennethorne and Sir John Taylor 1851/Gaunt Francis Associates 2001. Entry: round room, Rolls Chapel (now Weston Room), some library areas.

Tube: Chancery Lane, Temple; Tube/Rail: Charing Cross; 11,15,26,172,341

Lloyd's Register Group ●

71 Fenchurch Street EC3M 4BS

■ Sat 10am-5pm. First come basis, queuing outside if necessary. Last entry 4.30pm. Max 250 at one time. T Q G d

Sumptuous building with many original decorative and architectural features. Sympathetically extended by Richard Rogers Partnership whose glass and steel structure soars above as a fine example of high-tech architecture. RIBA Award winner. Thomas E Collcutt 1901/Richard Rogers Partnership 2000. Entry: Rogers building entrance and reception, Collcutt building reception, library, General Committee room.

Tube: Aldgate, Tower Hill; DLR: Tower Gateway; Rail: Fenchurch Street, Liverpool Street; 40,25,15,35,47

Mansion House

Walbrook EC4N 8BH

■ Sat tours only at 9am, 10am, 11am, 12noon, 2pm, 3pm, 4pm. Pre-book ONLY, apply in writing by 4 September to Mansion House Tours, Public Relations Office, City of London Corporation, Guildhall, PO Box 270, EC2P 2EJ. Indicate preferred tour times. Max 4 tickets per booking. Give names of all attendees in application. Tickets allocated by draw; successful applicants notified in writing. T d

Residence of the City of London's Lord Mayor, retaining its C18 character, with superb plasterwork and wood carving. George Dance the Elder 1739-52. Entry: public areas of house on ground and 1st floors.

Tube: Mansion House; Tube/DLR: Bank; Tube/Rail: London Bridge, Liverpool Street; 8,11,21,25,26,149,15

Masonic Temple, Andaz Liverpool Street (former Great Eastern Hotel)

Entrance on Bishopsgate EC2M 7QN

■ Sun 10am-5pm. Half-hourly tours. Last tour 4.30pm. Max 20 per tour. T

Grade II listed grand Victorian railway hotel refurbished with stylish contemporary interiors. Greek Masonic Temple with magnificent Grade I listed interior of marble and mahogany, built 1912 at immense cost. Charles Barry 1884/Conran & Partners and Manser Practice 2000. Entry: Temple only.

Tube/Rail: Liverpool Street; 8,11,26,35,42,47,48,78,100,133,141,149,153,214,242

Pipers' City of London Model at The City Centre

City of London's City Centre, within Guildhall Complex (entrance at 80 Basinghall Street, leading from Gresham Street) EC2V 5AR

■ Sat/Sun 10am-4pm. 12noon, 2pm talks, 'Update on the Square Mile around the City Model' with Peter Murray, New London Architecture Chairman and Master Architect of the Worshipful Company of Chartered Architects. T A

An overview of the latest developments and architecture in the City of London via the interactive 1:500 scale Pipers model that shows the future skyline with proposed new towers.

Tube: Mansion House, St Paul's, Moorgate; DLR/Tube: Bank; Tube/Rail: Liverpool Street; 43,8,21,76,133,100,242

St Botolph Building

138 Houndsditch EC3A 7DH

■ Sun 10am-5pm. Hourly tours, including art exhibition on 13th floor. Last entry 4pm. D R T

Grimshaw's design creates a highly adaptable commercial building for landlord DEKA Immoblien and agents CBRE. The upper 11 floors house high specification offices, while the first and second levels provide more flexible office space with the potential to become dealing floors. The St Botolph Building is the first major office building in the UK to use TWIN® lift technology, with 16 lifts operating independently in three shafts within the central atrium. Grimshaw 2010. Entry: main reception and 13th floor.

Tube: Aldgate, Aldgate East; Tube/Rail: Liverpool Street; 25,205,15,115,254

St Bride Foundation

Bride Lane, Fleet Street EC4Y 8EQ

■ Sat 10am-1pm/Sun 1pm-5pm. Sat: to view workshop, exhibition, theatre and bar only. Sun: half-hourly tours of backstage, library, theatre, bar and selected meeting rooms, first come basis. Display on 100 years of printing and Fleet Street's social history. Max 15 per tour. R T B d

Built as a printers' institute in the Anglo-Dutch style, with sandstone dressings, steeply pitched tiled roof and gables; many original features remain including the swimming pool and library. Robert C Murray 1894.

Tube: Temple, St Paul's; Tube/Rail: Blackfriars; 4,11,15,45,63,26,76,172

St Paul's Cathedral – Triforium Tour

Access is via a registration desk in the Cathedral crypt (entry via north west crypt door) EC4M 8AD

■ Sat 10am-4pm. Tours on the hour, pre-book ONLY at goo.gl/EZMRdt. Max 15 per tour. Duration 45mins. R T B

The tour includes: The C18 Cathedral Library; Sir Christopher Wren's first model and designs for the new Cathedral; the stunning views down the nave from the West Gallery. The tour to these special areas is via 160 steps only. We recommend that those with pre-existing medical conditions, mobility difficulties or concerns with heights do not attempt this climb. Sir Christopher Wren 1710. Entry: Triforium.

Tube: St Paul's, Mansion House; Rail: City Thameslink, Blackfriars; 242,25,4,11,15

Stationers' Hall

Ave Maria Lane, London EC4M 7DD

■ Sun 10am-5pm. Guided tours, first come basis. Last entry 4.30pm. D R T B

C17 livery hall with courtroom and garden. Oak panelling and stained glass windows. Undamaged in WW2. Selected items from the archives on display. 1673.

Tube: St. Paul's; Rail: City Thameslink; 4,15,76,26,11

The City Churches

■ Sat/Sun 10am-5pm. Times vary.

There are 42 churches within the City of London, the range of styles includes Norman, pre-fire Medieval, Wren's masterpieces and modern reworkings, and some of the largest enclosed spaces in the Square Mile. Four churches are listed here. A full list available from the City of London Information Centre, St Paul's Churchyard EC4M 8BX and from each church during the weekend.

St Helen Bishopsgate

Great St Helen's EC3A 6AT

■ Sat 10am-5pm/Sun 12.30pm-3.30pm. Half-hourly tours outlining the changing face of St Helen's building over the centuries. Quiz for children. Open House Guest Services on Sun at 10.30,4pm, 6pm. N D R T B C

One of the few City buildings to survive the Great Fire of London and dates from 1210 onwards. Unusual double nave with the best pre-Great Fire collection of monuments in any London parish church. Damaged by two terrorist bombs in the 1990s, then extensively and controversially reordered by Quinlan Terry in 1993. C13 onward.

Tube/DLR: Bank; Tube/Rail: Liverpool Street

St Lawrence Jewry

Guildhall Yard EC2V 5AA

■ Sat/Sun 10am-5pm. Hourly history talks 11am-3pm. Mosaics exhibition and demonstration. N E G d

C11 site with a stunning Wren building from the C17. Restored in the C20 (Cecil Brown), and now the official church of the City of London Corporation. Stunning ceiling and windows by Christopher Webb. Sir Christopher Wren C11/1677.

Tube: Mansion House, St Paul's, Moorgate

St Mary-le-Bow

Cheapside EC2V 6AU

■ Sat/Sun 10am-5pm. Guided tours Sat/Sun 11am, 12.30pm, 2pm, 3.30pm, first come basis. N T d

Founded by William the Conqueror's Archbishop Lanfranc in 1080 (of which the highly significant crypt largely survives) St Mary-le-Bow was rebuilt several times, most notably by Wren (1670) after the Great Fire and again by Laurence King (1964) after WWII destruction of Wren's design. Home of the Bow Bells.

Tube: St Paul's, Mansion House; Tube/DLR: Bank

St Stephen Walbrook

Walbrook EC4N 8BN

■ Sat/Sun 10am-5pm. N R T

Wren's own parish church with the building personally supervised by him in 1672. Within a rectangular outline is a square space defined by twelve columns and covered by a huge dome. Central stone altar by Henry Moore installed in 1987. Birthplace of the Samaritans. Sir Christopher Wren 1672.

Tube/DLR: Bank, Monument

Temple Inns of Court and Temple Church

■ Sat/Sun 10am-5pm. Last entry 4.30pm. C B T R D

At the anniversary of the sealing of the 1215 Magna Carta, the Inner Temple, Middle Temple and Temple Church will share an insight into the workings of the Temple over the last 800 years and a glimpse at the architecture through interactive tours, family events and a multitude of on-site activities, including Tours of Inner and Middle Temple Gardens, family friendly productions of Shakespeare Untold and a street food market. Picnic visitors welcome. Mock Trials will also be taking place at the Royal Courts of Justice on both days, including a Children's Court on Sun.

Tube: Temple, Chancery Lane; Tube/Rail: Blackfriars, Charing Cross; 4,11,15,26,76,341

Inner Temple

Crown Office Row EC4Y 7HL

Tours and self-guided access, first come basis. Pre-booked lunches available 12.30pm-2pm, book on www.innertemple.org.uk/OpenHouse2015.

A fine example of neo-Georgian architecture and three previous halls have occupied this site. The original C13 Knights Templar Hall was replaced in C14 and modified in C17, then completely rebuilt in 1870 in the then fashionable neo-gothic style by Sir Sydney Smirke. The existing hall was rebuilt by Sir Hubert Worthington in 1941, following the destruction of the Inn during WW2. Other buildings of note include Harcourt Building, Temple Gardens and King's Bench Walk. Wren designed the doorway of No. 4, and the certificates for the foundations bear his name. Entry: Hall, Bench Apartments, library, gardens, selected chambers. www.innertemple.org.uk/openhouse2015

Key. **A** Architect on site **B** Bookshop **C** Childrens' activities **d** Some disabled access **D** Full wheelchair access **E** Engineer on site **G** Green Features **N** Normally open to the public **P** Parking **Q** Long queues envisaged **R** Refreshments **T** Toilets

30 St Mary Axe (The Gherkin)

Middle Temple
Middle Temple Lane, EC4Y 9B¬T
■ Self-guided access, first come basis. Traditional wigs and gowns by Ede & Ravenscroft to view and try on.
London's finest surviving Elizabethan Hall (1573), 101ft long and 41ft wide, highly atmospheric, with double hammerbeam roof, screen and notable paintings. Entry: Hall, Bench Apartments, library, gardens, selected chambers.
www.middletemple.org.uk/openhouse2015

The Temple Church
Fleet Street, EC4Y 7BB
■ Magna Carta exhibit, choral performances, organ recitals, lectures, and Sun morning service. First come basis.
Medieval architecture meets Sir Christopher Wren's refurbishments in this awe-inspiring building (the cloisters and Middle Temple gateway bear his name) the Mother Church of the Common Law. Magna Carta exhibit: look into the faces of William Marshall and his liege King John in the place they would have debated and agreed clauses of Magna Carta. 1185. Entry: Temple Church Round, chancel, triforium. Family activities: self-guided quiz, What On Earth Magna Carta Chronical team (Sun).
Tube: Temple, Chancery Lane; Rail: Blackfriars, Charing Cross; 4,11,15,26,76,341
www.templechurch.com/openhouse2015

The Salvation Army International Headquarters
101 Queen Victoria Street EC4V 4EH
■ Sat 10am-5pm. Architect-led half-hourly tours, first come basis. Max 10 per tour. Last entry 4pm. Max 70 at one time. N D R T A
A transparent and welcoming working environment with full-height glazing and feature steel columns. Brief was to create a space 'modern in design, frugal in operation and evangelical in purpose'. Sheppard Robson 2004. Entry: Café 101, board and conference rooms, 1st floor chapel.
Tube: Mansion House, St Paul's; Tube/Rail Cannon Street, Blackfriars; 388,4,11,15,17,26

The Steward Building
12 Steward Street E1 6FQ
■ Sat 10am-1pm. Guided tours 10am, 11am, 12noon, pre-book ONLY via openhouse@ahmm.co.uk. Please include 'Steward' in subject line. D A
6-storey brick clad building set between two very different Spitalfields streetscapes, marking the transition between Bishop's Square and the fine grain of the surrounding conservation area. Allford Hall Monaghan Morris 2014.
Tube/Rail: Liverpool Street; 388,8,26,35,42.

Tower 42
25 Old Broad Street EC2N 1HQ
■ Sat 10am-3pm. Tours every 45 minutes. Pre-book ONLY via http://goo.gl/ucjTFo. Last tour 2.30pm. Max 50 per tour. T d
The City of London's tallest fully occupied building, consisting of three hexagonal chevrons, at 601ft was the first to break previous restrictions on tall buildings in London. During a comprehensive refurbishment in 1995, a new glass and steel entrance hall was built on Old Broad Street and the external steel cladding was replaced. Richard Seifert & Partners 1981/ GMW Partnership/Fletcher Priest 1995. Entry: ground floor entrance, level 42.
DLR/Tube: Bank; Tube/Rail: Liverpool Street

Trinity House
Tower Hill EC3N 4DH
■ Sat 10am-1pm. Last entry 12.30pm. Max 60 at one time. D T
Fine late Georgian exterior with interior painstakingly reconstructed after destruction by incendiary bomb in 1940. Good fittings, statues and works of art from original building. Samuel Wyatt 1796/Albert Richardson 1953. Entry: 1st floor ceremonial rooms.
Tube: Tower Hill; Rail: Fenchurch Street; 25,15,40

Watermark Place
1 Angel Lane EC4R 3AB
■ Sat 10am-5pm. Half-hourly tours, first come basis. Last entry 4pm. E D R T G
A landmark office building and European HQ of Nomura International, featuring spectacular riverfront views and rooftop gardens with award-winning kitchen garden maintained by staff volunteers. Many green features including carbon neutral pavilion. Fletcher Priest Architects 2009.
Tube/DLR: Bank; Tube/Rail: Cannon Street, London Bridge

Watermen's Hall
18 St Mary-at-Hill EC3R 8EF
■ Sat tours 9am, 10.30am, 12noon, 1.30pm. Pre-book ONLY in writing enclosing SAE to The Assistant Clerk, giving name/s, address and tel no. Max 2 tickets per application. State tour time preferred. Tickets sent by post. Max 30 per tour. d
Only remaining Georgian hall in the City of London, and perfect example of domestic architecture of the period. William Blackburn 1780. Entry: parlour, Freemen's room, Court room, Silver room, hallway.
Tube: Monument; Rail: Fenchurch Street; 15,25,35,45

Wax Chandlers' Hall
6 Gresham Street EC2V 7AD
■ Sat half-hourly tours from 10am. Last tour 4pm. Pre-book via openhousewaxchandlers2015.eventbrite.co.uk or by application on the day at the door. Max 20 per tour. D T
The sixth livery hall to be built on a site owned by the Company since 1501. 1958 building stands on part of 1854 hall largely destroyed in WWII. East wall recently refaced. Completely refurbished and remodelled internally 2006/7. Charles Fowler 1854/Seeley & Paget 1954/Foster + Partners 2003/ACQ Architects 2007. Entry: livery hall, court room.
Tube: Mansion House, Moorgate; DLR/Tube: Bank; Tube/Rail: Liverpool Street; 8,56,76,100,133,242

WALKS/TOURS

Broadgate Art Tour ●
Broadgate Circle EC2A 2QS
■ Sat 10am, 12noon, 2.30pm one-hour tours with Broadgate's art curator Rosie Glenn, departing from Broadgate Circle. First come basis. Max 15 per tour.
Broadgate houses an impressive art collection by acclaimed British and international artists. Out in the open air, stunning sculptures in bronze, ceramic, steel and stone, these modern masterpieces are accessible to all. Continuing indoors, paintings, tapestries and other pieces are enjoyed by people who work in the buildings.
Tube/Rail: Liverpool Street; 8,11,26,35,42,47
www.broadgate.co.uk/art

City Alleyways South West
Meet: Outside Guildhall Art Gallery, Guildhall Yard EC2V 5AE
■ Sat/Sun regular departures every 45 mins from 10.15am. Duration approx. 2 hours. First come basis. Last tour 2pm. Max 30 per walk.
A walk through some of the old alleyways of the City of London, passing Wren churches, Livery Halls and investigating the historic area of Carter Lane and Blackfriars, finishing at Blackfriars Station. Walk led by qualified City of London guide.
Tube: Barbican, St Paul's, Moorgate; DLR/Tube: Bank; 8,21,23,25,43,133,141,242

City Alleyways to the East
Meet: Outside Guildhall Art Gallery, Guildhall Yard EC2V 5AE
■ Sat/Sun regular departures every 45 mins from 10.15am. Duration approx. 2 hours. First come basis. Last tour 2.15pm. Max 30 per walk.
A walk through some of the old alleyways of the City of London, passing Wren churches, Livery Halls and many little known historical places, finishing at the Monument. Walk led by qualified City of London guide.
Tube: Barbican, St Paul's, Moorgate; DLR/Tube: Bank; 8,21,23,25,43,133,141,242

Riverside Walk ●
Meet: Outside Guildhall Art Gallery, Guildhall Yard EC2V 5AE
■ Sat/Sun regular departures every 45 minutes from 11am. Duration approx 1.5 hours. First come basis. Last tour 2.45pm. Max 30 per walk.
A walk past St Mary-le-Bow church to the River Thames, then along the riverside path under London Bridge to the Tower of London. Walk led by qualified City of London guide.
Tube: Barbican, St Paul's, Moorgate; DLR/Tube: Bank; 8,21,23,25,43,133,141,242

Sculpture in the City 2015 ●
■ Meet: Sat 10am or 12noon at corner of 99 Bishopsgate and Wormwood Street EC2M 3XF. Pre-book ONLY via pro.events@cityoflondon.gov.uk. Duration 1.5 hours. Max 25 per tour.
Sculpture in the City is an urban sculpture park of 14 contemporary art installations by leading international artists set within the iconic towers of the City of London.
Tube/Rail: Liverpool Street; 149,344,35,48,8,26
www.cityoflondon.gov.uk/sculptureinthecity

Supported by

CITY OF LONDON

Croydon

See openhouselondon.org.uk/croydon
to find out more about this area

Airport House
Purley Way, Croydon CR0 0XZ
- Sat/Sun 11am-3.30pm. Regular tours of Croydon Airport Visitor Centre, first come basis. N R T C P d

Unique Grade II listed 1928 building with rusticated features. Entrance façade features three 1.5-storey arched windows. Booking hall with glass domed atrium. Earliest example of an air traffic control tower. Facilities at adjacent 1928 Aerodrome Hotel also open to public.
Rail/Tram: East Croydon, West Croydon; Rail: Purley; 119,289 to Croydon Colonnades/Croydon Airport

Bernard Weatherill House
8 Mint Walk, Croydon CR0 1QQ
- Sat 8am-12noon. Hourly tours. Max 12 per tour. D T

New public service building provides 20,000ft2 of BREEAM Excellent accredited modern commercial accommodation spread over 13 storeys combined with a public access facility at ground floor in the heart of the building. Features include energy efficient twin-skin glazed façades, occupiable roof terraces and exposed internal concrete soffits. EPR Architects 2013. Entry: ground floor, access to terraces.
Rail/Tram: East Croydon, West Croydon; 60,166,405,412,466

Croydon Town Hall and Clocktower Complex
Katharine Street CR9 1ET
- Sat 10am-1pm. Access to Town Hall by timed tour only 10am, 11am, 12noon, 1pm. Duration 45 mins. D R T C

Guided tours of the original Town Hall, including Council Chamber and meeting rooms. Clocktower complex opened in 1993 and Museum of Croydon, opened in 2006. Charles Henman 1895/Tibbalds 1993/ FAT 2006. Entry: Town Hall including council chambers and meeting rooms; Museum of Croydon, including creative family workshop.
Rail/Tram: East Croydon, West Croydon; 109,119,154,197,466

Fairfield Halls
Park Lane CR9 1DG
- Sat tours at 9.15am, 11am, pre-book ONLY via johnspring@fairfield.co.uk. Duration 1.5 hours. Max 16 per tour. T d

One of the few surviving examples of a major early post-war concert hall and arts centre in the country and is reputed for its excellent acoustics. Built in a style similar to the Royal Festival Hall, it houses a 1794 seat concert hall and 763 seat theatre. Robert Atkinson & Partners 1962.
Rail/Tram: East Croydon; 50,109,166,264,312

Old Palace, Croydon
Old Palace Road, Old Town CR0 1AX
- One Sat tour at 11am. First come basis. Max 30 per tour. T P

Grade I listed manor house, former summer residence of Archbishops of Canterbury from C13-18. Elizabeth I and other monarchs regularly visited. Contains one of the finest great halls with its original roof from 1440s. C13.
Tram: Church Street, Reeves Corner; Rail/Tram: East Croydon, West Croydon

---

Connected Croydon - On Site

Ruskin Square on Site
AMP House, Dingwall Road, Croydon CR0 2LX
- Sat/Sun 10am-5pm. Site tours 12noon both days starting from AMP House, first come basis. Duration 1 hour. Last entry 4.30pm. Max 20 per tour. N R T A E d

Ruskin Square is a 2 million sq ft development by Schroder UK Real Estate Fund and Stanhope plc. The scheme comprises a planned 1.5 million sq ft of office space, 625 flats and 100,000 sq ft of shops, cafés and restaurants, all set within attractive new public realm space. Allford Hall Monaghan Morris/ShedKM.
Rail/Tram: East Croydon

Shirley Windmill
Postmill Close, Upper Shirley Road, Croydon CR0 5DY
- Sun 12noon-5pm. Regular tours, first come basis. Duration 1 hour. Last tour 4pm. N R T P d

The present brick tower windmill was built to replace a post mill destroyed by fire. Now renovated to near-working condition, it is the only surviving windmill in Croydon.
Rail/Tram: East Croydon; 466,130,119,194,198

St Bernard's Houses
Meet: by OHL banner, St Bernard's, Chichester Road CR0 5UL
- Sat 2pm-4.30pm. Half-hourly tours. Last tour 4.30pm. Max 28 per tour. d

Twenty-one houses, in three hillside terraces, built by Swiss architects Atelier 5 for Wates. The living areas on the upper floor are approached through a garden court. Bedrooms downstairs open on to a lower garden. Pevsner wrote, 'a group with few equals in Britain'. Atelier 5 1969-70. Entry: a selection of 3 houses, grounds.
Rail/Tram: East Croydon; 64,T33

The Stanley Halls
12 South Norwood Hill SE25 6AB
- Sat 10am-5pm. Tours on the hour, first come basis. Max 10 per tour. Last tour 4pm. Max 20 at one time. R T d

A public hall, theatre and gallery in grand Edwardian style. Grade II listed, Stanley made fun of the Victorian style with grand ornamentation. William Ford Robinson Stanley 1903. Entry: full access including behind the stage.
Rail: Norwood Junction; 75,157,196,197,410,130

Thornton Heath Library ●
109 Brigstock Road, Thornton Heath CR7 7JB
- Sat 9am-5pm. Tours 12noon, 2pm. Max 20 per tour. N D T

A Carnegie library (1914) with some fine original architectural features, recently refurbished to create a light, welcoming and spacious environment whilst its dramatic façade now makes a bold statement upon the High Street. A new white concrete and glass pavilion provides a highly visible reading area complemented by rich oak flooring and comfortable seating. On the lower level a rejuvenated children's library leads to a community garden. FAT (pavilion) 2010.
Rail: Thornton Heath; 198,250,450

Whitehorse Manor Infant and Junior Schools ●
Whitehouse Road, Thornton Heath CR7 8SB
- Sat 10am-1pm. Half-hourly tours, first come basis. Last entry 12.30pm. D T A

A stunning gold-fronted expansion to an existing primary school. The design builds on the character of the existing Victorian school building and brings togther a fragmented site with a series of inventive material and formal interventions. Hayhurst and Co 2014. Entry: classrooms, grounds.
Rail: Norwood Junction, Thornton Heath

Whitgift Almshouses
North End, Croydon CR9 1SS
- Sat tours 10.30am, 11.45am, 2pm, 3.15pm, pre-book ONLY on 020 8680 8499. Last tour 3.15pm. Max 30 per tour. T

Tudor almshouses dating from 1596 and founded by the Archbishop of Canterbury John Whitgift. Chapel and Courtyard with original C16 clock. Entry: courtyard, chapel, audience chamber.
Rail/Tram: East Croydon

WALKS/TOURS

Connected Croydon – On Site ●
- Meet: Sat 2pm at East Croydon train station main entrance on George Street CR0 1LF

Walking tour of central Croydon led by Croydon's placemaking team focusing on projects that form part of the Connected Croydon programme, a £50m programme of public realm and infrastructure projects currently being delivered in central Croydon, transforming London's biggest borough. Design teams involved include East, John McAslan + Partners, Hassell, We Made That, muf, Project Centre, StudioWeave, Jan Kattein, Allies and Morrison.
Rail: East Croydon, West Croydon; 60,166,405,412,466

The Seven Hills of Croydon
- Meet: Sun 12noon. Meeting point to be confirmed on booking. Pre-book ONLY via www.eventbrite.com – search 'Seven Hills of Croydon'. A

After WWII, Croydon transformed from a market town on London's outskirts into a C20 super suburb. This architect-led tour offers a walk around England's Alphaville via its 7 hills.
Rail/Tram: East Croydon, West Croydon; 50,109,154,194,197

Supported by

CROYDON
www.croydon.gov.uk

Key. A Architect on site **B** Bookshop **C** Childrens' activities **d** Some disabled access **D** Full wheelchair access **E** Engineer on site **G** Green Features **N** Normally open to the public **P** Parking **Q** Long queues envisaged **R** Refreshments **T** Toilets

Ealing

See **openhouselondon.org.uk/ealing**
to find out more about this area

Acton Town Hall
Acton High Street W3 6NG
- Sat 10am-5pm. Informal tours. Max 50 at one time. N G d
Extension to existing Edwardian Town Hall, includes marble-clad hall, entrance and grand staircase, stained glass and original fixtures and fittings. Robert Atkinson (extension) 1938. Entry: entrance, staircase, main hall.
Tube: Acton Town; Rail: Acton Central; 7,70,207,266,607

Chestnut Grove ●
56 Chestnut Grove W5 4JS
- Sat/Sun 1pm-5pm. Tours 1pm, 3pm. R T C G P d
A certified Passivhaus with a rear extension. Display on how to refurbish to meet new-build Passivhaus standards. Janet Cotterell, Junko Suetake 2013. Entry: two flats, most areas. Children's design activities.
Tube: South Ealing; 65,E3

Dormers Wells High School
Dormers Wells Lane, Southall UB1 3HZ
- Sat 10am-1pm. Regular architect-led tours. D T A P
Rebuilt as part of the BSF programme, the school aims to encourage educational aspiration through supporting social inclusion and community cohesion in a calm and uplifting environment. The design achieved the top, rarely awarded, 'Very Good' status by CABE, and is BREEAM Excellent. Nicholas Hare Architects 2012.
Tube: Greenford; Rail: Southall; 105,95

Ealing Abbey
Charlbury Grove W5 2DY
- Sun 1pm-5pm. Hourly tours. Last tour 4pm. Recital of Gregorian Chant. N D R T B P
Building began in 1897 and was still being worked on a century later. Architects include F and E Walters 1897 (the nave), Stanley Kerr Bates 1960 (transepts), and Sir William Whitfield 1997 (choir and apse). Entry: church, adjacent centre.
Tube/Rail: Ealing Broadway; E2,E9,297

Horizons Education and Achievement Centre for Care Leavers
15 Cherington Road, Hanwell W7 3HL
- Sun 10am-5pm. Half-hourly tours, first come basis. Last entry 4.30pm. Max 10 per tour. D T G P
Developed from the refurbishment of derelict former depot buildings, Horizons is a unique project that provides a community resource for young people leaving the care of Ealing Council. RICS London Building of the Year 2008. Gavin Leonard MA, DipArch RIBA, Borough Architect 2007.
Tube: Hanwell, Ealing Broadway; 207,607,427,E3,83

Norwood Hall
Khalsa Primary School, Norwood Green Road, Southall UB2 4LA
- Sat/Sun 10am-5pm. Max 30 at one time. R T P
Much modified and extended in late C19 with Arts & Crafts details but recognisably a Soane house with echoes of his own nearby house at Pitzhanger Manor. Original Soane drawings on display. 19-acre walled garden contemporary with house. Sir John Soane 1803. Entry: house, walled garden, C19 greenhouses, grounds.
Rail: Southall; 120

Villa Caroisla

Pitzhanger Manor House
Walpole Park, Mattock Lane W5 5EQ
- Sat 12noon, 3pm behind the scenes architect-led tours of the house currently undergoing restoration. Pre-book ONLY via pitzhanger@ealing.gov.uk or 0208 825 9808. N E T C G d
Former country residence designed by Sir John Soane for his own use, set in the grounds of Walpole Park. Grade I listed building, expressing Soane's idiosyncratic architectural style with its stripped back classical detail, radical colour schemes and inventive use of space and light. Sir John Soane 1800-10.
Tube/Rail: Ealing Broadway; 65,83,207,427,607

Subterranean Light
6 Gloucester Road W5 4JB
- Sun 10am-5pm. Half-hourly tours. Max 15 per tour. Last entry 4.30pm. G A
Unusual below garden contemporary light-filled basement extension to Edwardian semi that opens up to a lowered garden terrace with built in hot tub. Features include walk over roof lights, elegant promenade walkways, stairs and tiered planters that connect all spaces. KSKa Architects 2015. Entry: ground floor, terrace, basement, lower terrace, garden.
Tube: South Ealing; Tube/Rail: Ealing Broadway; 65,E2,E3
www.kska.co.uk

The White House
46 Park View Road W5 2JB
- Sat/Sun 10am-5pm. Half-hourly tours. Last entry 4pm. Max 14 at one time. R T Q A P d
Louis XVI Palace set in own private gardens, based on owner's grandmother's palace in Poland. 'Marble Arch' entrance – the first in London for 200 years. Extremely opulent interiors with marble, gold cornices and chandeliers. John Zylinski 2009.
Tube/Rail: Ealing Broadway; 207,83,112,607

Villa Caroisla
25C Montpelier Road W5 2QT
- Sun 1pm-5pm. Hourly tours. Last entry 4.30pm. Max 10 per tour. A G d
A contemporary take on backland living in Ealing, this four bedroom eco-home is built using timber framing and passive solar design techniques. Nick Baker Architects 2012.
Tube/Rail: Ealing Broadway; 226
www.nickbakerarchitects.com

Westside Young People's Centre
Churchfield Road, Ealing W13 9NF
- Sun 10am-5pm. Tours taking place. Last entry 4.30pm. D T
Westside is a pioneering facility, evolving the concept of a creative ideas 'factory', to bring together innovative programmes that support young people in every aspect of their lives. RIBA London Award Winner 2013. Gavin Leonard MA,

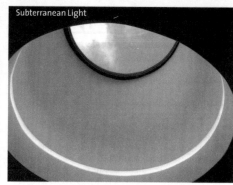
Subterranean Light

DipArch RIBA, Borough Architect 2012. Entry: all areas.
Rail: West Ealing; 207,607,427,83,E2,E3

WALKS/TOURS

Brentham Garden Suburb ●
- Meet: Sat/Sun 10.30am at The Brentham Club, 38 Meadvale Road W5 1NP. Duration approx 2 hours. No organised groups over 6 people please. N R T P
Britain's first co-partnership garden suburb, first houses built 1901. Parker and Unwin's plan introduced 1907, mainly Arts & Crafts style; fascinating social history. Organised by The Brentham Society.
Tube: Hanger Lane; Tube/Rail: Ealing Broadway; E2,E9

Ealing Common Walk
- Meet: Sat 2pm at Hanger Lane end of Inglis Road W5 3RN. Duration up to 2 hours. If heavy rain the walk will be cancelled. R d
Walk across Ealing Common taking in the range of architectural styles. Highlights: the home of a Wimbledon champion and the death mask of a prime minister.
Tube: North Ealing, Ealing Common; Tube/Rail: Ealing Broadway; 83,112,207,427,607

Hanwell Flight of Locks & Three Bridges ●
- Meet: Sat/Sun 1pm, 2pm, 3pm, 4pm at The Fox public house, Green Lane W7 2PJ. Duration 1 hour. N R P d
Restored flight of locks at Hanwell is a scheduled ancient monument, while Three Bridges is a unique stacked intersection of road, rail and canal, and Brunel's last major railway project. Walks led by knowledgeable enthusiasts in local waterway history. Isambard Kingdom Brunel 1794/1859.
Tube: Boston Manor; Rail: Hanwell; E8,83,207,195

Northala Fields: A Recycled New Park ●
- Meet: Sat 11am at the Northala Fields Dolphin Road car park off A40, Kensington Road UB5 6UR. Pre-book ONLY via 020 7537 3654 or peter@studiofink.eu. Duration 1 hour. Max 30 per tour. N E A G d
Using waste from other building work, such as the new Wembley stadium, the mounds of Northala Fields shield Ealing from the busy A40 whilst providing an impressive landmark and a brand new park. Walk led by a member of the design team. FoRM Associates.
Tube: Ealing Broadway, Northolt; E10,90,120,140,282,398

Supported by

www.ealing.gov.uk

● AJ Library Building   ● Green Exemplar   ● Landscape/Public realm   ● Infrastructure/Engineering   ■ Open Saturday   ■ Open Sunday   ■ Open Saturday and Sunday

openhouselondon.org.uk | Ealing | 31

Enfield

See **openhouselondon.org.uk/enfield**
to find out more about this area

Christ Church Southgate and the Minchenden Oak Garden
Waterfall Road, Southgate N14 7EG
- ◾ Sat 10am-5pm/Sun 9am-6.30pm. Hourly tours, first come basis. Material available for self-guided tours. Children's activities in the church. R T B C P d

Grade II listed church and grounds with fine collection of pre-Raphaelite stained glass windows by Morris & Co. including Burne-Jones, Ford Madox Brown and Rossetti. Highly decorated Lady chapel. Minchenden Oak Garden – containing ancient pollarded oak more than 800 years old. George Gilbert Scott 1861-62.
Tube: Arnos Grove, Southgate; Rail: New Southgate, Palmers Green; 121,298,299, W6

Deephams Sewage Treatment Works ●
Ardra Road, Edmonton N9 0BD
- ◾ Sat 10am-5pm. Half-hourly tours, first come basis. Last entry 4pm. Max 15 per tour. T R

Thames Water are upgrading the sewage treatment process while continuing to treat the 209,000 tonnes of flow that arrives at the works each day. Due for completion 2018.
Tube/Rail: Tottenham Hale; Rail: Ponders End; W8,191,192

Dugdale Centre
Thomas Hardy House 39 London Road, Enfield EN2 6DS
- ◾ Sat/Sun 10am-5pm. N D R T

New build multi-use studio theatre and conferencing venue with spacious café and gelateria. 2007.
Rail: Enfield Town; 191,W8,W9,307,313,317,121

Forty Hall & Estate ●
Forty Hill, Enfield EN2 9HA
- ◾ Sat/Sun 1pm-5pm. First come basis. N D R T B P

Recently fully refurbished in partnership with HLF, this Grade I listed Carolean mansion hall (1629-32) is set in a fine estate within the Forty Hill village conservation area. Home of Sir Nicholas Rainton, Lord Mayor of London 1632-33, Master of the Haberdasher's Guild. Last private owners were the Parker-Bowles family. Now fully accessible with gift shop and café. Changing programme of high quality arts and crafts exhibitions. Entry: ground and 1st floors.
Rail: Enfield Town; 191 (10 mins walk)

King George V Pumping Station ●
Swan & Pike Road, Enfield EN3 6JH
- ◾ Sat/Sun 10am-4pm. Regular tours, first come basis. Site closes 4pm prompt. E P

Designed to pump water from the River Lee into the George V reservoir, the building houses three old disused gas Humphrey pumps, and two electric pumps currently in service. William Booth Bryan 1913.
Tube: Turnpike Lane then 121 bus; Rail: Enfield Lock

Lamb's Cottage
Church Street N9 9DY
- ◾ Sun tours 11am, 12noon, 2pm, 3pm, first-come basis. P d

Late C17 timber-frame house with early C18 façade and period features. Grade II* listed. Last home of Charles and Mary Lamb. Entry: house, garden.

Rail: Edmonton Green; 102,144,149,192,259, W6, W8

Lee Valley Athletics Centre ●
Lee Valley Leisure Complex, 61 Meridian Way, Picketts Lock N9 0AS
- ◾ Sun 10am-1pm. Last entry 12.30pm. N D R T A G

A world-class indoor training facility, the only one of its kind in the South East, this naturally lit and ventilated building is highly sustainable. David Morley Architects 2007. Entry: all areas except offices and changing areas.
Tube/Rail: Tottenham Hale; Rail: Ponders End, Angel Road, Edmonton Green; W8

Millfield Arts Centre
Silver Street N18 1PJ
- ◾ Sat/Sun 10am-5pm. N R T G P d

Grade II* listed small Georgian suburban villa (1778) with later additions. Formerly orphanage and hospital, currently a multi-use community and arts centre. Entry: house, grounds and WWII bunker.
Tube: Wood Green then 144; Rail: Silver Street; 34,102,W6,144,444,217,231

Myddelton House
Bulls Cross, Enfield EN2 9HG
- ◾ Sat 10am-4pm. First come basis. Last entry 3.30pm. N D R T

Neo-classical yellow Suffolk stock brick villa with mid C19 extension to north and west front. Victorian conservatory to side. Adam style ceilings to ground floor. Home of the great horticulturalist EA Bowles. George Ferry and John Wallen 1818. Entry: ground floor only, selected rooms, tearoom, museum, gardens. NB. Does not include entry to contemporary buildings.
Rail: Turkey Street; 217,317

Old Vestry Offices
22 The Town, Enfield EN2 6LT
- ◾ Sat 10am-1pm. Last entry 12.30pm. Max 10 at one time. N

Tiny polygonal building originally for the beadle. Used as local police station until 1930s and then as offices. Grade II listed. NB. Steep narrow staircase unsuitable for people with mobility restrictions.
Tube: Oakwood; Rail: Enfield Town, Enfield Chase; 329,192,121,313,307

Parish Church of St Andrew Enfield
Market Place, Enfield EN2 6LL
- ◾ Sat 9.30am-3.30pm/Sun 12noon-3pm. N D T

Grade II* listed church (C13-19) with fine organ case and monuments.
Rail: Enfield Town, Enfield Chase; 121,191,192,231,307,313,317,329

Priory Hospital North London
Grovelands House, The Bourne N14 6RA
- ◾ Sat tours 10am-1pm. Pre-book ONLY via nickhazell@ priorygroup.com. Max 30 per tour. R T G P

Grade I listed neo-classical villa designed for Walker Gray. Grounds laid out by Repton. Elegant trompe l'oeil breakfast room. John Nash 1797. Entry: main house, ground and 1st floors, ice house.
Tube: Southgate; Rail: Winchmore Hill; 121,125,299, W6

Royal Small Arms Factory
RSA Island Centre, 12 Island Centre Way, Enfield (off A1055 Mollison Avenue) EN3 6GS
- ◾ Sat 10am-5pm. Regular tours, first come basis. Former Arms Factory employees present to answer questions. N T P d

Grade II listed arms factory closed to public for 170 years, buildings on site included a church (the original font is displayed in the central courtyard at the centre), a police

---

Lee Valley Athletics Centre

station and a school. Now restored as mixed-use village and commercial centre. Clock c1783. Shepheard Epstein Hunter (refurb) 2000.
Rail: Enfield Lock; 121,491

St Mary Magdalene Church
Windmill Hill, Enfield EN2 8QH
- ◾ Sat 10am-5pm. D R T P

Fine Victorian Gothic church with impressive windows and painted chancel. Paintings by Buckeridge and Westlake 1897 and restored 2012. William Butterfield 1883. Entry: church, vestry.
Tube: Oakwood; Rail: Enfield Chase, Enfield Town; 121,307,377,313

Suburban Studio
11 Second Avenue, Bush Hill Park EN1 1BT
- ◾ Sun 10am-5pm. Architect-led tours at 3pm. Last entry 4pm. Max 12 per tour. D T A G P

Timber-clad garden studio and refurbishment to Victorian house, with stunning garden – a courtyard addressed by 'floating' studio and house. Garden is a folded timber landscape with heated paddling pool, a sand pit and a fire pit. Sustainable features include a green roof. Winner of the NLA 'Don't Move, Improve' Award for best home extension 2011/12. Ashton Porter Architects 2011. Entry: studio, garden, library.
Rail: Bush Hill Park; 192,377

Winchmore Hill Friends Meeting House & Burial Ground
Winchmore Hill Quaker Meeting, 59 Church Hill N21 1LE
- ◾ Sat/Sun 2pm-5pm. Last entry 4.30pm. Max 20 at one time. D R T P

Established 1688, the present Grade II listed building of yellow stock brick dates from 1790. A simple building with central double door under a bracketed cornice hood, flanked by large sash windows, with delicate glazing bars. Panelled interior. Curved entrance wall allowed carriages to turn in the narrow lane. Notable burials in the grounds. 1790. Entry: ground floor.
Tube: Southgate; Rail: Winchmore Hill; 125,329, W9

Supported by

The Enfield Society
conserving our heritage and environme
www.enfieldsociety.org.uk

Key. A Architect on site **B** Bookshop **C** Childrens' activities **d** Some disabled access **D** Full wheelchair access **E** Engineer on site **G** Green Features **N** Normally open to the public **P** Parking **Q** Long queues envisaged **R** Refreshments **T** Toilets

Greenwich

See **openhouselondon.org.uk/greenwich**
to find out more about this area

Blackheath House
195 Shooters Hill Road SE3 8UL
- ■ Sun 12noon-5pm. First come basis, queuing outside if necessary.
Edwardian house lived in by an interior designer and his partner, with a contemporary extension. Sasa Works 2012.
Tube: North Greenwich; Rail: Blackheath; 53,422,178,89,54

Charlton House
Charlton Road SE7 8RE
- ■ Sun 10am-4pm. Self guided tours. Last entry 4pm. D R T P
London's only surviving great Jacobean mansion, set in Charlton Park, red brick with white stone dressings and beautifully proportioned hall. A Newton 1607-12/Norman Shaw (restored) late C19. Entry: Minstrel Hall, Long Gallery, Grand Salon, White Room, Newton, Prince Henry & Dutch Rooms, Old Library, grounds.
Rail: Charlton; 53,54,422

Christ Faith Tabernacle Cathedral, Ebenezer Building (formerly Granada Cinema)
186 Powis Street SE18 6NL
- ■ Sat 1pm-5pm. Last entry 5pm. Max 20 at one time. N R T G E d
Lavish and atmospheric former cinema with interior by Theodore Komisarjevsky, converted to Bingo Hall in 1960s. Grade II* listed. Cecil Masey and Reginald Uren 1937. Entry: auditorium, foyer, circle area. NB. Children under 18 not permitted.
Rail: Woolwich Arsenal; 51,53,54,96,99,122,161,177,178,180,244

Emirates Air Line tour ●
Meet: Emirates Greenwich Peninsula, Emirates SE10 0DX
- ■ Sat tours at 10am, 11am, 12noon. Pre-book ONLY via EALgroups@macemacro.com. Includes tickets to travel on cable car; entry to Aviation Experience Museum; in-flight guide. Max 20 per tour. E D R T
Tour exploring the civil engineering achievements of the construction of the cable car. Led by the Emirates Air Line engineers and front-of-house team. **ice**
Tube: North Greenwich

Greenwich Yacht Club
1 Peartree Way SE10 0BW
- ■ Sat/Sun 1pm-4.30pm. Regular architect-led tours, first come basis. Club members available for discussion. Annual art show and members' bar. Max 40 at one time. R T A d
Contemporary timber and aluminium building using existing pier, offering unique views of the river, The O2 and Thames Barrier. Frankl + Luty 2000. Entry: main club house, sail loft, boat yard. Outbuilding adapted as art show venue with panoramic river views.
Tube: North Greenwich; DLR: Cutty Sark for Maritime Greenwich; Rail: Greenwich; 129

InterContinental The O2
1 Waterview Drive SE10 0TW
- ■ Sat 10am-1pm. Hourly tours only. First come basis. Max 20 per tour.
New 18-floor hotel by the Thames next to the O2, with 3100m² pillarless ballroom (the largest in Europe), 453 rooms,

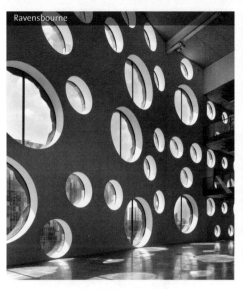
Ravensbourne

conference spaces and skybar. RTKL Architects 2015.
Tube: North Greenwich; 161,108,129,472,188

NOW Gallery and The Gateway Pavilions
The Gateway Pavilions, Peninsula Square, Greenwich Peninsula SE10 0SQ
- ■ Sat 10am-5pm/Sun 11am-4pm. Talks from Marks Barfield architects Sat/Sun 2pm. D A N T
Two curved glass pavilions, linked by a patinated brass-edged canopy. The combined buildings define the southern edge of Peninsula Square and act as a gateway to the south, the cable car and Central Park. Marks Barfield 2014.
Tube: North Greenwich; 161,129,472,108,188

Old Royal Naval College
Admiral's House, King William Court, Painted Hall, Chapel, Discover Greenwich, Queen Anne Court, Queen Mary Court. Main entry from West Gate (King William Walk), or East Gate (Park Row) and Romney Road crossing. Entry also from pier via Cutty Sark Gardens SE10 9NN.
- ■ Admiral's House: Sat/Sun 10am-6pm. Half-hourly talks. King William Court: access by hourly ticketed tours (10am-3pm only). Painted Hall, Chapel, Discover Greenwich: Sat/Sun 10am-6pm. Tours throughout the day, plus 'Meet Hawksmoor' 12noon, 1pm, 2pm, 3pm. Queen Anne Court/Queen Mary Court: Sat/Sun 11.30am-4.30pm. Access via hourly ticketed tours only. Last tour 3.30pm. Max 20 per tour. Meet on Grand Square to collect tickets and start/finish for ALL tours. Bookshop and refreshments only available in Discover Greenwich. C B R T d
Admiral's House – Designed for Charles II in 1661, finished by Hawksmoor and Vanbrugh as the Royal Hospital for Seamen and later the Royal Naval College (1873-1998). Managed by the Greenwich Foundation, housing Trinity Laban Conservatoire of Music and Dance. Grade I listed. John Webb 1672/1696.
King William Court – Wren-designed building completed under the direction of Hawksmoor and Vanbrugh, 1698-1712. Original wood panelling, refurbished by Dannatt Johnson in 2001 for University of Greenwich. Wren/Hawksmoor/Vanbrugh 1698-1712/Dannatt Johnson (refurb) 2001.
Painted Hall, Chapel, Discover Greenwich – Painted Hall ceiling by Sir James Thornhill 1708-27. Neo-classical Chapel designed

Old Royal Naval College - Painted Hall, Chapel

by James 'Athenian' Stuart 1789. Entry: Painted Hall, Chapel, Discover Greenwich Visitor Centre featuring an exhibition on the architecture of the site.
Queen Anne Court – Wren and Hawksmoor building from 1689, completed 1749 when Thomas Ripley built the pavilions facing the river. Highlights include council boardroom, grand staircase and restored Portland stonework. Refurbished in 2000 by Dannatt Johnson for University of Greenwich.
Queen Mary Court – Last major building on the site (1649-1751). Original layout, timber panelling, barrel vaulting and Portland stone. Refurbished in 2000 by Dannatt Johnson for University of Greenwich.
DLR: Cutty Sark for Maritime Greenwich; Rail: Greenwich, Maze Hill; Riverboat: Greenwich Pier; 177,180,188,199,286,386

Rachel McMillan Nursery School and Children's Centre
McMillan Street, Deptford SE8 3EH
- ■ Sat 10am-1pm. First come basis. T d
Opened in 1914, Rachel McMillan pioneered the benefits of an open-air environment for children. Named by English Heritage as the most significant nursery school of its date in England. London County Council Architects with Herbert Baker designed memorial 1914-33.
DLR: Deptford Bridge; Rail: Deptford; 188,199,47

Ravensbourne ●●⊗
6 Penrose Way, Greenwich Peninsula SE10 0EW
- ■ Sat 10am-5pm. Tours 10.30am, 11.30am, 1pm, 2pm, 3pm, first come basis. Children must be accompanied by an adult. Max 30 per tour. N D T G
This stunning location at Greenwich Peninsula is home to an inspirational new learning and teaching environment, over a series of interlinked floors around an impressive central atrium. It houses the latest digital media and design technologies, an HDTV studio, prototyping facilities and collaborative workspaces. BREEAM Excellent status with sustainable features including green roof, solar hot water and biomass boiler. RIBA Award Winner 2011. Foreign Office Architects 2010.
Tube: North Greenwich; Riverboat: North Greenwich Pier; 188,108,129,161,486,422,472

University of Greenwich, Stockwell Street

River Sculpture/Studio (Slice of Reality)

University of Greenwich, Stockwell Street ●●
Stockwell Street, Greenwich SE10 9BD
■ Sat/Sun 10am-5pm. Tours taking place, pre-book ONLY via conferences@gre.ac.uk. Max 20 per tour. N D R T B
Home to departments including architecture and landscape, this features one of the largest landscaped roofs in the world. Heneghan Peng Architects 2014. Entry: whole building and roof gardens.
DLR: Cutty Sark for Maritime Greenwich; Rail: Greenwich; 286,177,180,188

Woolwich Town Hall
Wellington Street SE18 6PW
■ Sat/Sun 10am-1pm. N T d
Florid Edwardian Baroque design with domed entrance hall, grand staircase and stained glass windows, a great example of civic architecture of the time belonging to the Classical tradition rather than the Gothic Revival favoured outside London. Alfred Brumwell Thomas 1906. Entry: Victoria Hall, council chamber, committee rooms, public hall.
Rail/DLR: Woolwich Arsenal; 51,53,54,96,99,122,161,380,422

WALKS/TOURS

Many Ways to Sit: The Social Dynamics of Gordon Square ●
■ Meet: Sat 10.30am next to the big TV screen, General Gordon Square SE18 6HX. First come basis. N D T
A tour and talk looking at the problems and potential of seating in public places, focusing on Gordon Square, Woolwich. A ten minute documentary film will be shown in a nearby venue, made in collaboration with users of Gordon Square. Gustafson Porter 2011.
DLR/Rail: Woolwich Arsenal; 54,53,161,178,180

Supported by

visit
greenwich
time after time

River Sculpture/Studio (Slice of Reality)
River Thames, off Thames Path, Meridian Gardens, nr Drawdock Road, Blackwall Point, Greenwich SE10 0PH
■ Sat 10am-5pm. N T A G d
Sliced vertical section of sea-going sand dredger. Original ship reduced in length by 85% leaving vertical portion housing the ship's habitable sections – bridge, poop, accommodation and engine room. Conversion by Richard Wilson 1999.
Tube: North Greenwich; 188,422,108

Royal Museums Greenwich: The Altazimuth Pavilion
Royal Observatory, Greenwich Park SE10 8XJ
■ Sat/Sun tours 2pm, 2.40pm, 3.20pm, 4pm, pre-book ONLY via 020 8312 6608. Suitable for ages 11+. Access only by narrow staircase. Max 10 per tour. N R T B P
Normally closed to the public, the exterior of this charming C19 dome features terracotta mouldings with the interior housing historic telescopes. 1899.
DLR: Cutty Sark for Maritime Greenwich; Rail: Greenwich, Maze Hill; Riverboat: Greenwich Pier; 129,177,180,188,199,286,386

Severndroog Castle
Castle Wood, Shooters Hill SE18 3RT
■ Sun 10.30am-4.30pm. Half-hourly tours, first come basis. Duration 25 mins. Last entry 4pm. Max 10 per tour. R T Q P
Grade II* listed triangular brick Georgian tower with Gothic windows sited in Oxleas Woods. Standing 63ft tall in woodlands it offers spectacular panoramic views across the capital. Built to commemorate the 1755 conquest of the Malabar Coast by Sir William James. Twenty five years after closing its doors to the public, restoration work has been completed. Richard Jupp 1784.
DLR/Rail: Woolwich Arsenal; Rail: Eltham, Welling; 89,122,161,244,486

Thames Barrier & Information Centre
1 Unity Way SE18 5NJ
■ Sat/Sun 10.30am-4.30pm. Last entry 4.30pm. Max 40 at one time, entrance subject to availability. R T d
Information centre sited by the dramatic Thames Barrier (1984), with a working model of the Barrier, films about its construction and exhibition explaining its past, present and future. Rendel, Palmer and Tritton 1984. Entry: information centre only. **ice**
Tube: North Greenwich, then 161,472; Rail: Charlton, then 177,180,472,161

The Fan Museum
12 Crooms Hill SE10 8ER
■ Sat 11am-5pm. Regular tours led by curator. Max 50 at one time. D R T B
Carefully restored Grade II listed early Georgian town houses, retaining the principal original domestic scale and character and architectural features, including elegant façades, staircase with 'barley sugar' baluster, panelled rooms and front courtyard with wrought iron railing and gates. It now houses the only museum devoted to the art and craft of fans. John Savery/John Griffiths (conversion) 1721. Entry: museum, orangery.
DLR: Cutty Sark for Maritime Greenwich; Rail: Greenwich, Maze Hill; 177,180,188,286,386,199

Trinity Hospital
Highbridge SE10 9PS
■ Sat 10am-4pm. R d
Early C17 riverside almshouse. Quadrangle with battlemented entrance facade and early C19 tower. Organised by the Warden of Trinity Hospital. Entry: courtyard, chapel.
Tube: North Greenwich; DLR: Cutty Sark for Maritime Greenwich; Rail: Maze Hill; 177,180,188,199,286,386

Navigate your way around Open House in your area with the app. See p14

Key. A Architect on site **B** Bookshop **C** Childrens' activities **d** Some disabled access **D** Full wheelchair access **E** Engineer on site **G** Green Features
N Normally open to the public **P** Parking **Q** Long queues envisaged **R** Refreshments **T** Toilets

Hackney

See **openhouselondon.org.uk/hackney**
to find out more about this area

13-18 Sidworth Street
13-18 Sidworth Street E8 3SD
■ Sat 10am-5pm. Regular tours. Last entry 4.30pm. Max 10-15 per tour. D T A G
Mixed-use residential building with atrium circulation, feature artwork, rooftop garden and glass-bottomed swimming pool. Lynas Architecture 2015.
Rail: London Fields, Hackney Central; 26,48,55,106,236,254,388

17-21 Wenlock Road
17-21 Wenlock Road N1 7SL
■ Sat tour 12.30pm only. Max 20 per tour. D A G
Join project architect Alex Smith and Roger Walsh of the developers Regal Homes for a presentation of the completed building from the park opposite and viewing selected spaces within. Hawkins Brown 2015.
Tube: Old Street, Angel; 43,205,214,394

24 St John's Church Road
24 St John's Church Road E9 6EJ
■ Sat 1pm-5pm/Sun 10am-5pm. Last entry 4.30pm. Sun 7pm-10pm open garden art discussion, first come basis (limited entry). R T A G d
Gracefully refurbished Victorian terrace introducing the UK's first heated clay ceiling system. Natural and reclaimed materials complement original features throughout. Modern extension with sedum roof. Art on display. Silke Stevens 2014.
Rail: Hackney Central, Hackney Downs, London Fields; 488,425,48,38,277

24 St Thomas's Place
24 St Thomas's Place E9 7PW
■ Sat 10am-5pm. Regular tours.
Back to brick refurbishment and extension to an early Victorian townhouse. The most noticeable features are the rear extension's variation on a typical butterfly roofline and the vertical garden. Building Designs 2015.
Rail: London Fields, Hackney Central; 55,48,254,26,106

30 Crown Place
30 Crown Place EC2A 4ES
■ Sat/Sun 10am-5pm. Hourly tours, first come basis. Last tour 4pm. Max 10 per tour. D
Striking 16-storey glass landmark office building with 3 terraces. An unusual form with a distinctive profile. Sustainable features include PV cells at roof level and ground floor geo-thermal heat source. Horden Cherry Lee Architects 2009. Entry: ground, 7th, 14th, 15th & 16th floors.
Tube/Rail: Liverpool Street; 23,149,214,242,271

52 Whitmore Road
52 Whitmore Road N1 5QG
■ Sat 10am-5pm. Practice Director Andrew Waugh on site. Last entry 4pm. T A G d
This mixed use building on Regents Canal illustrates capabilities of the cross laminated timber structure. The vast columnless, double height photography studio which stretches 9mx23m will be open, as will the canalside walkway and deck. Within the studio there will be an opportunity to explore an installation by artist Dan Tobin Smith. Waugh

Thistleton Architects 2012. Entry: photographer's studio.
Tube: Old Street

Adelaide Wharf
118/120 Queensbridge Road (at junction Whiston Road) E2 8PD
■ Sat 10am-3pm. Hourly architect-led tours. Pre-book ONLY via megan.van-niekerk@firstbase.com. NB. no tour at 1pm. Last tour 3pm. Max 20 per tour. D T A G
A pioneering mixed tenure residential scheme with some workspace extruded into a prototype block, folded to create a U-shaped court. Each apartment has an outdoor room part hung, part cantilevered out over the streets, courtyard or canal. Façade is composed of layers of roughly sawn larch that makes reference to the warehouses of packing crates that once occupied this site. RIBA Award Winner 2008. Allford Hall Monaghan Morris 2008.
Tube/Rail: Liverpool Street; 48,242,243,55,254,106

Arcola Theatre
24 Ashwin Street E8 3DL
■ Sat 10am-2pm. Half-hourly tours. Last entry 1.30pm. Max 12 per tour. N R T G d
Multi-award winning professional theatre with a strong community and sustainability ethos relocated to an emerging Hackney cultural quarter. Sustainability features include minimal intervention, large scale materials reuse and renewable energy technology. Refurbishment client-led with support from Cragg Management 1868/2011. Entry: Studio 1/2 (professional theatre), Bloomberg Arts Lab, Arcola Energy Lab.
Rail: Dalston Kingsland, Dalston Junction; 149,242,38,277,243

Black and White Building
74 Rivington Street EC2A 3AY
■ Sat/Sun 10am-5pm. Architect-led tours Sat 11am, 1pm. Last entry 4.30pm. T
Buckley Gray Yeoman transformed this 11,000ft² Victorian warehouse building with The Office Group into four floors of flexible workspace with offices, meeting rooms, co-working space, terraces and a lush roof garden. Buckley Gray Yeoman 2014.
Tube: Old Street; Tube/Rail: Liverpool Street, Shoreditch High Street

Calouste Gulbenkian Foundation
50 Hoxton Square N1 6PB
■ Sat 10am-5pm. First come basis. T d
The Foundation's artistic and social interests are at the heart of the design. A dramatic intervention to the first floor slab allows natural light from the rooflight above to permeate into the ground floor. Sustainable features include exposed concrete structure to provide thermal mass. Theis + Khan 2009. Entry: ground floor.
Tube/Rail: Old Street; Rail: Hoxton; 21,26,35,43,47

Cardinal Pole Catholic School ●
205 Morning Lane E9 6LG
■ Sat 10am-3pm. Half-hourly tours, first come basis. Displays. Last entry 2.30pm. D T A G
New-build school on challenging new inner-city site which unites school on one site for the first time in its 54 year history. Sustainable features include PV panels, air source heat pump. RIBA Awards Shortlisted 2013, Hackney Design Award Winner 2014. Jestico + Whiles 2012.
Rail: Hackney Downs, Hackney Central, Homerton; 30,236,276,W15

Clapton Girls' Academy
Laura Place E5 0RB
■ Sat 10am-12.30pm. Half-hourly tours. Talks/displays. Last tour 12noon. Max 25 per tour. T d
Sensitively refurbished Edwardian buildings providing

Black and White Building

an enhanced physical environment. Sustainable features throughout. Hackney Design Award winner 2010. Also open Clapton Portico – significant Grade II listed local landmark refurbished into a new teaching school. Brady Mallalieu Architects (Clapton Portico) 2006/Jestico + Whiles 2010.
Rail: Clapton; 38,48,55,56,106,253,254,308,425,488

Dalston C.L.R. James Library & Archives
Dalston Square, Dalston Lane E8 3BQ
■ Sat 9am-5pm/Sun 1pm-5pm. Tours Sat 11am/Sun 2pm, duration 1 hour, first come basis. Archives closed Sun except for tour. Max 15 per tour. N D T
4-storey multi-purpose, state of the art library and archives building. Earle Architects 2011. Entry: quick picks, adult, children's and study areas.
Rail: Dalston Junction, Dalston Kingsland; 30,38,56,242,277

Ed's Shed/Sunken House
75a De Beauvoir Road N1 4EL
■ Sat 10am-5pm. First come basis, queuing outside if necessary. Q G P
A cube clad in a cedar rainscreen, stained black – a single slot window at the front is all that indicates this is a house. The entire site was excavated to basement level in order to create the sunken foundation on which the house for Ed Reeve architectural photographer, now sits. Hemp insulation improves the thermal performance of the structure while the solid timber frame provides a significantly reduced carbon footprint. Adjaye Associates 2007.
Tube: Old Street; Rail: Haggerston, Dalston Junction, Dalston Kingsland; 67,149,242,243,394
www.edsshed.co.uk

Englefield Road
28 Englefield Road N1 4ET
■ Sat 1pm-5pm. Tours every 20-30 mins. Max 8 per tour. A G
Victorian terraced house conversion over three floors, with a contemporary rear extension creating additional, well-lit living space on the lower ground floor. united architecture 2014.
Rail: Dalston Junction, Dalston Kingsland; 277,30,38,56,242

Calouste Gulbenkian Foundation

Free Space Wenlock Barn Estate ●●
■ Meet: Sun 12noon for tours outside Wenlock Court, New North Road N1 7PL
A day of open gardens including estate tours and film screening. Tour begins at 12noon and screening at 3pm. Hosted by community engagement group Fourthland, includes discussion on community-led design. Max 25 per tour. R A G d
Three growing initiatives on the Wenlock Barn Estate. Each celebrate the long term benefits of growing food locally, the use of local materials and the importance of resident led design and construction.
Tube: Old Street; 76,394,141,21,271

Garden House
27 Buckingham Road N1 4DG
■ Sun 10am-1pm. First come basis.
New home and artist's studio in a land-locked site in Hackney. Features cantilevered steel stair and a bespoke terraced garden to the roof. Hayhurst and Co 2015.
Rail: Dalston Kingsland, Dalston Junction; 67,76,149,242,243

Gingerbread House ●
104 Balcorne Street E9 7AU
■ Tours Sat 9.30am, 10.30am, 11.30am, 12.30pm. Pre-book ONLY via studio@lauradewemathews.com. Max 15 per tour. A d
New build house on site of former box factory with clever use of volumes and daylight, despite the physical constraints of a small urban plot. Hackney Design Award Winner 2014. Laura Dewe Mathews 2012.
Tube: Mile End; Rail: Hackney Central; 277,425,388,26,30

Growing Communities' Eco Classroom ●●
Allen's Gardens, corner of Bethune and Manor Roads N16 5BD
■ Sun 10am-5pm. Regular tours, planting, salad tasting. Last entry 4.30pm. Max 30 at one time. N D T G
Wooden building with green roof, water harvesting, composting toilet and warmcell insulation, set in an organic market garden with a deck over pond and wildlife area. Classroom provides shelter for gardeners as well as a learning space. Constructive Individuals (Peter Smithdale) 2004. Entry: main building, surrounding organic market garden.
Tube: Manor House; Rail: Stoke Newington; 106,67,76,73,149

Hackney Empire
291 Mare Street E8 1EJ
■ Sat/Sun tours 11am, 12.30pm. Duration 45 mins. Pre-book ONLY, visit hackneyempire.co.uk. NB. Backstage and stage access may be limited. Max 20 per tour. D R T
Exuberant Grade II* listed auditorium and the most perfect example of Edwardian variety theatre remaining in London. Refurbishment restored the interiors added to the fly-tower and provided new back-stage areas, topping it off with the sign 'Hackney Empire' in massive terracotta 6.4m tall capital letters. Frank Matcham 1901/Tim Ronalds (refurb) 2004.
Tube/Rail: Bethnal Green; Rail: Hackney Central; 253,106,30,48,55

Hackney Marshes Centre ●
Hackney Marshes, off Homerton Road E9 5PF
■ Sat/Sun 9.30am-6pm. N D R T P
New community hub for Hackney Marshes comprising changing rooms, café and education facility. Housed in a welcoming, inclusive structure that is embedded within the landscape, culture and history of the marshes. RIBA, Civic Trust and Hackney Design Award Winner 2012. Stanton Williams 2010.
Rail: Hackney Wick, Homerton; W15

Hackney New School
1-9 Downham Road N1 5AA (access may be from 317-319 Kingsland Road E8 4DL)
■ Sat 10am-1pm. Half-hourly tours, first come basis. Last tour 12.30pm. D T A
A mixed-ability Free School with a focus on music, combining a 500 pupil secondary school and 200 pupil sixth-form. Situated within the Kingsland Road conservation area, this collection of brick buildings frames a series of precincts between the neighbouring streets and the canal basin. Henley Halebrown Rorrison 2015. Entry: main hall, typical classrooms, music and art rooms, bridges.
Rail: Haggerston; 67,149,242,243

Haggerston School
Weymouth Terrace E2 8LS
■ Sat 1pm-4.30pm. Hourly tours from 1.30pm led by parents who are architects. Presentation running in the hall and visuals of the school from past and present. Last tour 3.30pm. Last entry 4pm. Max 10 per tour. T A d
Grade II listed mixed comprehensive secondary school, retaining many original features. Distinctive for the large amount of timber used in the construction and contains some of Goldfinger's boldest and most handsome public interiors, including bush hammered concrete and coffered ceilings in the entrance and assembly hall block. Major refurbishment recently completed as part of BSF programme. Ernö Goldfinger & Hubert Bennett 1963-65/Avanti Architects 2011. Entry: main hall, reception areas, some classrooms, grounds.
Tube/Rail: Liverpool Street; Rail: Hoxton; 48,55,242,243

Kingsland Basin Moorings (CHUG)
Kingsland Basin Moorings (via towpath) N1 5BB
■ Sun 10am-5pm. Regular tours, first come basis. Max 5 per tour. N R T G d
Small is beautiful! 6 foot narrowboats provide individual design solutions for living and working. A unique community and shared open space, and a sustainable living concept. 1984. Entry: communal areas, interiors of 3-4 individual boats.
Rail: Haggerston, Dalston Junction; 67,149,242,243,394

Lauriston School
Rutland Road E9 7JS
■ Sat 10am-3pm. Regular architect-led tours, first come basis. Last tour 2.45pm. Max 15 per tour. T A G P R D
New build 2FE primary school. Classrooms are elevated in flexible, creative learning clusters to promote and facilitate various degrees of free and structured learning. The raised bridge structure maximises external space for play on this restricted site and creates a large covered all-weather area. Sustainable solutions as learning tools for children. Ann Griffin with Meadowcroft Griffin Architects 2011.
Tube/Rail: Bethnal Green; Rail: Hackney Central; 388,425,277
www.maccreanorlavington.com

Levitt Bernstein Studio
1 Kingsland Passage E8 2BB
■ Sat 1pm-5pm. N R T A d
Exhibition about masterplanning as a collaborative process including presentation of project being undertaken by Levitt Bernstein in collaboration with Proctor & Matthews and Cullinan Studios. Not the smooth corporate presentation of models, text and photographs, but the gutsy inner workings of a masterplanning studio: enquiring, self-referential, complicated, practical and messy.
Rail: Dalston Junction, Dalston Kingsland; 67,76,149,243,488

Our Lady's Convent High School
6-16 Amhurst Park N16 5AF
■ Sat 10am-1pm. First come basis. Last entry 12.30pm. T A
The 4-storey building – complete with a roof top multi-use games area above the sports hall – not only maximises the available external play spaces on what is a very small site, but also accommodates significant level changes across the site. The design also facilitatated the two-phase construction process, which was required to make the decant scenario possible. The chapel and its lightwell are clad in timber to highlight the significance of the space. Jestico + Whiles 2012.
Tube: Manor House, Seven Sisters; Rail: Stamford Hill

Restored Historic Almshouse at the Geffrye Museum
Kingsland Road E2 8EA
■ Sat 10.30am-4pm. First come basis. NB. Closed 12.30-2pm. Last entry 4pm. Max 16 at one time. T B C
Grade I listed C18 almshouse restored to original condition. Richard Halsaul and Robert Burford 1714/Branson Coates Architecture 1998. Entry: almshouse, museum, gardens.
Rail: Hoxton; 67,149,242,243,394

St Mary of Eton Church Mixed Use Development

Rivington Place
Rivington Place EC2A 3BA
■ Sat 12noon-6pm/Sun 12noon-5pm. Hourly tours until 4pm both days, first come basis. Last entry 30 mins before closing. Max 15 per tour. N D T R B
First permanent visual arts space dedicated to global diversity, inspired by African art and architecture as well as contemporary art and music. RIBA Award Winner 2008. Adjaye Associates 2007. Entry: ground, 1st, 2nd floors.
Tube: Old Street; Tube/Rail: Liverpool Street; Rail: Shoreditch High Street; 43,48,55,149,205,242,243

Shepherdess Walk
100 Shepherdess Walk N1 7JN
■ Sat 10am-4pm. Half-hourly tours, first come basis. Queuing outside if necessary. Last entry 3.30pm. Max 8 per tour. A P
Three houses and five apartments all with Solidspace inside – double height voids and split levels – connecting where we eat/live/work – homes full of volume, light and character. Jaccaud Zein Architects 2015.
Tube: Old Street; 394,43,205,214

St Mary of Eton Church Mixed Use Development
95 Eastway, Hackney Wick E9 5JA
■ Sat/Sun 10am-5pm. Last entry 4.30pm. N D
New housing surrounding a refurbished Grade II* listed church (Bodley & Garner 1892), with new community facilities. Matthew Lloyd Architects 2014.
Rail: Hackney Wick; 26,30,236,276,339,388

The Dalston Eastern Curve Garden ●
13 Dalston Lane E8 3DF
■ Sat/Sun 11am-6pm. Tours 2pm, 4pm. Last entry 5.45pm. Max 20 per tour. N R T G

Popular community garden in area lacking in green public space featuring biodiversity planting. Created on abandoned railway land, includes large wooden pavilion for events and workshops. Hackney Design Award Winner 2010 & 2011, Landscape Institute President's Award 2011. muf/J & L Gibbons/EXYZT 2010. Entry: garden, pavilion, pineapple house.
Rail: Dalston Junction; 30,56,277,38,242

The Lab by Spacelab
18 Wenlock Road N1 7TA
■ Sat 10am-5pm. Half-hourly tours. R T G d
The Lab by Spacelab is a co-working hub – a multi-functioning space that encourages flexibility, facilitates movement and fosters collaboration through a variety of strategically placed work and breakout spaces. Spacelab 2014.
Tube: Old Street, Angel; 43,205,214,394
www.spacelab.co.uk

The Studio
2 Nevill Road N16 8SR
■ Sat 12noon-4pm. Regular tours, first come basis. Last entry 3.30pm. Max 5 per tour. Q A G
A unique mews property which has undergone a complete retrofit where both architects designed and built the entire scheme themselves. The small house has a surprising amount of playful elements with sliding walls, hidden storage and contrasting materials. Bradley Van der Straeten Architects 2013. Entry: all areas.
Tube/Rail: Highbury & Islington; 73,476,149

Uniform Wares Showroom
Ground Floor, 83-85 Paul Street EC2A 4NQ
■ Sat/Sun 10am-5pm.
This studio fit-out for contemporary watch brand Uniform Wares draws upon the watchmakers "forensic devotion to detail" reflecting the cool craftsmanship and sleek refinement of their wares. Feilden Fowles 2013.
Tube: Old Street; 55,243,205,141,76

Village Underground
54 Holywell Lane EC2A 3PQ
■ Sat 10am-5pm. First come basis. T G Q
Recycled tube train carriages make affordable artists' studios on reclaimed land on top of an abandoned railway viaduct. Auro Foxcroft & Nicolas Laurent 2007.
Tube: Old Street; Tube/Rail: Liverpool Street; Rail: Shoreditch High Street; 149,243,67,55,8

Waddington Studios ●
127 Church Walk N16 8QW
■ Sun 1pm-5pm. Hourly tours, pre-book ONLY via benedetta.r@featherstoneyoung.com. Max 8 per tour. T A d
New build development of artist and photographic studios within a mews streetscape. The design, developed in close collaboration with the artist and owners, enhances the industrial aesthetic of the mews through its form and use of patterned Corten steel panels. Featherstone Young Architects 2013. Entry: studios only.
Tube/Rail: Highbury & Islington; Rail: Dalston Junction; 73,476

Woodberry Wetlands – Hidden Nature Reserve in Stoke Newington ●
Meeting point to be provided on booking.
■ Sun tours 1pm, 3pm. Opportunity to visit the site before official opening including the New River, East Reservoir and the mid C19 Grade II* listed Gas House and the Ivy House Sluice. Pre-book ONLY via woodberrywetlands@wildlondon.org.uk. T G d
Important wildlife site closed to the public since construction

Garden House

in 1833. Woodbury Wetlands project will see the site enhanced to create a publicly accessible nature reserve, due to open autumn 2015. Allen Scott Associates and Kaner Ollette 2015.
Tube: Manor House; Rail: Stamford Hill; 253,254,29,141,341

WALKS/TOURS

From Brownfield to Green Fields: A Walking Tour ●
■ Meet: Sat 10am outside 17-19 Great Eastern Street, EC2A 3EJ. First come basis, tour led by architectural designers Laura Rowland and Claire Beard from Between-Bricks. Max 20 on tour. D G
The streets of London are dominated by grey manufactured materials, with thousands of brownfield sites. This walk looks at the potential for greening brownfield sites to enhance our streetscapes.
Tube: Old Street; Rail: Shoreditch High Street; 55,149,243,242,8

Hackney's Timber Buildings – Walking Tour
■ Meet: Sat 10.30am at Murray Grove N1 7FB. A G
Hackney has a cluster of three of the most significant timber buildings in the world just a short walk apart (Stadthaus, at nine storeys is the world's tallest timber apartment block). This is an opportunity to view all three in the company of the architect Andrew Waugh of Waugh Thistleton. The tour will start at Murray Grove, go on to Bridport Place and end at Whitmore Road.
Tube: Old Street

Woodberry Down Urban Sustainability and Place-making Tour
Meet: Riverside Apartments, Goodchild Road N4 2BA
■ Sat 10am-1pm. Hourly tours. Last tour 4pm. G
Walking tour of the Woodberry Down regeneration estate showing key sustainable urban features including swales and reed beds, and a raft of green design features. Also included is a viewing of one of the new homes identifying key energy efficiency measures.
Tube: Manor House; 253,254,259,279

Supported by

⊖ Hackney

Hammersmith & Fulham

See openhouselondon.org.uk/hammersmith
to find out more about this area

79 Sterndale Road
79 Sterndale Road W14 0HX
- Sat/Sun 10am-5pm. Guided tours. Max 6 per tour.

Recently completed full refurbishment and new basement extension. A wonderful example of period character meeting contemporary design through clever use of light, colour and texture. The Vawdrey House 2015.
Tube: Hammersmith, Goldhawk Road; Tube/Rail: Shepherd's Bush, Kensington Olympia; 72,220,283,295
www.thevawdreyhouse.com

Brackenbury Road
108 Brackenbury Road W6 0BD
- Sat/Sun 10am-5pm. Last entry 4.30pm.

A London townhouse, celebrating the story of a family of drapers who lived in the building 100 years ago, explored through architecture and textile installations. Patrick Lewis Architects 2014.
Tube: Hammersmith, Goldhawk Road, Ravenscourt Park; 94,237,27,267,391

Bush Theatre
7 Uxbridge Road W12 8LJ
- Sat 10am-1pm. Regular tours, pre-book ONLY via Box Office on 020 8743 5050. Max 12 per tour. N R T B d

Designed in the English Renaissance style by the second most prolific architect of public libraries prior to WW1. Funded by John Passmore Edwards. Redesigned to create beautiful contemporary theatre space. Maurice B. Adams 1895/Haworth Tompkins (refurb) 2011. Entry: library, theatre, studio.
Tube: Shepherd's Bush Market; Tube/Rail: Shepherd's Bush; 49,72,94,95,207

Dorsett Shepherd's Bush Hotel
58 Shepherd's Bush Green W12 8QE
- Sun 2pm-6pm. Half-hourly architect-led tours, first come basis. Max 8 per tour. A

Breathing new life into a Grade II listed building; the Dorsett Hotel sees a former cinema transformed into a 4 star hotel complete with leisure and retail facilities. RIBA Awards shortlisted 2015. Flanagan Lawrence 2014.
Tube: Shepherd's Bush Market, Goldhawk Road; Tube/Rail: Shepherd's Bush

Fulham Palace
Bishop's Avenue SW6 6EA
- Sun 11am-5pm. Tours of upstairs offices not normally open to the public in main palace 11am, 12noon. Max 10 per tour, many stairs so unsuitable for disabled. Pre-book ONLY via 020 7736 3233 option 7. 1pm-4pm hourly tours of ground floor public rooms and Jessie Mylne Education Centre in converted stables, first come basis. Museum also open 11am-5pm. Restored vineries and walled garden open 10.15am-4.15pm. N R T B G P d

Former residence of the Bishop of London. Tudor courtyard with Georgian additions. Stiff Leadbetter 1764-6/Samuel Pepys Cockerell 1814/Butterfield Chapel 1867 (with Brian Thomas murals 1953).
Tube: Putney Bridge; 14,74,220,414,430

Greenside Primary School
Westville Road W12 9PT
- Sun 11am-5pm. Last entry 4.30pm. Max 50 at one time. Tours plus 'Bouncing Off the Wall!' C20 Graphic Arts Fair in the hall, celebrating the fine Gordon Cullen mural, 1952, restored 2014. Talk by Alan Powers, eminent C20 expert, architect and cultural historian at 12noon. D R T C P A

One of only two schools designed using Ernö Goldfinger's school building system – precast reinforced concrete frame with brick infill. Grade II* listed. Ernö Goldfinger 1952. Entry, foyer, mural, hall, one classroom, playground, garden.
Tube: Shepherd's Bush Market, Goldhawk Road, Ravenscourt Park; Tube/Rail: Shepherd's Bush; 94,237,283,260,207

LAMDA (The London Academy of Music & Dramatic Art)
155 Talgarth Road W14 9DA
- Sun 10am-4pm. Regular student led tours and demonstrations. Last entry 3.30pm. Max 10 per tour. R T C d

LAMDA's home since 2003. Consists of Victorian building with more recent extensions – including black box studio theatre and rehearsal rooms. Work has begun on the £28m redevelopment of the west end of the academy to include rehearsal studios, the 200-seat Simon Sainsbury Theatre and the Sackler Library and Study Centre. John Salmon Quilter 1894/Niall McLaughlin Architects 2003.
Tube: Barons Court, Hammersmith; 9,10,27,391

Maggie's Centre ●
Charing Cross Hospital, Fulham Palace Road W6 8RF
- Sun 12noon-4pm. Some tours. Last entry 3.30pm. Max 100 at one time. R T d

A non-institutional 'open house', Maggie's is a flexible space designed to be welcoming, uplifting and thought-provoking. The raised roof allows natural light to enter the whole of the building. Partitions divide up the open structure, placing the kitchen at the heart of the building. RIBA Award Winner 2009. Rogers Stirk Harbour + Partners 2008.
Tube: Hammersmith, Baron's Court; Rail: Putney; 190,211,220,295

Roca London Gallery
Station Court, Townmead Road SW6 2PY
- Sat/Sun 11am-5pm. Architect-led tours Sat 12noon, 3pm, first come basis. Last entry 4.30pm. Max 30 per tour. N E D T A

A space inspired by the various phases or states of water, offering a unique visual and interactive experience. Zaha Hadid Architects 2011.
Rail: Imperial Wharf; C3
www.rocalondongallery.com/

Rogers Stirk Harbour + Partners
Thames Wharf Studios, Rainville Road W6 9HA
- Sun 10am-5pm. Regular architect-led tours, first come basis. Last entry 3.45pm. Max 20 at one time. R T B Q C A d

RIBA award winning architects practice located in early C20 warehouses, overlooking the river Thames – formerly used to store oil tanks. Spectacular 2-storey lightweight roof added in 1989. Richard Rogers Partnership 1984-7. Entry: reception, 3rd floor. Drawing and modelmaking activities for children.
Tube: Hammersmith; 74,190,211,220,295

Sulgrave Gardens Passivhaus ●
Sulgrave Gardens W6 7RA
- Sat 10am-1pm. D A G

Sulgrave Gardens is the capital's largest mixed tenure development built using a Passivhaus approach – the most comprehensive energy efficient performance standard for buildings. Developed by Octavia. Cartwright Pickard 2013. Exterior tour only.
Tube: Goldhawk Road; Tube/Rail: Shepherd's Bush

79 Sterndale Road

The Hurlingham Club ●●
Ranelagh Gardens SW6 3PR
- Sat tours at 11am, 3pm only, first come basis, entry 15 mins prior to tour. No admittance at any other time. T d

Last of the grand C18 mansions which once fronted this part of the river, with magnificent interiors and extensive grounds. Dr William Cadogan 1760/George Byfield 1797-8.
Tube: Putney Bridge; 14,22,39,74,85,93,220,265,270,424

Tin House
2 Smugglers Yard, Devonport Road W12 8PB
- Sat 10am-1pm. C A P d

Making efficient use of an irregular urban site, this house is made up of interconnecting top-lit pavilions arranged to create a serene private courtyard. Henning Stummel Architects Ltd 2015.
Tube: Shepherd's Bush Market; Tube/Rail: Shepherd's Bush; 207,260,283

V&A Study Centre, Blythe House
23 Blythe Road
- Sat 10am-4pm. Courtyard and reception areas only, including the 'Krazy Kat Arkive'. Tours of the Clothworkers' Centre at 10.30am, 12noon and 2.30pm. Pre-book ONLY via 0207 942 2211. Max 15 per tour. d

A glimpse of the Victoria and Albert Museum's study centre at Blythe House near Olympia, including new reception area by Haworth Tompkins and display of Eduardo Paolozzi's 'Krazy Kat Arkive' of C20 Popular Culture. Sir Henry Tanner 1899-1903/Haworth Tompkins 2013.
Tube/Rail: Kensington Olympia; 9,10,27,28

William Morris Society – Kelmscott House
26 Upper Mall W6 9TA
- Sat/Sun 11am-4pm. Regular tours, first come basis. Printing demonstrations on Morris' Albion press throughout Sat. Max 40 at one time. N T B d

Residence of Sir Francis Ronalds, George MacDonald and (from 1878-96) William Morris. Organised by William Morris Society. C18. Entry: basement and coach house only.
Tube: Ravenscourt Park; 27,190,267,391,H91

Supported by

Haringey

See openhouselondon.org.uk/haringey
to find out more about this area

19 Mayfield Road
19 Mayfield Road N8 9LL
- Sun 10am-5pm. Half-hourly architect-led talks, first come basis. Last entry 4.30pm. A

This project opens up the kitchen to the garden and create a seamless transition with minimum impact to enable increased use of the garden and bring natural daylight into the domestic space. Luis Trevino 2012. Entry: rear extension, kitchen, garden.
Tube/Rail: Finsbury Park; Rail: Harringay; W3

87 Woodland Rise
87 Woodland Rise N10 3UN
- Sun 1pm-5pm. A G

Twentieth century meets twenty-first. Ground floor transformed into open plan, zoned, family living space, flowing into the garden. Knott Architects 2015. Entry: ground floor, garden.
Tube: Highgate; W7,43,134

639 Tottenham High Road
639 Tottenham High Road N17 8AA
- Sat 10am-1pm. First come basis. Last entry 1pm. N D T P

Grade II listed. Former gas showroom built in 1901 in attractive neo Jacobean style, red brick with terracotta dressing and stone decoration. Elaborate gables and turrets at either end. Damaged during 2011 riots, now fully refurbished by GLA and managed by London Youth Support Trust as Enterprise Centre and support for local community. Sergison Bates 2012. Entry: ground reception, first and second floor hallways.
Tube/Rail: Seven Sisters; Rail: Bruce Grove; 149,259,279,349,476

Alexandra Palace – Uncover the People's Palace
Meet at East Court (Ice Rink entrance), Alexandra Palace Way N22 7AY
- Sat 10am-12pm/Sun 10am-3pm. Half-hourly tours. Pre-book ONLY via www.alexandrapalace.com. Max 10 per tour. R T d

Alexandra Palace opened in May 1873 as a public centre of recreation, education and entertainment in North London and in 1936 became home to the world's first regular public high-definition television service, operated by the BBC. Join the last tours of the Victorian theatre and BBC studios before restoration work commences on a £26.8 million project funded by the Heritage Lottery Fund and Haringey Council. John Johnson & A Messon 1873.
Tube: Wood Green; Rail: Alexandra Palace; W3

Bruce Castle Museum
Lordship Lane N17 8NU
- Sat/Sun 1pm-5pm. Half-hourly tours. Trails and activity sheets for children. Medieval All Hallows Church open 2-5pm. Last entry 4pm. Max 20 per tour. N D R T B C P

Tudor Manor House built for Sir William Compton in 1514, substantially altered in C17 and C18. A museum since 1906 housing local history and exhibitions of Bruce Castle. Entry: ground floor; other areas visited on tours.
Tube/Rail: Seven Sisters, Wood Green; Rail: Bruce Grove; 123,243

Clyde Road

Clyde Road ●
75 Clyde Road N22 7AD
- Sat/Sun 10am-5pm. Tours taking place, first come basis. Last entry 4.45pm. A

A bold and innovative loft extension and whole house refurbishment to an Edwardian terraced house. Exploring the potential of an archetypal London terrace house under permitted development. Andrew Mulroy Architects Ltd/ Gregory Turner Interior Design 2012.
Tube: Bounds Green; Rail: Alexandra Palace; 102,299,184
www.mulroy.info

Hale Village ●
Meet: Outside Tesco Express N17 9NE
- Sat 10am-4pm. Hourly tours, except 1pm, first come basis. Last tour 3pm. Max 15 per tour. N D G

New high-density waterside development with green design features including bio mass and green roofs. Includes residential for sale and rent, student accommodation and range of community facilities. BDP/KSS/RMA 2008-2012.
Tube/Rail: Tottenham Hale; 123

Highgate School Chapel, Big School & Museum
North Road N6 4AY
- Sat 10am-1pm. Regular tours. Max 20 at one time. T

Restored and refurbished Grade II listed Victorian Gothic School Chapel; also 'Big School', opened as new library in 2013, including new mezzanine floor. Chapel interior completely renovated, including restoration of stone and brick surfaces, stained glass and ceiling paintings. Museum exhibiting school history since foundation in 1565 is housed in former Highgate Tabernacle, an 1830s Baptist chapel. F P Cockerell 1865-7/2014. Entry: school chapel, 'Big School'.
Tube: Highgate, Archway; 143,210,271

Highpoint
Highpoint, North Hill N6 4BA
- Sat 10am-5pm. Regular tours, pre-book ONLY via http:// ohlhighpoint.eventbrite.co.uk from 1 Sep. Max 12 per tour.

Grade I listed Modernist apartment blocks retaining many original features. Lubetkin & Tecton 1935/1938. Entry: (by accompanied tour only) common parts, including restored foyers and interior of a flat. NB. No photographs within the buildings or gardens permitted.
Tube: Highgate; 143,271,210,134,43

Hornsey Town Hall
The Broadway N8 9JJ
- Sat tours at 10.30am, 11.15am, 12noon, 12.45pm, 1.30pm, 2.15pm, 3pm. Pre-book ONLY via www.hthartscentre.co.uk/ openhouse. Max 15 at one time. N R T d

Grade II* listed building, the quintessence of municipal modernity of the period. Notable Ashburton marble staircases, fine wood panelled rooms and cork flooring. Marble and bronze foyers express the optimism of the period. Reginald H Uren 1934-5.
Rail: Crouch Hill; 41,91,W5,W7

Markfield Beam Engine and House ●
Markfield Road N15 4RB
- Sat/Sun 11am-5pm. Engine steaming 12.30-1.15pm, 2-2.45pm, 3.30-4.15pm. Sessions preceded by an introduction on the history of the site and engine. Display panels on development of sanitation in Victorian times and later and its effect on improving public health, particularly in densely populated urban areas. N E D R T B P

Grade II listed Victorian industrial building set within a park and next to the River Lea, with the original Wood Bros beam pumping engine in situ, as originally installed.
Tube/Rail: Tottenham Hale, Seven Sisters; Rail: South Tottenham; 41,76,123,149,243

Muswell Hill Everyman
Fortis Green Road N10 3HP
- Sat/Sun 10am-1pm. Last entry 12.45pm. Max 20 at one time. T d

Grade II* listed Art Deco cinema, converted to three screens in 1974 but retaining its fine original décor. This year celebrating its 79th year. George Coles 1936. Entry: foyer and large main auditorium.
Tube: Highgate, East Finchley; 43,102,134,144,234,W7

N17 Design Studio
451-453 Tottenham High Road N17 6QH
- Sat 10am-5pm. First come basis. Heritage tours of Tottenham at 11am, 12.30pm. Pre-book ONLY for tours via https://goo.gl/bdjYgQ. Max 10 per tour. D T N

John McAslan + Partners, with Haringey Council, has transformed an empty Tottenham shop into a design studio. John McAslan + Partners 2015.
Tube/Rail: Seven Sisters; Rail: Bruce Grove; 123,243,149,476,259
www.mcaslan.co.uk

St Benet Fink, Tottenham
Walpole Road Tottenham N17 6BH
- Sat 10am-5pm. Last entry 4.30pm. N D R T

Late Gothic revival red-brick Grade II listed church, with original fittings, including a fine organ by Willis. JS Alder 1912.
Tube: Turnpike Lane; Rail: Bruce Grove; 123,243,217,231,444

● AJ Library Building ● Green Exemplar ● Landscape/Public realm ● Infrastructure/Engineering
■ Open Saturday ■ Open Sunday ■ Open Saturday and Sunday

openhouselondon.org.uk | Haringey | 39

Highpoint

639 Tottenham High Road

Stapleton Hall Road ◉
66 Stapleton Hall Road N4 4QA
■ Sun 10am-4pm. Half-hourly tours, first come basis.
Queuing outside if necessary. Last entry 3.30pm. Max 8 per
tour. A P Q
Modern take on the traditional Victorian Terrace. Two
new houses designed by Stephen Taylor in conjunction
with Solidspace, with double height voids and split levels,
connecting where we eat/live/work – the interiors are bold,
light with character. Stephen Taylor Architects/Solidspace 2014.
Rail: Crouch Hill, Harringay; W3,210,W7,W5

The Eco-Hub at Lordship Recreation Ground ◉◉
Lordship Recreation Ground (Near the pond), Lordship Lane
N17 7QX
■ Sat 1pm-5pm. N D R T A G
AECB silver standard strawbale and timber-frame
construction with raised floor on timber piles. Part of
regeneration of Lordship Recreation Ground. Clay boards and
unfired clay blocks. Low energy consumption design with
green roof. Anne Thorne Architects 2012. Entry: café, corridor,
decking area, park.
Tube: Turnpike Lane; Rail: Bruce Grove; 123,243,W4

The Old Schoolhouse
Hornsey Historical Society, 136 Tottenham Lane (corner Rokesly
Ave) N8 7EL
■ Sun 10am-4pm. Regular guided and self-guided tours.
Special displays on houses and streets then and now,
Victorian school built in 1848 and local architect John Farrer.
Worksheets and plans of building for children. N D T B C P d
Small, early Victorian infant school, closed in 1934, and after
conversion and some demolition re-opened in 1981 as HQ of
Society. John Henry Taylor 1848/Marius Reynolds 1981. Entry:

main school room.
Tube/Rail: Finsbury Park; Rail: Hornsey, Harringay; 41,91,W3,W5

Tottenham Town Hall
Town Hall, Approach Road N15 4RY
■ Sat 10am-5pm. Learn about the history of Tottenham in the
Legacy Heritage Centre. D T
Complete external and internal refurbishment of Grade II
listed Town Hall, rescued from English Heritage 'at risk' register,
now returned to its former glory. Grand foyer and Moselle
Room with its stunning Moorish-Jacobean style ceiling has
been restored along with brickwork and repairs to the intricate
Italian terrazzo mosaic floor. A salvage strategy was employed
to recycle slate tiles, granite setts, bricks and stone window
sills. AS Taylor & AR Jemmett 1904/bptw partnership (refurb)
2011. Entry: common areas, Moselle room, Mayor's parlour.
Tube/Rail: Seven Sisters; Rail: South Tottenham;
41,76,123,149,476

Tower and Churchyard of St Mary's Hornsey.
Hornsey High Street N8 7QB
■ Sun 2pm-5pm. Regular tours of tower. Max 15 at one time.
Exhibition, self-guided tree and tomb trails, and significant
tombs. Garden of Remembrance on site of demolished C19
church. R P
Grade II* listed tower with restored chapel remaining from
Medieval parish church. Excellent views from top of tower.
Organised by Friends of Hornsey Church Tower.
Tube: Turnpike Lane; Rail: Hornsey; 41,144,W3

Tower Gardens Garden Suburb ◉
Information pick up point: 5 Tower Gardens Road N17 7PX
■ Sun 10am-4pm. Self-guided exterior tour of the estate.
Coffee and cake sale. N R T

One of the first garden suburbs in the world, with 2-storey
terraced cottages retaining many decorative architectural
features. The LCC created a 'housing of the working classes'
role for the architects' department under Riley, a brother of the
Art Workers guild. WE Riley 1910-24.
Tube: Turnpike Lane; Wood Green; Rail: Bruce Grove;
123,144,243,217,444,231

WALKS/TOURS

Muswell Hill Walk
■ Meet: Sat 2pm beside Muswell Hill Library, Queen's Avenue
N10 3PE. Duration approx 2.5 hours. Talk and display at
North Bank house at end of walk. Max 30 on tour. R P d
Tour takes in early and late Victorian, Edwardian and 1930s
buildings, and gives an historical interpretation of how a rural
enclave changed into a unique Edwardian suburb. Finishes at
North Bank House, Pages Lane, one of the old Victorian villas.
First visit to library accessible via stairs only. Walk is otherwise
flat for duration. Organised by Hornsey Historical Society.
Tube: East Finchley, Highgate, Bounds Green;
43,102,134,144,234,W7

Noel Park Estate Tour
■ Meet: Sat 11am, 1pm corner of Gladstone and Wood Green
High Road N22 6EH
A late C19/early C20 planned community built to provide
affordable housing for working-class families wishing to leave
the inner city, close to the rail network to allow commuting.
One of the first Victorian Garden Suburbs – every property had
a front and back garden. Roland Plumbe 1883.
Tube: Wood Green; 29,243

Tottenham High Road Regeneration Tour
■ Meet: Sat 10am at Seven Sisters station (outside exit 1) N15
4RR. First come basis. N D
The tour will concentrate on the completed and planned
public realm improvements and reuse of vacant spaces and
buildings along Tottenham High Road. The project is known as
Growth on the High Road and is part of the wider Tottenham
Regeneration Programme funded by the Greater London
Authority (Mayor's Regeneration Fund) and Haringey Council.
Various architects: Adams and Sutherland/Tom Ebdan/You
and Me 2012-2015.
Tube/Rail: Seven Sisters

Tottenham High Road: Spurs Redevelopment &
Rebuilding after the Riots ◉
■ Meet: Sun 11am outside Sainsbury's, 28-48
Northumberland Park N17 0TX. Duration 1.5 hours.
A walk to reveal and showcase the amazing heritage wealth
of Tottenham High Road and the many new developments, led
by members of the Tottenham Civic Society.
Tube/Rail: Seven Sisters; Rail: White Hart Lane;
W3,149,259,279,349

Supported by

Haringey Council

Key. A Architect on site **B** Bookshop **C** Childrens' activities **d** Some disabled access **D** Full wheelchair access **E** Engineer on site **G** Green Features
N Normally open to the public **P** Parking **Q** Long queues envisaged **R** Refreshments **T** Toilets

Harrow

See openhouselondon.org.uk/harrow
to find out more about this area

Brockley Hill Farm

Brockley Hill Farm, Brockley Hill, Stanmore HA7 4LN
- Sat 10am-5pm.

Grade II listed timber-framed 2-storey Wealden style farmhouse built c1550 with additions in C17 and C18, clad in weatherboarding, with tiled roof.
Tube: Edgware, then 107 bus

Canons Park ●

Canons Park, Edgware HA8 6RH
- Sun 10am-5pm. Hourly tours, first come basis. Duration 30mins. N D R T P

Grade II listed historic landscape containing several listed buildings, including an C18 'temple' and walled kitchen garden, converted in 1937 to an informally planted garden. Harrow Council C18/1930s.
Tube: Canons Park; 186,79,340,142

Canons Park Estate

Rose Garden Close, off Canons Drive, Edgware HA8 7RF
- Sun 10am-5pm. Hourly tours, first come basis. Duration 20-30mins. Last entry 4pm. D d

Private C18 seven-acre lake, part of the dismantled Canons Mansion grounds, now surrounded by 1930s character housing. Wildlife includes Canada geese, swans and ducks.
Tube: Edgware, Canons Park; 303,186,79,340,142

Ewart House ●

9 Richards Close, Harrow HA1 2BE
- Sat 10am-5pm. Regular tours, first come basis. Max 25 at one time. Max 10 per tour. D R T A G P

A low energy Extra Care and affordable housing scheme for older people. Winner of the Mayor's award for 'Best new place to live in London'. Includes solar thermal and PV panels, and rainwater harvesting. TM Architects 2010.
Tube/Rail: Harrow-on-the-Hill

Former Grosvenor Cinema, now Zoroastrian Centre For Europe

440-442 Alexandra Avenue, Harrow HA2 9TL
- Sat 11am-5pm. Hourly tours, and half-hourly talks on Zoroastrianism. Last entry 4.30pm. D R T P

Grade II* listed Art Deco building with well-preserved interior. Auditorium with deep coved ribs; proscenium arch flanked by fluted columns. F E Bromige 1936. Entry: auditorium, foyer.
Tube: Rayners Lane; 398,H10,H11,H12

High Street Harrow Public Realm ●

St Ann's Road (Station Road End) Harrow HA1 1AT
- Sat 10am-5pm. Hourly guided tours, first come basis. No tour at 1pm. Last tour 4pm. N D A

Utilising continuous paving and strategic planting, St Ann's Road has been transformed into a linear, unified street scape allowing pedestrians to appreciate its scale, openness and character. David Kohn Architects 2014.
Tube/Rail: Harrow-on-the-Hill; 114,182,183,186,H11

The Arc House & Lowlands Recreation Ground

Kenton Library

Kenton Lane, Kenton HA3 8UJ
- Sat 9am-5pm. N D P

A good example of the Middlesex County Architect's Department's style adopted after 1933, which gave distinctive architectural form of calibre and panache to the London suburbs, this is also one of the best examples of inter-war library design in London. Grade II listed with original internal fittings. Curtis & Burchett 1939.
Tube/Rail: Kenton, Harrow & Wealdstone; H9,H10,H18,H19,114.

Rayners Lane Station

Alexandra Avenue, Harrow HA5 5EG
- Sat 11am-5pm. Guided tours, first come basis. Last tour 4.30pm. N D

Rebuilt in the 1930s to a design by Holden and Uren, the station is cube-shaped, constructed in brick and glass and capped with a flat reinforced concrete roof. Charles Holden and Reginald Uren 1938. Entry: ticket hall.
Tube: Rayners Lane; 398,H9,H10,H12

Stanmore Place ●

Sales & Marketing Suite, Monarch Court, Howard Road, Honeypot Lane, Stanmore HA7 1BT
- Sat/Sun 10am-5pm. Regular tours, first come basis. Last entry 4pm. N T A P d

Stanmore Place is the regeneration of a former government site to create a new, sustainable urban quarter with creative and unique solutions to flooding, accessibility, transport and ecology. GRID Architects 2014.
Tube: Canons Park; 79,186,340

The Arc House & Lowlands Recreation Ground

Lowlands Rec, Lowlands Road, Harrow-on-the-Hill HA1 3GR
- Sat/Sun 7am-9pm. Architect on site Sat only. Last entry 8.30pm. N D R T A

A previously neglected open space next to Harrow Town Centre has been transformed into a public resource with new landscaping, café, community building, playground and outdoor amphitheatre. Adams & Sutherland 2015.
Tube/Rail: Harrow-on-the-Hill

WALKS/TOURS

Grange Farm Estate Regeneration Tour

Grange Farm Community Centre HA2 0QF
- Sat 10am-5pm. Hourly tours, first come basis. D T A

Resiform estate of 3-storey flats thought to be the last around in London, being prepared for regeneration. See the past, present and future of this unusual resin panel construction. Hawkins\Brown due 2020-22.
Tube: South Harrow, Rayners Lane; Tube/Rail: Harrow-on-the-Hill; Rail: Northolt Park; 114,140,258,398,H9,H10

Harrow Civic Centre Regeneration Walk and Talk

Harrow Civic Centre, Station Road, Harrow HA1 2XF
- Sat 10am-3pm. Hourly presentations by senior regeneration officers of local regeneration projects, first come basis. Last tour 2pm. Max 30 per tour. N D T A P

Harrow Council is about to embark on a £1.75 billion Heart of Harrow Regeneration Programme, the largest in a generation. Presentations will take place in Council Chamber of the Brutalist Modern Civic Centre from 1970s, designed by Eric G Broughton chosen after competition judged by Sir Basil Spence. This will be followed by 30 mins tour of the site, which is forming the core of the regeneration, and key sites across the railway in Wealdstone.
Tube/Rail: Harrow & Wealdstone; 140,182,186,258,340

Modernism in Metroland

- Meet: Sat 10am, 2pm outside Stanmore tube station, London Road, Stanmore HA7 4PD. First come basis. Max 25 per tour.

A walking tour of Stanmore's Art Deco and Modernist homes, from the birth of metro-land to the post-war era. Douglas Wood/Gerald Lacoste/Owen Williams/Reginald Uren/Rudolf Frankel c1934.
Tube: Stanmore; 142,324,H12

Supported by

Havering

See openhouselondon.org.uk/havering
to find out more about this area

Thames Chase Forest Centre

Langtons House

Bower House
Orange Tree Hill, Havering-atte-Bower, Romford RM4 1PB
■ Sat 10am-4pm. Regular tours. R T B P d
Grade I listed mansion house commanding the most
extensive southerly views over Essex towards Kent. Leading
landscape designer Charles Bridgman and Sir James Thornhill
(best known for his wall paintings at Blenheim Palace) were
involved with the design. Henry Flitcroft 1729. Entry: mansion
house, grounds.
Rail: Romford then 375

Elm Park Primary School
Elm Park, South End Road, Hornchurch RM12 5UA
■ Sat/Sun 10am-5pm. N D R T G P
Bright, spacious award winning school, providing flexible
spaces to accommodate a range of activities. The 2-storey
building has a sedum grass roof with classroom spaces
opening onto a double-height shared 'heart' space. Walters &
Cohen Architects 2011.
Tube: Elm Park; 165,252,365

Havering Museum
19-21 High Street RM1 1JU
■ Sat/Sun 11am-5pm. First come basis. Last entry 4pm. Max
70 at one time. D T B
A flagship cultural centre for the borough, in a converted
Romford brewery building near to the historic market place.
Permanent and temporary exhibition spaces tell the story of
this area from bronze age to present day. Exhibition pieces
have been carefully crafted into the existing structure to
create a modern intervention that retains the historic value of
the building. TTSP Architects (refurb) 2010.
Rail: Romford; 66,175,248,496

Langtons House
Billet Lane, Hornchurch RM11 1XJ
■ Sun 10am-5pm. Regular tours, first come basis. Exhibition
of historic photographs. Last entry 4.45pm. Max 30 at one
time. D T
Grade II listed neo-Georgian house with later additions.
Landscaped garden with lake, orangery and gazebo.
Entry: marriage rooms, orangery. Gardens open Sat and Sun.
Tube: Hornchurch; Rail: Emerson Park; 248,252,256,324,370

Rainham Parish Church of St Helen and St Giles
The Broadway, Rainham RM13 9YW
■ Sat 10am-1pm. Regular tours, first come basis. N
Grade I listed Norman church with notable chancel arch with
chevron and nailhead ornament, built by Richard De Lucy. 12C.
Entry: vestry, chancel.
Tube: Elm Park, Dagenham East; Rail: Rainham; 103,165,287,324

Romford Town Hall
Main Road, Romford RM1 3BD
■ Sat 12noon-4pm. Regular tours, first come basis.
Photographic exhibition of old photos of the town hall. D T
Grade II listed, the design was the result of an architectural
competition won by Collins & Geens. Unique fittings using
Bath stone, red cedar wood and Tasmanian oak, with full-
height entrance hall and tall central staircase window and

flagpoles. H R Collins & AEO Geens 1935. Entry: ground and 1st floor.
Tube: Hornchurch; Rail: Romford; 252,248,175,128,66

Royal Liberty School (formerly Hare Hall)
Upper Brentwood Road, Gidea Park, Romford RM2 6HJ
■ Sun 10am-5pm. Last entry 4.15pm. T P
Grade II listed Palladian villa with a west facing five-bay front
of Portland stone with two wings. Interior contains fine
original staircase. James Paine 1768. Entry: ground, 1st, 2nd
floors.
Tube: Hornchurch; Rail: Gidea Park; 496

St Mary Magdalene Church
Church Lane, North Ockendon, Upminster RM14 3QH
■ Sat 10am-1pm. Max 150 at one time. D R T P
Grade I listed. Norman nave c1170, North aisle C13. Poyntz
Chapel added 1300 and Jacobean pulpit.
Tube/Rail: Upminster; 370

Thames Chase Forest Centre
Broadfields, Pike Lane, Upminster RM14 3NS
■ Sat/Sun 10am-5pm. Displays on how the community forest
improves the quality of urban life, and how buildings can
be sympathetic to the forest. Craft and produce stalls. Last
entry 4.50pm. N D R T B G
Distinctive award-winning visitor centre of modern timber
construction forming an A-frame building roofed with
cedar shingles, attached to C17 listed barn – one of the best
preserved in the London area. Sustainable features include
timber construction, passive ventilation, underfloor heating,
biomass boiler. C17/Laurie Wood Architects 2010. Entry: forest
centre, barn.
Tube/Rail: Upminster; 347

The Queen's Theatre
Billet Lane, Hornchurch RM11 1QT
■ Sat 1pm-5pm. Backstage tours 1.30pm, 2.30pm, 3.30pm
(may not be suitable for wheelchair users), bookable in
advance from Box Office on 01708 443333. Max 30 per tour.
N R T C d
Opened by Sir Peter Hall, a robust example of 1970s civic
architecture and a vibrant and successful producing theatre.
Norman Brooks 1975. Entry: all front of house areas, and
backstage with tour. Children's activities/backstage treasure
hunt running 2pm, 3pm.
Tube: Hornchurch; 193,248,252,256,324

Upminster Old Chapel
70 St Mary's Lane (entry in side foyer), Upminster RM14 2QR
■ Sat/Sun 2pm-5pm. Tours 2.30pm, 3.30pm, 4.30pm. N D R T C P
Grade II timber-framed former Dissenters' Meeting House
(1800) with pedimented façade. Two blank windows flank the

Doric entrance porch. Fully refurbished, and re-opened to the
public in 2013.
Tube: Upminster Bridge; Tube/Rail: Upminster; 248,348,370,373

Upminster Tithe Barn Museum
Hall Lane, Upminster RM14 1AU
■ Sat/Sun 10.30am-4pm. Regular tours. Displays illustrating
'The Upminster Suburb Story'. Demonstrations of historical
exhibits. Last entry 3.30pm. N P d
C15 box-framed, 9-bay, aisled barn, weatherboarded with
crown-post, collar-tie reed-thatched roof. Ancient monument.
Tube/Rail: Upminster; 248

WALKS/TOURS

Elm Park Garden Suburb Walk
■ Meet: Saturday 10.30am at Elm Park Station entrance
(District Line) RM12 4RW. First come basis. Duration 2 hours.
For information call 01277 219892. Max 40 per tour. R T B d
Elm Park, an estate of 7000 proposed houses was built on
600 acres of farmland to totally transform a rural area,
opened together with a new District Line station in May 1935
by the Minister of Health. Costains had studied and learnt
important lessons from earlier Garden City development.
Home ownership of 6 styles of house according to income was
offered to many people who previously had had no prospect of
home purchase.
Tube: Elm Park; 165,252,365,372.

Supported by

🏛 Havering
LONDON BOROUGH

Open House London 2015

**Navigate your way
around Open House
in your area with the
app. See p14**

Key. A Architect on site **B** Bookshop **C** Childrens' activities **d** Some disabled access **D** Full wheelchair access **E** Engineer on site **G** Green Features
N Normally open to the public **P** Parking **Q** Long queues envisaged **R** Refreshments **T** Toilets

Hillingdon

See **openhouselondon.org.uk/hillingdon**
to find out more about this area

Battle of Britain Bunker at RAF Uxbridge
St Andrews Road (off Vine Lane), Uxbridge UB10 0RN
■ Sat/Sun 10am-5pm. Tours taking place, pre-book ONLY via 01895 238154 or 11gpenquiries@btconnect.com. Bunker has 76 stairs. Last tour 3.30pm. Max 40 per tour. N T P
The bunker, built in 1939 and restored to its wartime state, controlled the RAF Fighters and prevented the Luftwaffe winning the Battle of Britain. Entry: bunker with plotting room, controllers cabins, museum rooms. Wartime buildings and shop above ground.
Tube: Uxbridge; 427,607

Cranford Stable Block & St Dunstan's Church
Cranford Park, The Parkway, Cranford TW5 9RZ
■ Sat/Sun 10.30am-4.30pm. Activities, refreshments, guided history walks. Max 20 at one time. R T P d
Restored C18 stable block of now demolished Cranford House, former seat of the Earl of Berkeley. The front has arches with stone keystones facing a cobbled yard. Entry: ground floor area (west stable). Also open medieval St Dunstan's Church mentioned in the Domesday Book and famous for its early C14 wall paintings. Berkeley family tombs in cemetery.
Tube: Hatton Cross, Hounslow West; Rail: Hayes & Harlington; 105,111,81,222,498,E6,195

Eastcote House Gardens
High Road Eastcote, Eastcote HA5 2FE
■ Sun 10am-5pm. R T P d
Restored timber-framed C17 stables, C18 brick dovecote and large walled garden, all set in parkland of the former Eastcote House (dem. 1964). Family home of the Hawtrey family from 1527 to 1930. Interiors largely as originally constructed.
Tube: Eastcote (15 min walk), Ruislip; H13 from Ruislip

Harefield Hospital
Hill End Road, Harefield UB9 6JH
■ Sun 10am-5pm. Tours hourly from 11am, last tour 4pm. Meet at concert hall. Last entry 4.30pm. N R T P d
Founded as an Australian WW1 hospital, 2015 is Harefield's centenary. Guided tours will explore the C18 estate, the curved 1937 TB sanatorium and the modern heart hospital. WT Curtis 1937. Entry: concert hall and exhibition, grounds.
Tube: Northwood, Uxbridge; Rail: Denham; then U9 (only from Uxbridge),331

Manor Farm Site, Manor House
St Martins Approach, Ruislip HA4 8BD
■ Sat/Sun 11am-5pm. Tours of house 11am-2pm; Great Barn 12pm-3pm. N R T d
Oldest and largest (22 acres) heritage site in Hillingdon, Manor Farm has been occupied since C11. Sympathetically refurbished in 2008, now home to interpretation centre in C16 Manor House. Great Barn is the oldest in the Greater London area, containing many early features.
Tube: Ruislip; Tube/Rail: West Ruislip; 331,H13,U10,U1,398,114

Swakeleys Estate

St Martin's Church, Ruislip
High Street, Ruislip HA4 8DG
■ Sat 10am-5pm/Sun 1pm-5pm. N D T P
Church dates from 1250 with C15 additions and Victorian restorations. Grade II listed. Fine late medieval wall paintings and funeral hatchments. C13/Sir Gilbert Scott and Ewan Christian 1870.
Tube: Ruislip; Rail: West Ruislip; 114,E7,331

St Mary the Virgin Church
Church Road, Hayes UB3 2LY
■ Sat 10am-5pm/Sun 11am-5pm. N D R T P
The Parish Church of Hayes Middlesex has witnessed to the Christian Faith since at least 830 AD. This reflects several periods of architecture from the early perpendicular of the East Window to the Tower which was rebuilt in 1970.
Rail: Hayes & Harlington; H98,195,607,427,90

St Peter & St Paul Harlington
St Peter's Way, High Street, Harlington UB3 5AB
■ Sat 10am-5pm/Sun 1pm-5pm. Regular tours. N D T P
Grade I listed church (C16) with Norman font and Norman stone arch carved with cats' heads. Interesting monuments including Easter sepulchre. Ancient yew tree in churchyard. Good restoration between 1830 and 1860.
Tube: Hatton Cross; Rail: Hayes & Harlington; 140,U4

Swakeleys Estate
Swakeleys Road, Ickenham (access from Milton Road) UB10 8LD
■ Sat 10am-5pm. Max 15 at one time, entry every 20-30 mins. T P
By far the most important house in Ickenham and an outstanding example of Jacobean architecture built in the 1630s. Constructed of red brick, laid in English bond on an H plan. Great Hall includes the 1655 Harrington Screen, C18 marble fireplace and panelling. The Great Hall and the main staircase hall with its wall paintings will be open to the public along with much of the grounds from which the very particular style of Jacobean architecture can viewed. Entry: Great Hall, main staircase hall, gardens.
Tube: Ickenham, Uxbridge; Rail: West Ruislip; U1,U2,U10

The Great Barn, Harmondsworth
Manor Court, High Street, Harmondsworth UB7 0AQ
■ Sat 10am-5pm. Owlsworth carpenter on site pm only. Women's Land Army live horse-drawn display 3pm. E D P
This great medieval barn (1426), over 190 feet long and nearly 40 feet high, is the last of a series of enormous, cathedral-like barns built on this site in Harmondsworth. Displays on the conservation/repairs carried out in 2014 by Owlsworth for English Heritage. 1426/Peter McCurdy and English Heritage (restored) 1986/Owlsworth (restored) 2014. Entry: barn, grounds adjacent to barn.
Tube/Rail: Heathrow T1,2,3, then bus U3; Rail: West Drayton, then bus U3,350

Uxbridge Lido
Hillingdon Sports and Leisure Complex, Gatting Way, Uxbridge UB8 1ES
■ Sat/Sun 10am-5pm. R T
This 1930s 'Moderne Art Deco' designed lido was refurbished in 2010 to include a £33m sports complex. It has closed down multiple times throughout its history but is currently enjoyed by the public. GP Trentham 1935. Entry: lido, Clive Hamilton suite.
Tube: Uxbridge; U1,U2,U3,44,331

Uxbridge Quaker Meeting House
York Road Uxbridge, UB8 1QW
■ Sat 10am-4pm/Sun 1pm-4pm. First come basis. Last entry 3.30pm. Max 20 at one time. T
Grade II listed typical Georgian Quaker meeting house (1818), retaining its original features with an elders' gallery and full size opening screens. Entry: large meeting house. NB. Exhibition on 'Quakers and Uxbridge from 1658'.
Tube: Uxbridge; 222,331,427,607,U4

Supported by

HILLINGDON
LONDON

Hounslow

See openhouselondon.org.uk/hounslow
to find out more about this area

Adobe Village Hounslow Heath Infant and Nursery School

Martindale Road TW4 7HE

■ Sat 10am-5pm. First come basis. Last entry 4.30pm. D R T C P

A unique striking playscape and adobe home structure that integrates outside learning with innovative earth forms. Construction is 'rammed' earth made from earth filled tubes. The children contributed to the scheme by sketching out their ideas for their eco-classroom. Adobe construction recently gaining recognition for sound-reducing properties. Small Earth 2011. Entry: adobe home, adobe village, large sandpit, moon gate.

Tube: Hounslow West; Rail: Hounslow; 237,117,235,116

Boston Manor House ●

Boston Manor Road, Brentford TW8 9JX

■ Sat/Sun 12noon-5pm. Tours 12.30pm, 2pm, 3.30pm, first come basis. Max 30 per tour. T d

Jacobean Manor House set in parkland with lake and ancient trees. Richly decorated C17 plaster ceilings in State Rooms. Donald Insall (restoration) 1963. Entry: state room, dining room.

Tube: Boston Manor; Rail: Brentford; E8

Gunnersbury Park & Museum ●

Gunnersbury Park Museum W3 8LQ

■ Sun 11am, 1pm behind the scenes architect-led tours to explore the restoration project. Meet outside the museum. Pre-book ONLY via gunnersbury@ealing.gov.uk. T P A

Former home to the Rothschild family, now a local history museum set in beautiful C19 mansion on an elevated terrace overlooking lawns and parkland. Major restoration project is under way. Alexander Copland 1802/Sydney Smirke (extended) 1835.

Tube: Acton Town; E3

Hogarth's House

Hogarth Lane, Great West Road W4 2QN

■ Sat/Sun 12pm-5pm. Hourly tours of areas usually closed to the public, first come basis. Last tour 4pm, last entry 4.45pm. Max 6 per tour. N T B P d

Early C18 red brick home of artist William Hogarth extended significantly c1749-1764. Delightful walled garden containing famous ancient mulberry tree. A unique oasis in modern west London. Entry: attic, basement, store rooms, study rooms.

Tube: Turnham Green; Rail: Chiswick; 190

Kempton Great Engines Trust ●

Kempton Park Water Treatment Works, Snakey Lane, Hanworth TW13 7ND

■ Sat/Sun 10.30am-4pm. First come basis. Last entry 3.30pm. E R T B C P d

Magnificent industrial cathedral (a National Monument) housing two triple expansion steam engines and two steam turbines. The engines were at the heart of the water treatment works supplying north London with drinking water taken from the Thames. Quiz pack, play area.

Rail: Kempton Park; 290, H25

Adobe Village Hounslow Heath Infant and Nursery School

London Museum of Water & Steam ●

Green Dragon Lane, Brentford TW8 0EN

■ Sat/Sun 11am-4pm. Engine tours and archive tours. E D R T B A P

Recognised as the most important historic site of the water supply industry in Britain. The museum is housed within a unique collection of Grade I and II listed buildings. Even though they were purpose-built as purely functional, the architect took great care to make the buildings aesthetically pleasing. The main entrance lobby to the engine house looks similar to the vestibule of a grand town house, with the window encasement finished off in fine Georgian style. William Anderson 1838.

Tube/Rail: Gunnersbury; Rail: Kew Bridge; 65,237,267,391

Osterley Park House

Jersey Road, Isleworth TW7 4RD

■ Sat/Sun 11am-5pm. Timed tickets may apply. Last entry 4pm. Max 200 in house at one time. R T B P d

One of Britain's most complete examples of Robert Adam's work. Set in over 350 acres of park, garden and farmland. Robert Adam 1761. Entry: house, park, garden.

Tube: Osterley; Rail: Isleworth; H28,H37,H91

St Mary's Convent

10 The Butts, Brentford TW8 8BQ

■ Sat tours 10am, 12noon. Tour with PRP architects 3pm. Pre-book ONLY via 020 8568 7305. Duration approx 1.5 hours. Max 8 per tour. T P A d

Convent in C18 Grade II listed house with original features. Various additions including west wing (1913-15) and harmonious care home facilities and chapel by PRP Architects (1998-2001). Entry: lobby, community room, chapel, heritage room and Foundress' room (no wheelchair access to heritage and Foundress' rooms). Archival exhibition and historical talk.

Tube: Boston Manor; Rail: Brentford; 235,237,267,E2,E8

West Thames College (Spring Grove House)

London Road, Isleworth TW7 4HS

■ Sat 10am-4pm. Regular tours. Last tour 3.30pm. Max 10 per tour. R T G P d

Remarkably intact prime example of late Victorian architecture and interior design, including stained glass windows and mosaics. Grade II listed with one remaining fine Georgian room. Previous owners include Pears 'Soap' family and Sir Joseph Banks, President of the Royal Society, who sailed in the 'Endeavour' with Captain Cook. Restored and refurbished during 2011-12. Sir John Offley/various 1754 onwards. Entry: house and key rooms.

Tube: Osterley, Hounslow East; Rail: Isleworth; 117,H37,235,237,110

Osterley Park House

WALKS/TOURS

Bedford Park ●

■ Meet: Sun 2.30pm at Victorian Society (garden), 1 Priory Gardens W4 1TT. Duration approx 2hrs. P

Bedford Park is known as the first garden suburb. Some 400 homes, mostly in red brick with red tiled roofs, Dutch-style gables, balconies and artists' studios. Norman Shaw, EW Godwin, EJ May and Maurice B Adams 1875-1886.

Tube: Turnham Green; 94,272,E3

Gunnersbury Park Landscape Tour ●

■ Meet: Sun 2pm at entrance to Gunnersbury Park Museum, Gunnersbury Park W3 8LQ. Pre-book ONLY via gunnersbury@ealing.gov.uk, limited places. N D R T P

Landscape architect tour of Gunnersbury Park to discuss the planned restoration of the park. The tour will give an insight into the future transformation of the heritage landscape which hosts over 20 listed features including an orangery, walled garden, bathhouse and the remnants of a horseshoe pond.

Tube: Acton Town; E3

Hounslow Open House Guided Cycle Tour

■ Meet: Sat 12.45pm at Brentford Market Place TW8 8LB. First come basis. Duration approx 2.5 hours. Steady-paced cycle suitable for all. Children aged 8-15 must be accompanied by an adult.

Guided architectural bike tour led by local Hounslow Cycle Campaign group around Open House buildings.

Rail: Brentford

Turnham Green Walk ●

■ Meet: Sun 2.30pm outside Chiswick Town Hall, Heathfield Terrace W4 4JN. Duration approx 1 hour.

Beginning at the Victorian/Edwardian Town Hall, this walk takes in the former Sanderson home (famous for their wallpapers) including the CFA Voysey industrial building, a statue of William Hogarth, a police station and the first fire station to be built with a hose tower.

Tube: Chiswick Park; Rail: Gunnersbury; 237,267,E3

Supported by

London Borough of Hounslow

Key. A Architect on site **B** Bookshop **C** Childrens' activities **d** Some disabled access **D** Full wheelchair access **E** Engineer on site **G** Green Features **N** Normally open to the public **P** Parking **Q** Long queues envisaged **R** Refreshments **T** Toilets

Islington

See **openhouselondon.org.uk/islington**
to find out more about this area

30 Cardozo Road
30 Cardozo Road N7 9RL
■ Sat 10am-5pm. First come basis, queuing outside if
necessary. Last entry 4.30pm. Max 20 at one time. G d
A partially subterranean house, designed to give generous
accommodation on a small plot while preserving the long
views across the site from the street. Jack Woolley 2013.
*Tube: Caledonian Road, Holloway Road; Tube/Rail: King's Cross
St Pancras; 17,91,259,274*

AL_A Studio
14a Brewery Road N7 9NH
■ Sat/Sun 10am-4pm. Images and models of both current
and past projects will be on display. T A
The architects for the V&A Exhibition Road project, Central
Embassy in Bangkok and the 2015 MPavilion in Melbourne,
open their top-lit studio, formerly an Islington Council
transport depot. AL_A 2012.
*Tube: Caledonian Road; Rail: Caledonian Road & Barnsbury;
91,17,259,274*

Angel Building ●
407 St John Street EC1V 4AB
■ Sat 10am-5pm/Sun 1pm-5pm. First come basis. Last entry
4.15pm. Max 75 at one time. D T A G
Re-invention of an early 1980s office block from Derwent
London. Elegant and robust detailing, the existing concrete
frame has been re-used and re-wrapped with a highly energy-
efficient glazed skin. Striking Ian McChesney art piece in foyer
and stunning London-wide views from terrace. RIBA and BCO
Award Winner 2011, Stirling Prize shortlist 2011. Allford Hall
Monaghan Morris 2010. Entry: atrium, top floor terrace.
Tube: Angel; 19,38,341,73,214,30,205

Ashmount Primary School ●
83 Crouch Hill N8 9EG
■ Sat/Sun 10am-1pm. Regular architect-led tours of whole
school. D T G
Carbon neutral building. BREEAM Award for Highest Scoring
Project in the Education Sector. Penoyre & Prasad 2012.
Tube/Rail: Finsbury Park then W7 bus; Rail: Crouch Hill
www.ashmountprimaryschool.co.uk

Bunhill Heat and Power Energy Centre ●
Central Street EC1V 3QB
■ Sat 10am-5pm. Regular tours, first come basis. Max 10 per
tour. Display on design and build outside the Energy Centre.
Last entry 4.30pm. G d
A ground-breaking decentralised energy scheme located in
the south of the borough and part of Islington's wider strategy
to reduce fuel poverty and yield financial and environmental
benefits to the community. Tim Ronalds Architects 2012.
Tube: Old Street, Barbican

Caledonian Park Clocktower
Market Road N7 9PL
■ Sat 11am-4pm. Hourly tours only, pre-book ONLY via
www.islington.gov.uk/caledonianpark. Last tour 3pm. R d
Opened in 1855 as centrepiece of Metropolitan Cattle Market.
The seven storey clock tower offers magnificent views over

W Plumb Family Butchers

London. The original working clock mechanism adds further
interest. J.B. Bunning 1850-5. Entry: all levels
*Tube: Caledonian Road; Rail: Caledonian Road & Barnsbury,
Kings Cross St Pancras; 274,390,17,91,259*

Charterhouse Chapel
Charterhouse Square EC1M 6AN
■ Sun 2pm-5pm. Last entry 4.45pm. Max 30 at one time. D T
Founded as a Carthusian Monastery in 1371, later sold as a
Tudor mansion. Elizabeth I and James I both spent time here. In
1611 endowed as a school (now in Godalming) and almshouse,
which it remains to this day. Entry: chapel court, chapel cloister,
chapel.
Tube: Barbican; 4,56,153

Crossrail Farringdon Construction Sites ●
Crossrail site office, Farringdon Road EC1M 3HN
■ Sat/Sun. See www.crossrail.co.uk/openhouse for booking
details and meeting point. E
Sitting right at the heart of the London transport network,
Farringdon Station is fundamental to Crossrail meeting its
aspiration of delivering a world-class railway that meets the
ever growing transport needs of London. When complete,
it is planned that over 140 trains per hour will flow through
the Farringdon interchange. Aedas/PLP Architecture/John
Robertson Architects due 2018.
Tube/Rail: Farringdon; 8,17,25,45,63
www.crossrail.co.uk/openhouse

Cullinan Studio ● ●
5 Baldwin Terrace N1 7RU
■ Sun 11am-1pm. Tours every 45 mins. Max 10 per tour. Display
of recent work. Last entry 12.30pm. D R T A G
Newly-retrofitted canal-side Victorian foundry building
converted into BREEAM Excellent offices. Sustainable features
include air-source heat pump, PV panels, recycled newspaper
insulation. Cullinan Studio Architects 2012.
Tube: Angel, Old Street; 38,43,73,205,341
www.cullinanstudio.com

Finsbury Health Centre ●
17 Pine Street EC1R 0LP
■ Sat/Sun 10am-5pm. Last entry 4.30pm. Max 25 at one time. D T

Angel Building

A pioneering idea. Grade I listed open access health centre that
allied Modernist design aesthetics with progressive social
policies, encapsulating progressive post-war politics a decade
before the establishment of the NHS, for which it was a model.
Tecton & Lubetkin 1938. Entry: all areas excluding clinical
rooms and offices.
Tube: Angel; Tube/Rail: Farringdon, King's Cross St Pancras; 63

Finsbury Town Hall
Rosebery Avenue EC1R 4RP
■ Sun 10am-5pm. Regular tours. Last entry 4.45pm. Max 10 at
one time. D T
Opened by Lord Rosebery, an ornate building with elegant
décor influenced by the Art Nouveau movement. Several
notable rooms including the Great Hall with unique stained
glass, antique mirrors and Clerkenwell Angel statuettes.
C Evans Vaughan 1895. Entry: Great Hall, council chamber,
marriage room, staircase.
Tube: Angel; Tube/Rail: Farringdon; 19,38,341

four23 London Studio
Berry House, Berry Street EC1V 0AA
■ Sat/Sun 1pm-5pm. Regular tours, first come basis. Sat
5-10pm special Open House film screening 'The Architect
and the Painter' exploring the creative environments of Ray
and Charles Eames. T D R
Former precious metals workshop re-imagined by interior
designer Harriet Paterson into a unique work and exhibition
space for leading communication design studio four23.
Frederick J Gibbons 1937.
Tube/Rail: Farringdon, Liverpool Street; 55,56,4,243,153
www.four23.net

Graduate Centre – London Metropolitan University
166-220 Holloway Road N7 8DB
■ Sat 9.30am-1pm. Display of recently completed projects by
ArchitecturePLB and Bisset Adams. Last entry 12.30pm. Max
30 at one time. D T
Award-winning landmark building providing postgraduate
and teaching facilities with a distinctive design. The building
is composed of three intersecting volumes clad entirely with
embossed stainless steel panels creating a shining and ever-
changing surface. Daniel Libeskind Studio 2004. Entry: lecture

---

● AJ Library Building ● Green Exemplar ● Landscape/Public realm ● Infrastructure/Engineering ■ Open Saturday ■ Open Sunday ■ Open Saturday and Sunday

Islington Penthouse

theatre, seminar rooms and postgraduate hub area.
Tube: Holloway Road; Tube/Rail: Highbury & Islington; 43,271,153,393

Hugh Myddelton Primary School
Myddelton Street EC1R 1YJ
■ Sat/Sun 10am-5pm. Access via half-hourly tours only, first come basis. Last tour 4.30pm. Max 10 per tour. R T d
Existing classrooms have been refurbished to provide new nursery and foundation stage accommodation, and external areas redesigned to maximise play space. A first floor extension provides additional accommodation. Gold timber contrasting with cobalt blue render creates a vibrant new entrance and lively street façade. Julian Sofaer 1966/Architype 2009.
Tube: Angel; 19,38,341,4,73

Impact Hub King's Cross ●
Impact Hub King's Cross, 34B York Way N1 9AB
■ Sat 10am-5pm. Hourly tours, first come basis. Last entry 4.45pm. Max 20 per tour. G D R T
Innovative workspace for social entrepreneurs with recycled fittings and furniture. Housed within Grade II listed building. Meeting rooms contain hanging glass and writable glass walls. Architecture 00 2008.
Tube/Rail: King's Cross St Pancras; 10,17,30,45,59,63,91,205,259

Ironmonger Row Baths
1 Norman Street EC1V 3AA
■ Sat/Sun 10am-5pm. Regular tours. Free parking on Sat after 1.30pm and all day Sun. Last entry 5.30pm. N D R T P
Grade II listed building, refurbished from May 2010 to November 2012. Original features: Turkish baths, laundry, swimming pool. Historical details of 1931 bath, maps and photos in a purpose built history room. AWS & KMB Cross 1930s /Tim Ronalds Architects 2012. Entry: All areas except spa if single gender day.
Tube: Old Street; 55,43,205,214,243

Islington Penthouse ●
Flat 4, 15 Highbury Crescent N5 1RS
■ Sat/Sun 1pm-5pm. T P
A penthouse with a hidden side and top. Within and above an Italianate villa in Highbury, HÛT created a series of unexpected inside and outside spaces using concrete, scaffolding boards, steel, glass and recycled timber. HÛT Architecture 2014.
Tube/Rail: Highbury & Islington

Kings Place
90 York Way N1 9AG
■ Sat/Sun tours of concert venues, backstage areas and Pangolin Gallery 10am, 11.15am, 1.15pm. Max 20 per tour. Duration 1 hour. D R T

Iconic mixed-use building with glass and limestone façades comprised of three basic components: a smaller scale block on Battlebridge Basin; The Rotunda, a long rectangular block facing York Way; running west to east a street-like atrium. Advanced acoustic design with interior veneer carved from single oak tree. RIBA Award Winner 2009. Dixon Jones 2008.
Tube/Rail: King's Cross St Pancras; 10,17,91,214,390,259

Marx Memorial Library
37a Clerkenwell Green EC1R 0DU
■ Sun 10am-5pm. Regular tours and talks. Last entry 3.30pm. Max 50 at one time. N R T B d
Built as a Welsh Charity School, and a library since 1933. Lenin worked here 1902-03 and his office is preserved. Grade II listed. Fresco on 1st floor. Late C15 tunnels. Sir James Steere 1738. Entry: Lenin Room, lecture hall, reading room, basement tunnels.
Tube/Rail: Farringdon, King's Cross St Pancras; 55,63,243

Morelands (AHMM offices) ●
Morelands 5-12 Old Street EC1V 9HL
■ Sat 1pm-5pm. Architect-led tours/talks 2pm, 3pm, 4pm. Model shop open throughout with model making demonstrations. 2pm-4pm Sketch Club on rooftop terrace. D R T A
Home to a variety of creative industries and the office of AHMM since 1995, the Morelands interventions stitch together a convoluted tangle of disparate warehouse blocks, alleys and entrances. The most recent refurbishment achieved BREEAM Outstanding. 5th floor completed in 2013. Allford Hall Monaghan Morris 2013.
Tube: Old Street, Barbican; Rail: Farringdon; 4,55,56,243

Oak Rooms, New River Head ●
New River Head, 173 Rosebery Avenue EC1R 4UL
■ Sat/Sun 10am-4pm. Hourly tours. Pre-book ONLY via londonopenhouse@thameswater.co.uk clearly marking 'Oak Rooms – Open House' in the subject line. Please do not turn up on the day without pre-booking. Max 16 per tour.
Formerly the boardroom of the C17 water house the Oak Room is a fine late Renaissance room demonstrating the New River Company's wealth. Fine 1697 carved oak interior, attributed to Grinling Gibbons, the overmantel and panels over the doors and shelving portray water plants and animals, fish and anglers' tackle. Unknown 1696/Austen Hall (refurbished) 1914-20. Entry: Oak Room, Oak Room approaches.
Tube: Angel; Tube/Rail: Farringdon; 19,38,153,341

Pollard Thomas Edwards ●
Diespeker Wharf, 38 Graham Street N1 8JX
■ Sat 10am-5pm. Last entry 4.30pm. T A
Conversion of a Victorian canalside warehouse, formerly a timberyard, into spacious offices, garden and glazed extension with one of the best waterside views in London. Pollard Thomas Edwards 1990s/2003. Entry: upper and lower ground floors, courtyard.
Tube: Angel, Old Street; 38,43,73,214

Priory Green
Hugh Cubitt House, 48 Collier Street N1 9QZ
■ Sat 10am-5pm. Last entry 4.30pm. Max 10 at one time. D T
Modern movement estate, received Conservation Area status after extensive refurbishment by Peabody. Pioneering in use of concrete and some of the most sculptural stairways ever designed for social housing. Includes 4 blocks, Old Laundry building and landscaped areas. Tecton & Lubetkin 1957. Entry: external areas, internal access to old laundry building. NB. no entry to flats.
Tube: Angel; Tube/Rail: King's Cross St Pancras; 73

Richard Desmond Children's Eye Centre at Moorfields Eye Hospital
3 Peerless Street EC1V 9EZ
■ Sun 10am-1pm. Half-hourly tours, first come basis. Last entry 12.30pm. Max 10 per tour. D T A
A world-class, contemporary healthcare building, dedicated to the treatment of children's eye conditions. Combines functional excellence with an award-winning and non-institutional design. Penoyre & Prasad 2007. Entry: all public areas accessible including waiting rooms, receptions.
Tube: Old Street; 43,135,205,214

Stanton Williams
36 Graham Street N1 8GJ
■ Sat 12pm-5pm. D T C A J
Award-winning architects' studio, with panoramic views over Regent's Canal. Display of recent projects, models and design materials. Model making demonstration and childrens' activities. Pollard Thomas Edwards architects (building)/ Stanton Williams (fit-out) 2003.
Tube: Angel; 30,38,73,214,205

Studionorth
277 New North Road N1 7AA
■ Sat/Sun 10am-5pm. First come basis, queuing outside if necessary. Last entry 4.30pm. Max 20 at one time. R T A d
Shopfront gallery features a special exhibition showing drawings, models, and anecdotes from Jan Kattein Architects' high street regeneration projects. Jan Kattein Architects 2006. Entry: gallery, studio, workshop, garden.
Tube: Angel; 21,38,73,141,271

The Goldsmiths' Centre ●
42 Britton Street, EC1M 5AD
■ Sat 10am-5pm. Tours 10.30am, 12noon, 2pm, 4pm. First come basis. Last entry 4.30pm. Max 15 per tour. D R T A G
RIBA Award winning centre for the training and advancement of the goldsmith's craft. Completed in 2012 it combines an early Grade II listed Victorian board school and modern 4-storey block clad in York stone and brass. Lyall, Bills and Young 2012. Entry: café, atrium, exhibition space, 4th floor conference rooms and terrace, training workshops and studios.
Tube/Rail: Farringdon; 63,45,17,243,55
www.goldsmiths-centre.org

W Plumb Family Butchers
493 Hornsey Road N19 3QL
■ Sat 10am-7pm/Sun 10am-5pm. Max 25 at one time. E D R
Grade II listed, ornate former Victorian butcher's shop c1900 with Art Nouveau wall tiling, geometric tiled floor, scrolled meat rails and mahogany cashier's booth with etched and brilliant cut glass. Very well preserved. Entry: butcher's shop.
Tube: Archway; Rail: Upper Holloway; 41,91,210

Wesley's Chapel and House
49 City Road EC1Y 1AU
■ Sat 10am-4pm/Sun 12.30pm-2pm. Regular tours. Groups over 6 people should pre-book via 020 7253 2262. Last entry Sat 3.30pm/Sun 1.30pm. Max 50 at one time (15 in Wesley's house). N T B C d
Fine Georgian complex built by John Wesley as his London base. George Dance the Younger 1778. Entry: chapel, museum, John Wesley's house, gardens. Q&A and 'search for' leaflet
Tube: Old Street (Exit 4), Moorgate; Tube/Rail: Liverpool Street; 21,43,76,141,205,214,271

Supported by

 ISLINGTON

Key. A Architect on site **B** Bookshop **C** Childrens' activities **d** Some disabled access **D** Full wheelchair access **E** Engineer on site **G** Green Features **N** Normally open to the public **P** Parking **Q** Long queues envisaged **R** Refreshments **T** Toilets

Kensington & Chelsea

See **openhouselondon.org.uk/kensington**
to find out more about this area

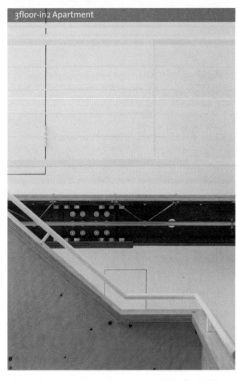
3floor-in2 Apartment

Chelsea Academy

3floor-in2 Apartment ●
17 Elgin Crescent W11 2JD
■ Sun 3pm-6.30pm. Tours every 20mins, first come basis, queuing outside if necessary. Shoes off. Max 30 per tour. A G E
This project unites two old flats with the insertion of dramatic full height vertical space; a stair rises through three new minor levels that shape this new tall atrium and link into the two main previous floor levels. Sunlight beams into the lower, previously shaded north spaces. The variations in height and depth simultaneously animate private and more playful spaces. Andrew Pilkington Architects 2013.
Tube: Notting Hill Gate, Ladbroke Grove, Westbourne Park;
23,52,452,328,31
www.elliottwood.co.uk

18 Stafford Terrace – The Sambourne Family Home
18 Stafford Terrace W8 7BH
■ Sat 10am-5pm. First come basis. Entry at set intervals – cards will be given out with entrance time. Last entry 4pm. Max 15 at one time. T B Q
From 1875, the home of the Punch cartoonist Edward Linley Sambourne, his wife Marion, their two children and their live-in servants. Today, the house is recognised as the best surviving example of a late Victorian middle-class home in the UK. It is remarkably well-preserved and complete with its original interior decoration and contents. Joseph Gordon Davis 1871.
Entry: ground floor and basement only.
Tube: High Street Kensington; Tube/Rail: Olympia;
9,10,27,28,49,328

155 Holland Park Avenue
155 Holland Park Avenue W11 4UX
■ Sat/Sun 10am-5pm. Tours every half hour. Pre-book ONLY via 020 7602 2489. Max 10 at one time.
Fantasy interior in Victorian flat intended to be enjoyed as a dreamlike escape from the outside world. Each room a play on a different style – Gothic, Renaissance, Baroque, Roccoco, Victorian, Regency and Modern.
Tube: Holland Park; 31,94,148,228

264 Westbourne Park Road
264 Westbourne Park Road W11 1EJ
■ Sat/Sun 10am-5pm. Closed from 12noon-3pm. First come basis, queuing outside if necessary. Shoes off. Last entry 4.45pm. Max 6 per tour. Q A G
New building as an urban accent, consisting of two independent houses placed on top of each other. While contemporary in design the building draws from the tectonic composition of the adjacent Victorian houses with their clearly expressed bases. Sustainable features: rain water harvesting, extensive roof garden, solar water heating and heat recovery. Studio Bednarski 2011.
Tube: Ladbroke Grove, Westbourne Park; Tube/Rail: Paddington;
7,70,452,52,23

Ark Brunel Primary Academy ●
Middle Row W10 5AT
■ Sat 10am-5pm. Architect-led tours 10am-1pm. First come basis. Last tour 12.30pm. A T G
Part of a mixed-use scheme that maximises the use and value

of the tight urban site to create a new 3-storey school with increased capacity and external play areas. PV panels produce renewable energy and a green roof encourages biodiversity and provides insulation. BREEAM Excellent. Penoyre & Prasad Architects 2014.
Tube: Westbourne Park; Tube/Rail: Kensal Rise, Kensal Green;
23,52,70,228,295

Artist Studio
6 Kensington Court Mews W8 5DR
■ Sat 12noon-10pm. Half-hourly tours, first come basis. Last entry 9.30pm. Max 10 per tour. A
Black Ice is the first in a series of Groves Natcheva short films showing architecture through a stream of dramatic life. The film will be screened at the Architects' studio, followed by a guided tour of the space the film seeks to bring into created life. Groves Natcheva Architects 2010. Entry: studio spaces.
Tube: High Street Kensington; 9,10,49,52,452,70

Brewster Gardens
42 Brewster Gardens W10 6AJ
■ Sat 1pm-5pm. Last entry 4.30pm. A
A side and rear extension to a Victorian house in North Kensington. The extension is built from a subtle traditional brick, with bespoke frameless glazing. Architecture for London 2015. Entry: ground floor, garden.
Tube: Latimer Road; Tube/Rail: Kensal Green; 7,70,220,272,283

Brompton Cemetery Chapel, Colonnades and Memorials
Old Brompton Road SW5 or Fulham Road SW10 9UG
■ Sat/Sun 1pm-5pm. Tour 2pm starting at the Cemetery Chapel. For info on tours tel 0207 351 1689. Max 35 at one time. R T B d

London's finest Grade I listed Victorian cemetery of 40 acres with many memorials, designed by architect who had previously worked on rebuilding of Windsor Castle. Benjamin Baud 1840. Entry: chapel, cemetery grounds.
Tube/Rail: West Brompton; 14,74,190,211,328,C3,414

Chelsea Academy ●
Lots Road SW10 0AB
■ Sat 10am-2pm. Hourly tours at 10am, 11am, 12noon, 1pm ONLY, first come basis. Max 20 per tour. N D T A
One of a new generation of schools on a very tight urban space. The architectural language is classical, formal and restrained recalling the local terraces, but enlivened with subtle variations. Numerous energy-saving measures are incorporated. RIBA Award Winner 2011. Feilden Clegg Bradley 2010.
Tube: Fulham Broadway; Rail: Imperial Wharf; 11,22,C3

Hidden House ●
39 Russell Garden Mews W14 8EU
■ Sun 10am-6pm. Regular tours, first come basis. Shoes off. Architect Ian Hogarth on site. Last tour 5.45pm. Max 20 per tour. R Q A G
A new build 2600 sq ft mews house as featured on Grand Designs. Four floors with a large basement living space and night club dance floor wrapped around a courtyard with a pond and waterfall. The house achieved BREEAM Excellent home rating. Sustainable features include air source heat pump, photovoltaics, super-insulation and water recycling. Hogarth Architects 2011. Entry: all areas.
Tube/Rail: Kensington Olympia, Shepherd's Bush; 49,C1,27,9,28

● AJ Library Building ● Green Exemplar ● Landscape/Public realm ● Infrastructure/Engineering
■ Open Saturday ■ Open Sunday ■ Open Saturday and Sunday

Institut français du Royaume-Uni

17 Queensberry Place SW7 2DT

■ Sat 12noon-7pm/Sun 12noon-6pm. Regular tours for adults and kids of the Institute and newly renovated Reading Room. Historical documentary screenings. Presentation of future library after renovation. Max 15 at one time. N R T B d

1939 Art Deco listed building refurbished in 1950, then restructured and modernised. Contains an authentically classic cinema, private salons, multimedia library and bistro. Patrice Bonnet 1939/Jean-Francois Darin 1996/Stefanie Fisher 2010/Bisset Adams 2013. Entry: library, hall, exhibition.
Tube: South Kensington; 14,49,70,74,345,C1

Kensington Palace

Kensington Palace W8 4PX

■ Sun tours 11am, 1pm, 3pm. Sign up at reception on arrival to book. 45min tour of exterior architectural features. Does not include entry to palace interior. Max 20 per tour. D R T B

Original Jacobean house with additions made by architects Hawksmoor and Wren. Tour of the gardens and exterior of the Palace about the architectural and design from the C17 up to today's conservation projects.
Tube: High Street Kensington, Queensway, Notting Hill Gate; 9,10,14,52,70,390

Kenure House

24 Princedale Road W11 4NJ

■ Sat/Sun 10am-1pm. Half-hourly tours, first come basis. Last entry 12.30pm. Max 6 per tour. G T

Dual-fronted landmark home in one of London's most prestigious conservation areas. Coupling a restored façade on one street with a confident modern mews to another, it offers a true meeting of historic charm and high specification contemporary living. Echlin 2015.
Tube: Holland Park; Tube/Rail: Shepherd's Bush; 31,94,148,228,316

Leighton House Museum

12 Holland Park Road W14 8LZ

■ Sat/Sun 10am-5pm. Last entry 5pm. T B Q

Originally home and studio of Lord Leighton, President of the Royal Academy, the house is one of the most remarkable buildings of C19. Extraordinary Arab hall with fountains and tiling; superb staircase. The museum also houses an outstanding collection of high Victorian art including paintings by Leighton himself. George Aitchison 1864-79/Purcell Miller Tritton (refurb) 2010.
Tube: High Street Kensington; Tube/Rail: Kensington Olympia; 9,10,27,28,49

Lindsey House

100 Cheyne Walk SW10 0DQ

■ Sat 2pm-4pm. First come basis, queuing outside if necessary. Last entry 4pm. Max 20 at one time. Q

Built on the former site of Sir Thomas More's garden, the house has a fine C17 exterior and many notable past residents including Whistler and I K Brunel. 1670s. Entry: entrance hall, garden.
Tube: Sloane Square, South Kensington; 239,19,49,345

Peter Jones

Sloane Square SW1W 8EL

■ Sat/Sun 12noon-5pm. Hourly tours, first come basis. Duration 45 mins. Meet in customer services department on 6th floor. Last tour 4pm. Max 20 per tour. D T

Grade II* listed building, with recently completed 5-year renovation programme involving complex mix of new build and restoration. Britain's first ever curtain walling and various features listed between 1969-71 such as spiral staircase. Sloane

The Ismaili Centre

Room has one of best views over Chelsea and beyond. RIBA Award Winner 2005. Crabtree, Slater & Moberley 1936-8/John McAslan + Partners 2004. Entry: main building, Sloane Room, other normally inaccessible areas. Display in Sloane Room.
Tube: Sloane Square; 11,19,22,211,319,C1,137

The Ismaili Centre

1-7 Cromwell Gardens SW7 2SL

■ Sun 10am-4pm. Regular tours. Last tour 4pm. Max 100 at one time. N T

Part of an international family of Ismaili Centres, this is the first religious, cultural and social space for the Shia Ismaili Muslim community in the West. From the serenity of the entrance fountain to the remarkable roof garden, it draws upon Muslim traditions in architecture and design while remaining conscious of its context. A sanctuary of calm amidst the bustle of the city. Casson Conder Partnership 1983.
Tube: South Kensington; 14,70,74,345,414,C1

The Roof Gardens & Babylon Restaurant (formerly Derry & Toms) ●

6th Floor, 99 Kensington High Street (entrance on Derry Street) W8 5SA

■ Sun 8am-11am. First come basis, queuing outside if necessary. Head Gardener on site. Last entry 10.45am. Max 500 at one time. N Q G d

A fine example of 30s architecture, now home to 1.5 acres of beautifully themed gardens with Spanish Garden, Tudor Courtyard and English Woodland Garden. All three gardens have recently undergone extensive refurbishment. The space has been an escape from London for over 75 years. Bernard George/Ralph Hancock 1938. Entry: 6th floor.
Tube: High Street Kensington; Tube/Rail: Victoria, Paddington; 9,10,27,28,49,52,328

Trellick Tower

5 Golborne Road W10 5UT

■ Sun 10am-4pm. Half-hourly tours, pre-book ONLY via trellick2015.eventbrite.co.uk. d

Goldfinger's 31-storey 'Unité d'Habitation' built as social housing and now one of London's most desirable addresses. Monumental in style, with its free-standing service tower and surreal boiler house, it retains beautiful detailing and a rich use of materials. Ernö Goldfinger 1972. Entry: lobby, 2 or 3 flats.
Tube: Westbourne Park; 18,23,28,31,52,70,328

V&A FuturePlan

V&A FuturePlan: Exhibition Road Building Project Roof Tour

Victoria and Albert Museum, Cromwell Road SW7 2RL

■ Sat/Sun 10am-5pm. 7 tours per day, duration 1hour. NB. Tours include steep steps. Not suitable for children, those with mobility issues, or anyone with vertigo. Last tour 4pm. Architectural activities for children: discovering architecture backpack trail available daily, collect from Learning Centre. G B T R C

The V&A are undertaking their largest building project in over 100 years, to create a new courtyard, grand entrance and subterranean gallery for temporary exhibitions. Join the project team on the roof of the Museum to view the building site at a critical stage. AL_A due 2017.
Tube: South Kensington; Rail: Victoria; C1,14,74,414

Victoria and Albert Museum (V&A)

Cromwell Road SW7 2RL

■ Tours Sat 11am, 2pm, 4pm, pre-book ONLY via 0207 942 2211. Max 20 per tour. N R T B

Introducing the rich and varied architecture of the V&A Museum, allowing access to some areas usually closed to the public. V&A and RIBA Architecture Gallery, ongoing restoration of historic interiors, and the latest gallery projects including the Exhibition Road Building by AL_A. Francis Fowke/Sir Aston Webb and others 1856 onwards.
Tube: South Kensington; Rail: Victoria; C1,14,74,414

WALKS/TOURS

World's End Estate walk

■ Meet: Sun 2.30pm, 4.30pm at 16 Blantyre Street SW10 0DS. Duration 2 hours. T d

Designed by Eric Lyons and constructed in the mid-70s, the World's End Estate is a deliberate architectural attempt to not only overcome many of the issues of previous high-rise developments, but also to eliminate monotonous and bland facades through the use of alternative designs and materials. Eric Lyons (Principal) 1969-76.
Tube: Sloane Square, Earls Court; Rail: Imperial Wharf; 11,22,19,49,328

Supported by

THE ROYAL BOROUGH OF
KENSINGTON
AND CHELSEA

Key. **A** Architect on site **B** Bookshop **C** Childrens' activities **d** Some disabled access **D** Full wheelchair access **E** Engineer on site **G** Green Features **N** Normally open to the public **P** Parking **Q** Long queues envisaged **R** Refreshments **T** Toilets

Lambeth

See **openhouselondon.org.uk/lambeth**
to find out more about this area

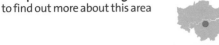

15b Herne Hill Road
15b Herne Hill Road SE24 0AU
◼ Sat/Sun 10am-6pm. First come basis. R A G
Renovation of flat in Victorian terrace house, creating new
living area within restructured roof space using unusual and
reclaimed materials, and retrofit of substantial insulation.
Colin MacInnes 2011-2015. Entry: living space, bedrooms.
Tube: Brixton; Rail: Denmark Hill, Loughborough Junction;
35,45,345,P4,P5

54 Cambria Road ●
54 Cambria Road SE5 9AS
◼ Sat 10am-5pm. Last entry 5pm. Max 15 at one time. T C A G P d
Self build conversion of C19 terrace: reorganised living spaces,
reclaimed materials, natural insulation, solar thermal and
PV, biofuel heating, vegetable growing, bees, hens. Baraitser
Smith (conversion) 2008. Entry: house and garden. Informal
discussion around eco conversion of C19 housing stock, and
bird house building for children.
Tube/Rail: Brixton; Rail: Loughborough Junction;
P4,35,45,176,345

111 Tyers Street
111 Tyers Street SE11 5HS
◼ Sat 1pm-5pm. First come basis. A P E
A quirky, bespoke new-build private house over five floors on a
tiny triangular site in the heart of Vauxhall. Howel-Evans and
Opher Architects 2015.
Tube/Rail: Vauxhall; 36,185,196,77,88.

357 Kennington Lane – DSDHA Studio
357 Kennington Lane, Vauxhall SE11 5QY
◼ Sat 1pm-5pm. Regular tours, first come basis, queueing if
necessary. Max 20 per tour. T A d
3-storey former perfume factory that now hosts DSDHA
Studio. The practice moved into the new premises in April 2014.
Tube/Rail: Vauxhall; 36,185,196,436

ArtsLav
180 Kennington Lane SE11 4UZ
◼ Sat/Sun 10am-5pm. First come basis, queueing outside if
necessary. Last entry 4.45pm. T
Once a Victorian Gentleman's lavatory, ArtsLav is now a
thriving arts hub in a listed and semi-restored Kennington
landmark. Original features include marble urinals, glass
water tank, mosaic floor, ventilator shaft and horse trough.
Entry: all areas.
Tube: Kennington; Tube/Rail: Elephant & Castle;
3,59,159,196,360

Carnegie Library
188 Herne Hill Road SE24 0AG
◼ Sat 9am-5pm. Regular tours of non-public areas and garden.
Exhibition and historical display. Last tour 4pm. N D R T
Picturesque Grade II listed building combining classical
framework with Tudor-style mullioned and transomed
windows. Red brick with terracotta. Bell cupolas and lakeland
slate roof. Wakeford & Son 1905.
Rail: Denmark Hill, Herne Hill, North Dulwich, Loughborough
Junction; 3,42,68,468,P4

Central Hill Estate
Corner of Central Hill and Vicars Oak Road SE19 1DT
◼ Sun 1pm-5pm. Guided tours, first come basis. N P A
A tree-lined housing estate designed by Ted Hollamby and
Rosemary Stjernstedt in Crystal Palace designed around
community, open spaces, gardens and views to London.
Rail: Gipsy Hill, Crystal Palace; 3,322,417,450,202

City Heights E-ACT Academy ●
33 Abbots Park SW2 3PW
◼ Sat 10am-1pm. Tours taking place, pre-book ONLY via
admin@chea.org.uk. Last entry 12.30pm. D T E A G
Situated on two sites, the academy combines the rebuilding of
Fenstanton Primary School for 638 children, and the creation
of a new 1100-place academy. The academy specialises in
language skills and is partnered with Dulwich College. Shared
facilities including sports pitches and a pavilion will be located
on a second site close by. Green design features include solar
panels and passive ventilator. Jestico + Whiles 2014.
Tube/Rail: Brixton; Rail: Tulse Hill; 2,68,196,201,322

Clapham Library ●
Mary Seacole Centre, 91 Clapham High Street SW4 7DB
◼ Sat/Sun 10am-5pm. Last entry 4.30pm. Max 5 at one time.
N D T
The building is based around a spiral theme that allows a
building of multiple uses to feel like one space to reinforce a
sense of community spirit. Studio Egret West 2012.
Tube: Clapham Common, Clapham North; 35,37,88,137,155

Clapham Manor Primary School ●
Belmont Road SW4 0BZ
◼ Sat 10am-1pm. Practice Director Philip Marsh on site. Last
entry 12.30pm. Max 20 at one time. D R T A
A polychromatic extension inserted into a tight urban context
offering this DCSF outstanding school a new identity with
much-needed new learning spaces and an organisational hub,
whilst maintaining external play space. RIBA Award Winner
2010. de Rijke Marsh Morgan (dRMM) 2008.
Tube: Clapham Common; Rail: Clapham High Street;
35,37,417,137,345

Cressingham Gardens
Cressingham Gardens Rotunda, Tulse Hill SW2 2QN
◼ Sat/Sun 10am-5pm. Regular tours, first come basis.
Exhibition in Rotunda. R T C P d
Low-rise leafy estate located next to beautiful Brockwell Park
noted for its innovative design, incorporating pioneering
architectural elements and echoing the natural topography.
Ted Hollamby 1967-78. Entry: Rotunda, private homes.
Tube/Rail: Brixton; Rail: Herne Hill; 415,432,2

Foxley Road
19 Foxley Road SW9 6ET
◼ Sat/Sun 1pm-5pm. First come basis, queueing outside if
necessary. Architects Gavin & Shigemi Challand onsite. T A
Refurbishment of a one-bedroom garden apartment in a
listed Georgian house. The interiors combine ingenious and
space-saving design solutions with bold and theatrical use of
materials. N.P. Rothery 1824/Catfish Studio Ltd (refurb) 2014.
Entry: private apartment, garden.
Tube: Oval; 3,36,59,133,159,185,415,436
http://www.catfishstudio.ltd.uk/foxleyroad/

Lambeth Palace
Lambeth Palace Road SE1 7JU
◼ Sat 10am-4pm. Tours every 15 mins, duration 1 hour. Pre-
book ONLY via www.archbishopofcanterbury.org.uk. Last
tour 3pm. Max 25 per tour. R d

The Foundry – Social Justice Centre

The Archbishop of Canterbury's London home, dating from
C13, with C19 work by Blore and crypt vestibule opened 2000.
Entry: chapel and crypt courtyard, guardroom, Great Hall,
picture gallery.
Tube: Lambeth North; Tube/Rail: Waterloo, Vauxhall;
3,77,344,507,C10

National Theatre
South Bank SE1 9PX
◼ Sat 10am-5pm/Sun 11.30am-5pm. Short tours to showcase
elements of Haworth Tompkins refurbishment completed
this year, first come basis. Meet main foyer (Sat)/Dorfman
foyer (Sun). Architect on site Sun only. Last tour 4.45pm.
Max 10 per tour. N R T B A G P d
A chance to see this key Grade II* listed work of British
Modernism since the completion of NT Future work. Lasdun's
NT includes theatres and associated spaces. RIBA Award
Winner. Denys Lasdun and Partners 1967-76/Stanton Williams
(refurb) 1997/ Haworth Tompkins (refurb) 2012-15.
Tube/Rail: Waterloo; Rail: Waterloo East; 1,4,26,59,68,171,176,188

Pop Brixton
53 Brixton Station Road SW9 8PQ
◼ Sat/Sun 1pm-5pm. Guided tours. T G N A d
Pop Brixton showcases ad-hoc and quick-thinking design on
a large scale, recycling and repurposing components so as to
quickly provide a temporary platform for community events
and fledgling businesses. Carl Turner 2015.
Tube/Rail: Brixton; 2,133,159,3,118

Pullman Court
Streatham Hill SW2 4SZ
◼ Sun 10am-5pm. d
Grade II* listed Modern Movement building, with balcony

Quadruple 4-Cube Glass Room

walkways and period internal features. Frederick Gibberd 1936. Entry: flats (differing types), common parts, gardens.
Tube/Rail: Brixton; Rail: Streatham Hill; 159,137,133,109,250

Quadruple 4-Cube Glass Room ◐
27 Telford Avenue SW2 4XL
■ Sat 3.30pm-6.30pm. Architect-led tours every 20 minutes, first come basis. Last entry time 6.30pm. Max 20 per tour. C E A P d
A perfect square made up of four equal cubes, responding to a brief to maintain the spirit of the history of the house but to inject a modern interior to the kitchen and radically increase natural light. Miesian detached columns support the centre of each perimeter edge, allowing the corners to be cantilevered. Andrew Pilkington Architects 2013.
Tube/Rail: Balham; Rail: Streatham Hill; 57,59,109,118,133,159,137

Rambert
99 Upper Ground, SE1 9PP
■ Sat 10am-5pm. First come basis, tours on the hour. Last entry 4pm. Max 15 per tour. D T
Rambert's award winning new home provides the company with state of the art facilities for the creation of new choreography and music for dance. It also enables the company to unlock the riches of the Rambert archive – one of the oldest and most complete dance archives in the world. Allies and Morrison 2013. Entry: studios, workshops, wardrobe and offices covered as part of tour.
Tube/Rail: Waterloo; RV1

Royal Festival Hall, Southbank Centre ◐
Belvedere Road SE1 8XX
■ Sat/Sun behind the scenes tours at 10.30am, 12.30pm, 2.30pm, first come basis, duration 1 hour. NB. Due to nature

of areas covered, no children under 16 and unsuitable for those with vertigo or special access requirements. No high heels or big bags. N D R T B
The Royal Festival Hall is a Grade I listed building, originally built for the Festival of Britain in 1951. Today, following the successful major refurbishment of the world class concert hall and public spaces in 2007, millions of people visit the Hall each year to enjoy Southbank Centre's cultural programme. RIBA Award Winner 2008. LCC Architects Department 1951/Allies and Morrison (refurb) 2007.
Tube: Embankment; Tube/Rail: Charing Cross, Waterloo; 172,181,176,26,188,RV1,68,76,77,168,171,341

South London Botanical Institute
323 Norwood Road SE24 9AQ
■ Sun 1pm-5pm. Regular tours, first come basis. Last entry 4.30pm. N R T C P d
Brick-built Victorian villa c1876 set back from road with sweeping drive. Few interior changes since 1910 when retired Indian government administrator Alan Octavian Hume founded the Institute. Newly decorated Lecture Room with bespoke wallpaper designed around plants and herbarium specimens in style of William Morris, with a nod to the founder's Indian connections. c.1876. Entry: herbarium, botanical library, garden with wide variety of plants. Small plant sale, botanical activities.
Rail: Tulse Hill; 68,196,322,2,P13,201,468,415,432

The Cinema Museum
The Master's House, 2 Dugard Way (off Renfrew Road) SE11 4TH
■ Sat/Sun 10am-5pm. Regular tours, first come basis. SE1 Picture Palaces exhibition on site. Last tour 3.30pm, last entry 4pm. Max 15 per tour. D R T B P
The Master's House of the Lambeth Workhouse is ornate

Victorian Gothic with polychrome brickwork, contrasting stone and narrow horizontal terracotta panels in dog-tooth pattern. R Parris and TW Aldwinkle 1871.
Tube: Kennington; Tube/Rail: Elephant & Castle; 3,59,133,156,196

The Clock House: 5 Chestnut Road
5 Chestnut Road SE27 9EZ
■ Sat 10am-5pm. Tours at 10am, 12noon, 2pm, 4pm, first come basis. T P d
Victorian house extended with large contemporary, highly colourful living space. Pre-patinated copper roof, large areas of glass, Douglas Fir detail. Glass floor/ceiling between living areas. See also The Clockworks. Michael Crowley Architect 2001. Entry: lower 2 floors.
Rail: West Norwood; 2,432,196,68,468

The Clockworks
6 Nettlefold Place SE27 0JW
■ Sat 11am-5pm. Tours at 11am, 1pm, 3pm, 4.30pm. Last entry 4.30pm. Max 50 at one time. D R T B P
Internationally pre-eminent museum and integral workshops devoted to electrical timekeeping and the distribution of accurate time (1840-1970). Practical education and conservation in action. See also The Clock House entry. Michael Crowley Architect 2012. Entry: gallery, workshops, library.
Rail: West Norwood; 2,432,196,68,468

The Coca-Cola London Eye ◐
County Hall, Belvedere Road SE1 7PB
■ Sun 9am-10.30am. Lecture with Director David Marks or Julia Barfield including a 15 minute Q&A followed by a rotation on the London Eye. By ballot through Open House ONLY. Please see p17 for details. 100 tickets maximum allocation. NB. Over 12 years only. D T B A
The world's tallest cantilevered observation wheel which has rapidly become a much-loved symbol of modern Britain. RIBA Award Winner 2000. Marks Barfield Architects 1999.
Tube: Westminster; Tube/Rail: Waterloo; RV1,211,24,11

The Edible Bus Stop
Arch 511, Ridgway Road SW9 7EX
■ Sun 2pm-6pm. Last entry 5.45pm. G D
Recently refurbished low cost, high impact fit out of a former mechanics garage. Utilising reclaimed and recycled materials to create a functional design studio and workshop for The Edible Bus Stop. Will Sandy (landscape architect).
Tube: Brixton; Rail: Loughborough Junction; P5,35,45,345,P4

The Foundry – Social Justice Centre ◐
17 Oval Way, Vauxhall SE11 5RR
■ Sat 10am-5pm. Hourly tours. Last entry 4.30pm. Max 10 per tour. N D T A
Home to Social Justice and Human Rights charities and campaigning organisations, The Foundry is a former shoe polish factory with high social and sustainability standards and recent winner of RIBA London Building of the Year Award 2015. Architecture 00 2014.
Tube: Oval; Tube/Rail: Vauxhall; 196
www.aplaceforchange.co.uk

The Livity School
Adare Walk SW16 2PW
■ Sat 10am-4pm. Hourly tours, first come basis. Last entry 3pm. Max 20 per tour. D T A
A special educational needs primary school for children with autistic spectrum condition and profound learning difficulties. Turning the school 'upside down' meant that all children could benefit from external space in a very tight site. An internal ramped elevated walkway wrapping around the atrium and

Key. A Architect on site B Bookshop C Childrens' activities d Some disabled access D Full wheelchair access E Engineer on site G Green Features N Normally open to the public P Parking Q Long queues envisaged R Refreshments T Toilets

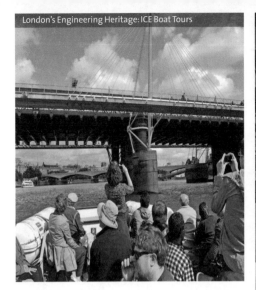
London's Engineering Heritage: ICE Boat Tours

Rambert

Pullman Court

the ribbon of folded stainless steel cladding are only two of the building's unique features. Haverstock 2012.
Rail: Streatham Hill; 118,133

The Old Vic
The Cut SE1 8NB
■ Sat tour at 10.30am, first come basis. Duration 1.5 hours. Max 30 on tour. R T
World-famous playhouse, Grade II* listed, with Georgian exterior and restored Victorian interior. Only London theatre of the time still open. Rudolph Cabernel 1818/RHWL (refurb) 1983. Entry: foyers, bars, public areas and auditorium, limited backstage areas.
Tube/Rail: Waterloo; Rail: Waterloo East; 1,4,26,59,68,168,171,172

West Norwood Health and Leisure Centre
25 Devane Way, West Norwood SE27 0DF
■ Sat 10am-5pm. N D T
Innovative new centre providing a mix of community and health facilities to promote well-being, including a 25m swimming pool, health and fitness suite and gym, dance studio, community meeting rooms, and GP and dental surgeries. Allford Hall Monaghan Morris 2013.
Rail: West Norwood; 2,68,196,315,432,468

Young Vic ◉
66 The Cut SE1 8LZ
■ Sun tours at 10.30am, 12noon, 2pm, 3.30pm. Pre-book ONLY via openhouse@youngvic.org. D T G
A major £12.5 million rebuilding theatre project. Main auditorium retained with extra height and with 2 newly built smaller, naturally-lit studios. Foyer has double-height mezzanine. Exterior includes mesh façade and painted screen by artist Clem Crosby. RIBA Award Winner 2007 and shortlisted for the RIBA Stirling Prize 2007. Haworth Tompkins 2007. Entry: front of house, some theatrical spaces.
Tube/Rail: Waterloo; Tube: Southwark; Rail: Waterloo East

WALKS/TOURS

Clapham Old Town and Venn Street ◉
■ Meet: Sun 2pm by the Clock Tower next to Clapham Common tube SW4 0BD. A guided walk with the lead designer, landscape architect Ian Hingley. Duration 2 hours. Max 20 on tour.
Once dominated by parked cars and fast moving through traffic, Clapham's Old Town was radically redesigned using the principles of 'shared space' and 'naked streets' to dramatically improve the pedestrian environment. The first place in the UK to use 'Copenhagen' style side road crossings. The first phase, Venn Street, has become the Old Town's premier destination for alfresco dining, and now also hosts a regular weekend market. Urban Movement + LB Lambeth 2011.
Tube: Clapham Common

London's Engineering Heritage: ICE Boat Tours ◉
■ Departs: Sat 11am, 1pm from Festival Pier SE1 8XZ
First come basis. Max 150 per tour. Arrive in good time to board, departures are prompt. Bar onboard MV Kingwood selling drinks. Please note food is not available and not allowed to be brought on board. Bring rainwear if you wish to sit on open deck. Duration 1.5 hours. E R Q
Experience the capital's inspirational engineering with live commentary from London's leading engineers on aspects including: Bazalgette's legacy, flood risk management, current and future engineering landmarks and London's historical structures. Organised by the Institution of Civil Engineers.
Tube/Rail: Waterloo; 211,24,11

West Norwood Cemetery & Greek Chapel
■ Meet: Sat at 2pm, 2.30pm, 3pm inside main cemetery gate, Norwood Road SE27 9JU. Tour duration 90 mins. Cemetery grounds open at all times, bookstall 1pm-5pm. Max 35 per tour. T B P
Opened 1837, with monuments to famous Victorians. 69 Grade II/II* listed structures, including Greek Chapel c1872, architect uncertain, mausolea by EM Barry and GE Street and entrance arch by W Tite. 1837.
Tube/Rail: Brixton; Rail: West Norwood, Tulse Hill; 2,68,196,322,432,468

Supported by

Lambeth

Navigate your way around Open House in your area with the app. See p14

Lewisham

See openhouselondon.org.uk/lewisham
to find out more about this area

6 Segal Close
6 Segal Close SE23 1PP
■ Sun 1pm-5pm. Last entry 4.45pm. P
Single-storey building, part of first phase of Walter Segal self-builds in Lewisham 1970-81. Number 6 was built by architect Jon Broome, the assistant to Walter Segal on the scheme. There have been some small additions and reconfiguration of rooms, done sympathetically to original build and construction methods. Walter Segal 1979-81.
Rail: Honor Oak Park; 122,171

Boone's Chapel
Lee High Road SE13 5PH
■ Sat/Sun 1pm-5pm. First come basis. Max 30 at one time. N D A
Grade I listed former almshouse chapel restored in 2008 as an architect's studio and exhibition space. Brick and Portland stone chapel (1682) with contemporary service building and small garden in grounds of the Merchant Taylors' Almshouses. Green features include recycled materials, sheep's wool insulation and lime plaster. 1682/2008. Exhibition material on the social history of the building.
Rail: Blackheath, Lewisham, Hither Green; 321,178,261,122

Deptford Green School
Deptford Green, Edward Street, New Cross SE14 6AN
■ Sat tours 10am-11.30am. Last entry 11.15am. T A G
Winner of LABP best educational building award in 2013. The design of the building reflects the importance of the student voice and wider community sports access. The design provides an impressive new street frontage whilst minimising the building's footprint. Classroom sizes are 25% larger than statutory, and halls can open out to seat 1000 for whole school assemblies while being a flexible performance space for the school's drama specialism. Highly sustainable design and rated BREEAM Excellent. Watkins Gray International 2012. Entry: roof top classrooms, conference hall and tours of classrooms.
Rail: New Cross, New Cross Gate; 171,172,225,436,453

Deptford Lounge ●
9 Giffin Street, Giffin Square SE8 4RJ
■ Sun 10am-5pm. Regular tours, first come basis. Last tour 3pm. Max 15 per tour. N D R T G
Part of a visionary concept that combines a replacement primary school with the Deptford Lounge – a new state-of-the-art district library that also provides new community facilities. Sustainable features include 10% renewable energy through Biomass CHP and BREEAM Very Good rating. Pollard Thomas Edwards 2012. Entry: rooftop ball court, Deptford Lounge, shared areas between the Lounge and Tidemill School.
DLR: Deptford Bridge; Rail: Deptford; 1,47,188,199,453
www.deptfordlounge.org.uk

Eco Vale ●
Eco Vale, rear of 270-332 Wood Vale SE23 3DZ
■ Sat 10am-5pm. Last entry 4.30pm. G A d
Three new eco-houses: biodiversity roof, exhaust air heat pump, timber clad, triple glazed modern eco-house on backland site. Chance de Silva 2015.
Rail: Honor Oak Park; 363,63,P12

End House
87a Manwood Road SE4 1SA
■ Sun 9.30am-12.30pm. First come basis, queuing outside if necessary. Last entry 12.15pm. Max 10 at one time. G d
A fresh, contemporary end of terrace house that makes clever use of a small site by using a simple form to offer privacy combined with open plan living. Sustainable features include recycled newspaper insulation and breathable walls. Edgley Design 2010.
Rail: Ladywell, Crofton Park, Honor Oak Park; 284,P4,171,172,122

Forest Hill Pools
Dartmouth Road SE23 3HZ
■ Sat/Sun 10am-5pm. Last entry 4.30pm. No tours. N D R T
New facility providing community pools, fitness, café and meeting rooms whilst retaining the original Victorian pool superintendent's building. 1885/Roberts Limbrick Architects (redevelopment) 2012. Entry: reception, café.
Rail: Forest Hill; 185,197,176,122,356

Forest Mews
Rockbourne Mews SE23 2AT
■ Sat tours every 45 minutes. Pre-book ONLY via jessica@stolon.co.uk. A G d
Three bespoke houses, each with a studio and courtyard, set around a communal courtyard. Each courtyard of the house forms the centre of the open plan ground floor, with living on one side and studio on the other. Inspired by views of ivy growing over trees in wintertime – all three houses are clad with striking green walls, trained to a geometric pattern. Robert and Jessica Barker 2014.
Rail: Forest Hill; 185,197

Glass Mill Leisure Centre
41 Loampit Vale SE13 7FT
■ Sat/Sun 10am-5pm. Last entry 4.30pm. No tours N D R T
Glass Mill has superb environmental credentials and offers a range of the most up-to-date facilities including a regional competition-standard 8-lane swimming pool with seating for 300 spectators, a 100-station gym and climbing wall. The centre has a crèche, 2 aerobics studios and a café. LA Architects 2013.
DLR/Rail: Lewisham; 21,47,136,321,436

Greenstreet Self-build Housing
1 Greenstreet Hill, Drakefell Road SE14 5SR
■ Sun 10am-5pm. Ground floor max 12 at one time; access to upper floor by tour only, max 5 per tour. First come basis. Last entry 4.30pm. R T A G P d
One of eleven self-build houses on site, inspired by the Walter Segal method. Completed in 1997 and owned by CHISEL Housing Association. Houses are timber-framed and hung with balconies. Potter and Holmes 1997.
Rail: Nunhead, Brockley, Queens Road Peckham; 343,484,171,36,436

Horniman Museum and Gardens ● ●
100 London Road SE23 3PQ
■ Sat/Sun 10.30am-5.30pm. Sun behind the scenes tours of the Gardens with Head of Horticulture Wes Shaw at 2pm, 3pm. Pre-book ONLY via www.horniman.ac.uk. Duration 45 mins. Last entry 5.20pm. Max 20 per tour. N D R T B
A landmark building – Charles Harrison Townsend's original Arts & Crafts building using his ideas on the Arts & Crafts aesthetic. The 16.5 acre gardens re-opened after major redevelopment by Land Use Consultants including a Pavilion by Walters + Cohen plus a bandstand terrace with views over London. C H Townsend 1901/Land Use Consultants/Elliott

Eco Vale

The Pavilion

Key. A Architect on site B Bookshop C Childrens' activities d Some disabled access D Full wheelchair access E Engineer on site G Green Features N Normally open to the public P Parking Q Long queues envisaged R Refreshments T Toilets

Walter Segal Self-build Houses

Wood Partnership 2012.
Rail: Forest Hill; 176,185,363,P4,356

Manor House Gardens Ice House
Manor House Gardens (Old Road) SE13 5SY
■ Sat/Sun 12noon-5pm. Last entry 4.50pm. Max 10 at one time. R T
Grade II listed ice well and underground chambers (1773) in Manor House Gardens park, which provided ice for nearby Manor House, former home of Sir Francis Baring. Cited in 2002 Civic Trust Awards.
DLR/Rail: Lewisham; Rail: Lee, Hither Green; 122,261,278,321

South East London Combined Heat & Power Energy Recovery Facility ●
Landmann Way, off Surrey Canal Road SE14 5RS
■ Sun 10am-3pm. If disabled access required, call 020 3567 6100 in advance. Last entry 2pm. E T d
First new generation 'state of the art' Energy Recovery Facility providing long-term sustainable solution for waste disposal, and producing electricity for National Grid. Designed to minimise visual impact whilst remaining a high quality landmark building. Alan J Smith Partnership 1993. Entry: specified tour route.
Tube/Rail: Canada Water; Rail: Surrey Quays, New Cross Gate, New Cross, South Bermondsey; 47,188,199,225,P12

Spring Gardens
Ennersdale Road SE13 6JQ
■ Sat 10.30am-4.30pm. No visitors under the age of 18. Last entry 4.30pm. Max 20 at one time. R T G
The first purpose-built hostel for homeless people, offering high-quality accommodation for 85 residents in buildings arranged around a beautiful garden with existing mature trees. Kitchen garden with chickens. Light, open and airy and with additional training spaces. Sustainable features include solar panels and grey water system. Peter Barber Architects/Buller Welsh Architects 2010. Entry: communal areas, activity rooms, gardens.
Rail: Hither Green; 181,273

The Capitol (formerly Forest Hill Cinema)
11-21 London Road SE23 3TW

■ Sat/Sun 10am-4pm. Architectural tours on the hour, including behind-the-scenes to largely untouched first floor area. Pre-book ONLY via 020 8291 8920. Last tour 4pm. Max 8 per tour. R T
Formerly Capitol Cinema, Grade II listed rare survival of a complete 1920s cinema in Art Deco style, later a bingo hall and now a Wetherspoons pub. Stanley Beard 1929.
Rail: Forest Hill; 185,176,122,P4

The Pavilion ●
The Pavillion, Pagoda Gardens, Blackheath SE3 0UZ
■ Sat 10am-5pm. First come basis. Last entry 4.30pm. T A G d
Recipient of ES Homes and Property Award 2015 and voted UK's Top Eco Home on the Guardian online, this is an uncompromisingly modern house in the Blackheath Conservation area adjacent to Grade II* listed Pagoda. Features include Code Level 5, full home automation, verdant gardens and open plan living flooded with natural light.
E2 Architecture 2014.
Rail: Lewisham, Blackheath
www.e2architecture.com
www.elliottwood.co.uk

The Seager Distillery Tower
1 Mill Lane Deptford SE8 4HN
■ Sat 10am-5pm/Sun 10am-1pm. Hourly tours, first come basis. Last tour Sat 4pm, Sun 12noon. Max 20 per tour. Q T d
Part of a regeneration project by Galliard Homes on site of former Seager distillery, which includes refurb of a C19 warehouse, conversion of former C19 Holland House, a new Crescent building, Pavilion and 27-storey residential tower with viewing gallery. John McAslan + Partners 2005/BUJ Architects 2011. Entry: 27th floor viewing gallery.
DLR: Deptford Bridge; Rail: Deptford High Street

TNG Wells Park Youth Venue
111 Wells Park Road SE26 6AD
■ Sat/Sun 10am-5pm. Hourly tours, first come basis. Last entry 4pm. Max 20 people per tour. N D R T A G
TNG is a new-build venue designed by RCKa working closely with Lewisham Council, its partners and the local community. The project provides a range of vocational, leisure and support services for the young people of Lewisham. Opened

by the Mayor in 2013, TNG has been heralded as a beacon of youth service provision across the region. It received a Commendation in the Civic Trust Awards and a RIBA Regional London award in 2014. RCKa 2013. Entry: all except offices.
Rail: Sydenham, Sydenham Hill

Walter Segal Self-build Houses ●
5, 6, 8 & 10 Walters Way, Honor Oak Park SE23 3LH
■ Sun 1pm-6pm. Regular tours, first come basis. Videos of Segal buildings and self-build showing. Last entry 5.45pm. Max 20 at one time. R T d
A close of 13 self-built houses. Each house is unique, many extended and built using a method developed by Walter Segal, who led the project in the 1980s. Houses have benefited from extensions and renovations. Sustainable features include solar electric, water and space heating. Walter Segal 1987. Note: Two steps to each house
Rail: Honor Oak Park; P4,P12,171,63

WALKS/TOURS

Historic Walk of Blackheath
■ Meet: Sat/Sun 11am outside Hare & Billet public house, Hare & Billet Road SE3 0RB. Duration 1.5 to 2 hours. First come basis. Max 30 per tour.
Historic walk along the south side of Blackheath exploring some highways and byways for mostly early-mid C19 domestic architecture off the beaten track. Arranged by Neil Rhind for the Blackheath Society.
Rail: Blackheath; 380,53,386

Ladywell Fields ●
■ Meet: Sat 11am at northern entrance of Ladywell Fields, Ladywell Road SE13 7XB. Duration approx 1.5 hours. N D A
A river restoration project within an existing park. The scheme has created new river channels, backwaters, pools and riffles, and greatly improved habitats within the river corridor along with improved access and educational benefits. Led by Mehron Kirk, landscape architect at BDP.
Rail: Ladywell

Mountsfield Park Community Gardens ●
■ Meet: Sat 1.30pm at Stainton Road entrance to Mountsfield Park SE16 1AN. N D A
Transformation of a derelict area within an existing park to create an exciting new community garden linked to a renovated playground. Designed in collaboration with the Friends of Mountsfield Park and LB Lewisham. Led by Mehron Kirk, landscape architect at BDP.
Rail: Hither Green, Catford Bridge, Catford; 181,225,202

Supported by

Lewisham

Merton

See openhouselondon.org.uk/merton
to find out more about this area

9 Parkside Avenue
9 Parkside Avenue SW19 5ES
■ Sun 12noon-4pm. Regular architect-led tours, first come basis, queuing outside if necessary. A
Complex series of interlocking spaces within a simple overall volume, the house has references to the dramatic and hidden sources for lighting spaces seen in Baroque churches and the work of Sir John Soane. Sustainable features include solar panels. Holden Harper 1999. Entry: house, garden.
Tube/Rail: Wimbledon

15 Edge Hill ●
15 Edge Hill SW19 4LR
■ Sat 10am-5pm. Owner/architect-led regular tours. Last tour 4.30pm. Closed 1pm to 1.30pm. Max 15 per tour. T A d
New build rear extension to Victorian house, entailing remodelling of ground floor to create a large open plan flow-through living, dining and kitchen space. Close integration with the garden is achieved by careful design of levels and paving surfaces. Asif Malik 2011. Entry: ground floor, garden.
Tube/Rail: Wimbledon; 57,131,200

31b St Mary's Road
31b St Mary's Road SW19 7BP
■ Sat 10am-4.30pm. Closed 12noon-2pm. Half-hourly tours, pre-book ONLY via jaci2000@fastmail.co.uk. Last tour 4pm.
Celebrating its half century, one of a small number of Peter Foggo, single storey, flat roofed houses inspired by the US Case Study Houses scheme and Mies van der Rohe's Farnsworth House. It features skylights, two wings, mahogany paneling, floor-to-ceiling windows and a large open-plan living room looking out onto a landscaped garden. Peter Foggo & David Thomas 1965. Entry: all except 1 bedroom.
Tube/Rail: Wimbledon; 493,93,200

106 Gladstone Road
106 Gladstone Road SW19 1QW
■ Sat/Sun 10am-5pm. A d
Inside this unassuming Victorian house is a unique, contemporary total refurbishment with additional rear and roof extensions. Seamless skylights, concrete floors, exposed brickwork, projecting glass box, whitewashed ash slats and oak ribs create an enthralling new take on a period house. Studio 1 Architects 2015.
Tube/Rail: Wimbledon; 219,57,131,156

Baitul Futuh Mosque
Ahmadiyya Muslim Association, 181 London Road SM4 5PT
■ Sat/Sun 10am-5pm. Regular talks and tours, pre-book ONLY via 020 8648 5255. Talks given in Urdu, Arabic, German and English. N D R T B P
Purpose-built mosque and the largest in Europe, with 15m diameter dome and minarets 36m and 23m high, accommodating 13,000 worshippers. The building is a blend of Islamic and modern British architecture and incorporates much of the structure of an old dairy site. Facilities include halls, library, crèche, studios. Voted one of top 50 buildings in the world by Independent Magazine. Sutton Griffin Architects 2003. Entry: all areas.
Tube: Morden; Rail: Morden South; 93,154,213,80

106 Gladstone Road

Elliott Wood ●
241 The Broadway SW19 1SD
■ Sun 10am-5pm. Max 20 at one time. E R T G
A Victorian villa with impressive 2-storey vaulted steel and glass office space with mezzanine for structural engineers Elliott Wood. Civic Trust Commendation 2006. Sustainably refurbished in 2012 with Alex Ferguson architects with natural ventilation, cooling from ground pipes and solar panels. Richard Paxton Architects (original refurbishment) 2004.
Tube: South Wimbledon; Tube/Rail: Wimbledon; 163,164,93,57,131,219

Mitcham Cricket Club Pavilion
4 Cricket Green, Mitcham CR4 4LA
■ Sat 10.30am-4.30pm. Players on hand. Sat 2.30pm Mitcham Cricket Green Community and Heritage Walk, taking in the diverse buildings within the conservation area including The Canons, Cranmer Green, Three Kings Piece, Vestry Hall, monuments and historic cricket grounds. Exhibition on women in cricket. First come basis. Max 30 on tour. R T
Locally listed and the club's pavilion for over 100 years, Mitcham Cricket Green has had cricket played on its pitch for over 300 years.
Tube: Colliers Wood; Tram: Mitcham; Rail: Mitcham Junction, Mitcham Eastfields; 200,127,118, S1

Mitcham Methodist Church
Cricket Green, Mitcham CR4 4LB
■ Sat 10.30am-4.30pm. First come basis. D R T
Designed by the foremost post-war architect of Methodist churches whose writing on church design was influential, as were his innovations in the use of concrete. A dynamic folded slab roof extends beyond the church's end wall to create a covered walkway. Materials and finish are good quality and the church retains the vast majority of its interior fittings. Recently listed Grade II. Edward Mills 1959. Entry: church, vestry, garden.
Rail/Tram: Mitcham Junction; Tram; Mitcham; 118,200,280,127,S1

Morden Hall Park ●
Morden Hall Road, Morden SM4 5JD
■ Sat/Sun 11am-3pm. 1.5 hour behind the scenes history tours at 11am, 1pm including access to Morden cottage and Morden Hall, and regular short tours of stableyard and turbine. Last tour and entry 2.30pm. Max 20 per tour. N D R T B
Award winning Stable Yard, part of the original Morden Hall estate – an oasis in Suburbia. Stable Yard renovated using renewable technologies, including the first Archimedes Screw hydroelectric turbine in London. RICS award winner. Cowper Griffith (refurb) 2011.
Tube: Morden; Tram: Phipps Bridge; 93,157,154,164,293

New Studios, Wimbledon College of Arts ●
Merton Hall Road SW19 3QA
■ Sat 10am-5pm. Architect-led tours 11am-1pm, first come basis. D T A
This 2-storey studio building is an exemplar building of sustainable design, providing simple, flexible workspace for Wimbledon College of Arts students. It was awarded the Green Apple Award in 2014 and the design stage assessment achieved the second highest BREEAM score in the world. Penoyre & Prasad 2014.
Tube/Rail: Wimbledon; Rail: Wimbledon Chase; Tram: Dundonals Road; 152,163,164
www.arts.ac.uk/wimbledon

New Wimbledon Theatre
93 The Broadway SW19 1QG
■ Sat 10am-5pm. Pre-book via Box Office window or wimbledonadmin@theambassadors.com. Historical and architectural tours, pirates' treasure hunt, ghost tour, career talks, musical theatre Open Mic sessions. R T C G d
Striking Edwardian theatre with beautiful main auditorium in classic three-tier design, seating 1652. Recent major refurbishment. Cecil Masey & Roy Young 1910.
Tube/Rail: Wimbledon; 57,93,131,219,493

The Chapter House, Merton Priory
Merton Abbey Mills, Merantun Way SW19 2RD
■ Sat/Sun 10am-5pm. Sun talk at 2pm by architects Haverstock and the Merton Priory Trust on revitalisation of Chapter House remains. Max 50 at one time. N D B C P
Fascinating excavated foundations of the Chapter House of Merton Priory c1100-1200, one of the most important of all Augustinian monasteries prior to its destruction in 1538 by Henry VIII. The remains lie under Merantun Way (A24). Archaeologist David Saxby on site. Entry: Chapter House archaeological site. Archaeology for kids and fabric block printing demonstration.
Tube: Colliers Wood; Tube/Rail: Wimbledon; 57,131,152,200,219,470

The Wheelhouse
Merton Abbey Mills, Merantun Way SW19 2RD
■ Sat/Sun 10am-5pm. N D R T B P
Listed building with unique 7-spoke Victorian waterwheel, the only daily working example in South London, originally used by Liberty's for rinsing printed silk, and now the home of a craft pottery.
Tube: Colliers Wood; Tube/Rail: Wimbledon; 57,131,152,200,219

Wimbledon Windmill
Windmill Road SW19 5NR
■ Sat 10am-5pm. Regular tours, first come basis. Architect for restoration and curator on site. Hands-on models and equipment for children. Max 50 at one time. R T B A C d
Rare example of a hollow post mill (1817). Grade II* listed, it now contains a museum depicting the history and development of windmills in Britain. Many working models, windmill machinery, equipment and tools.
Tube/Rail: Wimbledon; 93

Supported by

merton

Key. A Architect on site B Bookshop C Childrens' activities d Some disabled access D Full wheelchair access E Engineer on site G Green Features
N Normally open to the public P Parking Q Long queues envisaged R Refreshments T Toilets

Newham

See **openhouselondon.org.uk/newham** to find out more about this area

University Square Stratford (University of East London & Birkbeck, University of London)

Abbey Mills Pumping Station ●
Abbey Lane E15 2RW
- Sat/Sun tours at 10am, 11am, 12noon, 1pm, 2pm, 3pm. Pre-book ONLY via londonopenhouse@thameswater.co.uk clearly marking the subject 'ABBEY MILLS: Open House'. Do not turn up without pre-booking. Max 20 per tour. E T P

Abbey Mills pumping station 'A', built by engineer Joseph Bazalgette, Edmund Cooper and architect Charles Driver. Built between 1865 and 1868, it has been described as the cathedral of sewage.
Tube: Bromley-by-Bow, Bow Road; DLR: Pudding Mill Lane; 25,86

Cody Dock ●
11c South Crescent, Canning Town E16 4TL
- Sat/Sun 10am-5pm. First come basis. 2pm 1.5 hour guided tour of Cody Dock and Imperial Gaswork site. R T C G P d

One of east London's most exciting arts and heritage spaces, Cody Dock's new gardens and paths provide the gateway to exploring the Lower Lea Valley and The Line sculpture trail. Constructed for Harper Twelvetrees as part of Imperial Chemical Works 1871. Entry: community gardens, riverside walks, sculpture trail, River Princess café and gallery space.
DLR: Star Lane

Courtyard House
2a Macdonald Road E7 0HE
- Sat 10am-5pm. Half-hourly tours, pre-book ONLY via http://dpq.eventbrite.co.uk. Closed 1-2pm. Last entry 4.30pm. Max 8 per tour. A P d

RIBA London award-winning contemporary timber-frame house designed around four courtyards. A black clad exterior gives way to a light open-plan interior with exposed ceiling joists and flexible living space. Dallas Pierce Quintero 2015.
Rail: Wanstead Park, Forest Gate; 308,58,330
http://dp-q.com

Crossrail – Custom House Station ●
Crossrail Custom House Station, Victoria Dock Road E16 3BU
- See www.crossrail.co.uk/openhouse for times, booking details and meeting point. E

The only new station constructed above ground in the central section of the Crossrail route will welcome regional and international visitors to ExCeL conference centre, along with creating a transport interchange with DLR and local buses. It was manufactured in 825 parts near Sheffield then transported to London and assembled on site, a process taking a year and a day to become structurally complete. Due 2018.
DLR: Custom House; 241,325,541,678
www.crossrail.co.uk/openhouse

Crossrail – Pudding Mill Lane ●
Cooks Road E15 2PE
- Sat 10am-5pm. Guided tours every 90 minutes. See www.crossrail.co.uk/openhouse for booking details and meeting point. Last entry 4pm. Max 15 per tour. E P d T

The eastern entry point for the new Crossrail tunnels under central London. This key part of the Crossrail project facilitated the construction of the new Pudding Mill Lane DLR station, the largest and most modern station on the DLR network.
DLR: Pudding Mill Lane; 25,108,276,425,D8
www.crossrail.co.uk/openhouse

East Village London E20
Celebration Avenue E20 1YY
- Sun 1pm-5pm. Tours of East Village, the former Athletes' Village, with a tour of Vesta House and two show homes overlooking Queen Elizabeth Olympic Park. Pre-book ONLY via www.getlivinglondon.com/openhousetour. D R T C G P

Formerly the Olympic Village during the 2012 Games, East Village is a brand new neighbourhood for London with new homes, communal gardens, public squares, tree-lined streets, waterways and wetlands, school and health centre. Various architects 2012-2014.
Tube/DLR/Rail: Stratford

House Mill ●
Three Mills Lane E3 3DU
- Sat/Sun 11am-4pm. Regular tours. Last tour 3.30pm. Max 18 per tour. R T B P d

The UK's oldest and largest tidal mill. 5-storey, timber-framed, brick-clad watermill with four waterwheels, originally built 1776 to mill grain for distillery trade. Operational until 1940. Organised by River Lea Tidal Mill Trust. Entry: ground, 1st floors of mill and rebuilt house.
Tube: Bromley-by-Bow; DLR: Devons Road; 25,108,D8,205

Lea Valley Velodrome ● ● Ⓝ
Queen Elizabeth Olympic Park, Abercrombie Road E20 3AB
- Sat 10am-5pm. Guided tours, first come basis. N E D R T A G

One of four permanent facilities from the London 2012 Olympics, this landmark building was inspired by the design creativity and engineering rigour of the bicycles which race inside it. Hopkins Architects 2011.
Tube/DLR/Rail: Stratford; DLR/Rail: Stratford International; Rail: Hackney Wick; 308,97,W15,388

Old Ford Water Recycling Plant ● Ⓝ
Dace Road E3 2NW (site can be accessed from the Greenway)
- Sat 9am-4pm. Hourly tours, first come basis. Last tour 4pm. Max 12 per tour. T G d

The largest community-scale wastewater recycling facility in the UK, using membrane technology to convert raw sewage to non-potable water to supply Olympic Park venues. Clad in timber, gabion baskets and corten steel to blend within the Old Ford Nature Reserve (a site of SWCI Conservation

Importance). Sustainable features include sedum roofs. Lyall Bills and Young Architects 2012. Entry: Old Ford Island and treatment building.
Tube/Rail/DLR: Stratford; Rail: Hackney Wick; DLR: Pudding Mill Lane; 276,388

Silvertown
Meet: Gate 3, Mill Road E16 2BE
- Sat/Sun hard hat tours 10.30am, 12.30pm, pre-book ONLY via info@silvertown.com. Duration 1 hour with Q&A. Max 8 per tour.

A 62-acre development, set to be London's new creative capital. At the heart lies Millennium Mills, an iconic former flour mill which has been derelict for decades. A small section of the Rank Hovis Premier Mill remains, with a restored Grade II listed grain silo. Due 2017.
DLR: West Silvertown, Pontoon Dock; 474
http://www.silvertownlondon.com

Sir Ludwig Guttmann Health and Wellbeing Centre ●
40 Liberty Bridge Road, Olympic Park E20 1AS
- Sat 10am-1pm. Regular tours. Last entry 12.30pm. D R T A G

A landmark award-winning civic building on the London 2012 Olympic Athletes' Village site, providing accomodation for NHS primary care needs along with an additional 1500m² of premises for the East Village Community Development Trust. Its sculptural form exploits its siting upon a pedestal-like promontory between railway cuttings to boldly announce its presence amongst much larger neighbours, whilst a public street-facing arcade invites visitors to penetrate into the atrium and courtyard at the heart of the building. BREEAM Excellent. Penoyre & Prasad 2011. Entry: 4-storey atrium, ground floor terrace, selected treatment areas (on tours only).
Tube/DLR/Rail: Stratford; DLR/Rail: Stratford International

St Mary the Virgin
Church Road, Manor Park, Little Ilford E12 6HA
- Sat 10am-5pm/Sun 1pm-5pm. N D T P

Small Grade I listed C12 chapel in lovely churchyard setting, it retains original architectural features and has interesting brasses, monuments and stained glass windows.
Tube: East Ham; Tube/Rail: Manor Park; 25,86,101,104,147,474

●AJ Library Building ●Green Exemplar ●Landscape/Public realm ●Infrastructure/Engineering ■Open Saturday ■Open Sunday ■Open Saturday and Sunday

Sugarhouse Studios

Stratford Circus

Theatre Square E15 1BX

■ Sat 10am-5pm. Tours at 12noon, 1pm of theatre spaces, technical booths (programmed events dependent). Max 10 per tour. N D T

Space, light, inspiration – a contemporary building achieves the original vision to create a modern user-friendly facility with multi-functional spaces. Levitt Bernstein 2001. Entry: foyer, café, theatres.

Tube/DLR/Rail: Stratford; 25,69,27b,108,473

Stratford Picture House

Gerry Raffles Square, Salway Road E15 1BN

■ Sat/Sun 1pm-5pm. Hourly tours, first come basis. Last tour 4pm. Max 10 per tour. N D R T

Contemporary cinema in the heart of Stratford, a linear east-west glass and steel building, dramatically revealing its structure and functions to the passer-by. Four screens with state-of-the-art sound. Burrell Foley Fischer 1997.

Tube/DLR/Rail: Stratford; 25,69,86,104,108,158,238,241,257,262

Sugarhouse Studios

107 High Street Stratford E15 2QQ

■ Sat/Sun 10am-5pm. Hourly tours until 5pm. Open studios from tenants all day. Max 20 per group. D T A G

Varied collection of workspaces gathered around a communal yard in Stratford. Between an appropriated warehouse and the new-build Yardhouse, it houses a diverse collection of artists and designers, including Assemble, and a rich variety of workshops, studios and event spaces. Assemble 2014.

Tube: Bow Road; DLR: Bow Church; Tube/DLR/Rail: Stratford; 8,25,108,276,455

The City of London Cemetery and Crematorium at Aldersbrook

Aldersbrook Road E12 5DQ

■ Sat tours 10am, 1pm/Sun tour 10am. Max 20 per tour. Duration approx 2 hours. Talk from Superintendent on the history/heritage of site. N T G P d

A stunning Grade I listed 200 acre site designed and landscaped in 1856 to deal with the environmental/health/ space issues of London's cramped and over-used churchyards. Rich in architecture from the Victorian era. William Haywood & William Davidson 1855-56/Edwin George Chandler 1974. Entry on tour: chapels, monuments, archives.

Tube: East Ham, Wanstead then 101 bus; Rail: Manor Park

The Crystal – A Sustainable Cities Initiative by Siemens
● ● ●

One Siemens Brothers Way, Royal Victoria Docks E16 1GB

■ Sat/Sun 10am-7pm. Regular tours, first come basis. Last entry 6.30pm. E R T B G d

London's newest landmark building and the world's first centre dedicated to improving our knowledge of urban sustainability through its programme of exhibitions and lectures. One of the most sustainable buildings in the world. Wilkinson Eyre Architects 2012. Entry: ground floor.

Tube: Canning Town; DLR: Royal Victoria; Emirates Cable Car

Theatre Royal Stratford East

Gerry Raffles Square E15 1BN

■ Sun backstage tours at 1pm, 2pm, first come basis. N D R T

Built as a playhouse and entertaining audiences for over 100 years. A recent £7.5million refurbishment it now ensures the best of both worlds: an original Victorian auditorium with beautiful Frank Matcham interior, plus state-of-the-art backstage and front of house facilities. Grade II* listed. JG Buckle, Frank Matcham 1884. Entry: theatre, backstage areas.

DLR/Tube/Rail: Stratford; 25,108,69

University Square Stratford (University of East London & Birkbeck, University of London)

1 Salway Road E15 1NF

■ Sat 10am-4pm. Half-hourly tours 10.30am-3.30pm, first come basis. Last entry 3.30pm. Max 20 per tour. D T

A new higher education hub with 8600m² of flexible, state-of-the-art teaching, performance and administrative spaces, reaching up to 5 storeys, oriented around a large, light-filled atrium. Make Architects 2013. Entry: atrium, specialised lecture theatres, simulated courtroom, performing arts spaces, music and performance studios.

Tube/DLR/Rail: Stratford; 25,69,86,97,104

WALKS/TOURS

Beyond the Olympic Park – The Real Lea Valley ●

■ Meet: Sat/Sun 2pm, in front of Olympic Swimming Pool, Stratford E20 2ZQ. Duration 3 miles/2.5 hours ending at Trinity Buoy Wharf. Space limited, confirm booking via ralphward@blueyonder.co.uk. Map/full description found at www.londonurbanvisits.co.uk. N d

Stroll down the banks of the river Lea to the Thames, uncovering the past and future of one of London's least known locations-to-be. Led by Ralph Ward, Visiting Professor at the University of East London and Michael Owens, director of Bow Arts and founder of London Urban Visits. Landmarks include the Line sculpture trail, the C18 House Mill, the cathedral of sewage at Abbey Mills, the site of Cedric Price's unrealised Fun Palace, Cody Dock and Trinity Buoy Wharf.

Tube/DLR/Rail: Stratford; Rail: Hackney Wick; 339
www.londonurbanvisits.co.uk

ICE Engineering Highlights Cycle Tour of the Queen Elizabeth Olympic Park ●

■ Meet: Sun 2pm outside the Timber Lodge Café, Honour Lea Avenue, Queen Elizabeth Olympic Park E20 3BB. Bikes not provided. Wear appropriate clothing. Santander Cycle Hire at Stratford and Stratford International. Duration 2 hours. E A

Join leading engineer Andrew Weir (Director, Expedition Engineering)/architect Kay Hughes (Director, Khaa). Tour will explore the Olympic Park's enabling works and the construction of the venues, through to the utilities and their supporting infrastructure. Organised by the Institution of Civil Engineers.

Tube: Leyton; Tube/Rail/DLR: Stratford

The Line Sculpture Walk ●

Start point: River Lea, opposite Print House Bar & Kitchen, 133 High Street E15 2RB

■ Sat/Sun 10am-5pm. Self-guided walk. N D R T

A modern and contemporary art walk that follows the meridian and the waterways that run between the O2 and the Queen Elizabeth Olympic Park.

Tube: Bow Road; DLR: Pudding Mill Lane, Stratford High Street; 25,108,276,425,D8

Walk in the Olympic Park: Function and Beauty in Landscape ●

■ Meet: Sun 2pm at the podium next to the Arcelor Mittal Orbit, Queen Elizabeth Olympic Park E20 2AD. Walk led by Dr Phil Askew, Project Sponsor Parklands and Public Realm. Pre-book ONLY via www.landscapeinstitute.org/events.

An opportunity to walk the Queen Elizabeth Olympic Park looking at the design approaches which have shaped this new park for London. Walk from south to north exploring the South Park and its post-Games landscape designed by James Corner Field, operations designer of New York's High Line with planting design by Piet Oudolf, and the Games time London 2012 Gardens. Find out how the Legacy of the Olympics is unfolding, how the park considers sustainability and how new approaches to green space design are key to making cities healthy and liveable for the future. Finish at the Timber Lodge in the North Park.

Tube/DLR/Rail: Stratford; DLR/Rail: Stratford International; 25,69,86,97,104,108,158,308,473

Supported by

Newham London

Key. A Architect on site **B** Bookshop **C** Childrens' activities **d** Some disabled access **D** Full wheelchair access **E** Engineer on site **G** Green Features **N** Normally open to the public **P** Parking **Q** Long queues envisaged **R** Refreshments **T** Toilets

Redbridge

See **openhouselondon.org.uk/redbridge**
to find out more about this area

Bancroft's School
611 High Road, Woodford Green IG8 0RF
■ Sat 10am-1pm.
A dignified and impressive design with later additions. Spiral staircase leads to the top of the tower, giving excellent views of east London. Formerly a Drapers' Company charitable school in Mile End Road, Bancroft's moved to its present site in 1889. Sir Arthur Blomfield 1889. Entry: chapel, great hall, library, dining hall, tower, grounds.
Tube: Woodford; Rail: Chingford; 20,179, W13

Barnardo's Garden Village
Tanners Lane, Barkingside, Ilford IG6 1QG
■ Sat/Sun 10am-5pm. First come basis. Tours at 11am, 1.30pm, 4pm. Max 30 per tour. Proposals on new residential development on display. N T P d
The Victorian 'village' was started in the 1870s and had expanded to over 70 'cottages' on 60 acres by Barnardo's death in 1905. The village today contains the only remaining children's church in the country with lower pews and child-themed stained glass windows, and an iconic spired clock. Grade II listed site also has a monument to Barnardo by Sir George Frampton. New Head Office building completed 2013. Ebenezer Gregg 1876-1895. Entry: church, green, memorial.
Tube: Barkingside; Rail: Ilford; 150,169,128,167,462

Fullwell Cross Library
140 High Street, Barkingside, Ilford IG6 2EA
■ Sat 9.30am-4pm. N D T B
The library was built together with the swimming baths on an open site in Barkingside High Street. Circular library design copies nearby roundabout. Complex is set back from the pavement, intended to form a new local civic centre with a public space. Refurbished 1990 and 2011. Display on history of Barkingside. Interactive WW1 events during the day – contact library for more details. Frederick Gibberd/Coombes & Partners/ H C Connell 1958-68.
Tube: Barkingside, Fairlop; 128,150,167,169,247,275,462

Ilford War Memorial Hall
Ilford War Memorial Gardens, Eastern Avenue, Newbury Park IG2 7RJ
■ Sat/Sun 11am-4.30pm. D
Grade II listed memorial hall situated within the War Memorial Gardens. Panels inside the building record the names of the Ilford men killed during WWI. The Hall was designed to serve as the entrance to the now demolished children's ward of the Ilford Emergency Hospital. C J Dawson & Allardyce 1927.
Tube: Newbury Park; 66,169

Quaker Meeting House, Wanstead
Bush Road E11 3AU
■ Sun 1pm-5pm. Last entry 5.15pm. N R T P d
Modernist building based on four hexagons within an Epping Forest setting. Contains a sunny meeting room for Quaker worship facing onto a wooded burial ground of simple headstones, including that of Elizabeth Fry and, recently the Meeting House's architect Norman Frith who died in 2015. Norman Frith 1968. Entry: foyer, meeting room, social room,

kitchen, grounds, wildflower meadow.
Tube: Leytonstone; 101,308

Redbridge Town Hall, Council Chamber
128-142 High Road, Ilford IG1 1DD
■ Sat 10am-5pm. Tours on the hour 11am-2pm, first come basis. Tour by council's constitutional expert including council chamber. Max 15 per tour. D T
Built in 3 stages consisting of the Old Town Hall (1901) with facade in free classic style and some original decorations, library (1927) and additional buildings (1933). B Woolard 1901. Entry: ground and 1st floors.
Tube: Gants Hill; Rail: Ilford; 25,86,123,128,129,145,147,150,167,169,179,296,364

Sukkat Shalom Reform Synagogue
1 Victory Road, Wanstead E11 1UL
■ Sun 10am-5pm. First come basis. Last entry 4.45pm. R T P d
Red-brick, Grade II listed with sumptuous interior and stained glass windows above ark. Originally the Merchant Seaman's Orphan Asylum Chapel, acquired by the synagogue in 1995 and restored with Heritage Lottery Fund grant. Somers Clarke 1863. Entry: main building.
Tube: Snaresbrook; W13

The Hospital Chapel of St Mary & St Thomas
48 Ilford Hill, Ilford IG1 2AT
■ Sat 10am-4pm/Sun 1pm-4.30pm. Regular tours. Last entry half hour before close. N D R T B
Founded c1145 by the Abbess of Barking as a hospice for thirteen old and infirm men, the present building is C12 and C19. Grade II* listed with many interesting monuments, including Burne-Jones windows. Organised by Friends of the Hospital Chapel.
Tube: Gants Hill; Rail: Ilford; 25,86,123,150,179, EL1, EL2

The Temple
Wanstead Park E11 2LT
■ Sun 12.30pm-4.30pm. N R T B C d
C18 garden building in style of a Doric temple, one of the last remaining structures surviving from Wanstead Park's days of grandeur. C18 statuary fragments and Roman finds on display. Take home an individualised print of Wanstead House. Entry: ground and first floor.
Tube: Wanstead; 66,101,145,308, W13, W14, W19

Uphall Primary School Nursery
Uphall Road, Ilford IG1 2JD
■ Sat/Sun 10am-1pm. Max 10 at one time. P d
Unusual 1930s ship-shaped school building, converted to nursery. Dropped ceilings and child-height porthole windows give suitable scale of space whilst complementing external elevations. Grade II listed. Civic Trust commendation 2000. Artist Sally Labern of the drawing shed worked with the school's children to create a neon artwork around the Olympic principles of inclusiveness using the original 1930s clear red neon – viewable until dusk. Tooley and Foster c1937. Entry: nursery, playground.
Tube: Barking; Rail: Ilford

Valentines Mansion
Emerson Road, Ilford IG1 4XA
■ Sun 11am-3pm. Last entry 2pm. N D R T C G
Large, late C17 Grade II* listed house with fine staircase and Venetian window and with Georgian additions, used as a family dwelling until the early 1900s. Reopened to the public in Feb 2009 following extensive restoration works of period furnished rooms, Victorian kitchen and pantry, temporary exhibition gallery. 1696/Richard Griffiths Architects 2009.

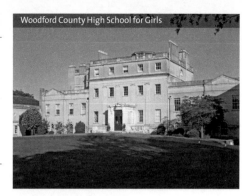
Woodford County High School for Girls

Entry: ground, 1st & 2nd floors.
Tube: Gants Hill; Rail: Ilford; 128,296,150,396,167

Woodford County High School for Girls
High Road, Woodford Green IG8 9LA
■ Sun 1pm-5pm. Half-hourly tours, first come basis. Last entry 4.30pm. N R T d
Formerly Highams Manor, an elegant Georgian manor house built for the Warner family with grounds by Repton. William Newton 1768. Entry: house, grounds (ground floor only for those in wheelchairs).
Tube: Woodford; 20,179,275, W13

Woodford Parish Church Memorial Hall
209 High Road, South Woodford E18 2PA
■ Sat 1pm-5pm. R T d
A Grade II listed building, built in 1902 in the Arts & Crafts style, on land where once stood Woodford Hall which was the childhood home of William Morris. J. Kingwell Cole 1902.
Tube: South Woodford; 179, W13,123,20

WALKS/TOURS

Wanstead Heritage Walk ●
■ Meet: Sun 10am outside Wanstead Station, 21 The Green, Wanstead E11 2NT. Duration 2 hours.
A guided walk from Wanstead Station to The Temple, Wanstead Park, highlighting the ancient chestnuts, St Mary's Church, a view of the Basin and Stable Block and other historical remnants of the Grade II listed historical landscape that formed the grounds of Wanstead House. Finishes at The Temple where walkers can find out more about the history of the rise and fall of this important Palladian mansion.
Tube: Wanstead; 66,101,145,308, W13, W14

Supported by

London Borough of
Redbridge

Richmond

See **openhouselondon.org.uk/richmond**
to find out more about this area

Style Council

All Hallows Parish Church
Chertsey Road, Twickenham, Middlesex TW1 1EW
■ Sun 1pm-5pm. Self guided tours and bell tower tours. Historian Kathryn Elliott on site. N D R T C P
A City of London church, previously in Lombard Street. Moved to present site in 1940 with original tower and richly carved interior furnishings. Christopher Wren 1694/Robert Atkinson (rebuilt) 1939-40. Children's activity sheets.
Tube/Rail: Richmond; Rail: Twickenham; 281,H37

Bushy House
National Physical Laboratory, Queens Road, Teddington TW11 OEB
■ Sat 10am-5pm. T P
Original house was built for Edward Proger, c1663/5. From 1797 the residence of William, Duke of Clarence (later William IV) and his mistress Dora Jordan. Now part of the National Physical Laboratory. William Samwell 1663/5. Entry: house, vinery, gardens. No pets with the exception of guide dogs.
Rail: Teddington; R68,33,281,285,465

Garrick's Temple to Shakespeare, Hampton
Garrick's Lawn, Hampton Court Road, Hampton TW12 2EJ
■ Sun 10am-5pm. Last entry 4.45pm. Max 30 at one time. D R T C
Georgian garden building (1756). Tribute to Shakespeare built in the Ionic style by actor David Garrick. Arcadian Thames side setting in restored C18 gardens by Capability Brown. Design activities for children; interactive digital presentations for adults and children. Garrick/Shakespeare exhibition.
Ferry: Hampton pedestrian ferry from Molesey; Rail: Hampton, Hampton Court; 111,216,R68

Grove Gardens Chapel
Richmond Cemetery, Grove Gardens, off Lower Grove Road (entrance opposite Greville Road) TW10 6HP
■ Sun 1pm-5pm. First come basis. Max 30 at one time. D T A
Small, charming Gothic chapel of imaginative design with plate tracery and mosaic triptych. Former cemetery chapel, now restored for mixed community use. Thomas Hardy was apprenticed to the architect. Sir Arthur Blomfield c1873.
Tube/Rail: Richmond; 371

Ham House and Garden
Ham Street, Ham TW10 7RS
■ Sat 10am-5pm. Regular short talks. Last entry to house 3.30pm. R T B C d
Built in 1610 for a Knight Marshall of James I, Ham House was greatly extended in the 1670s. One of a series of grand houses and palaces built along the Thames, Ham House and Garden is an unusual complete C17 survival. Fine interiors and historic gardens. Entry: areas of house, gardens, outbuildings. Art activities and trail for children.
Tube/Rail: Richmond; Rail: Kingston; 371,65

Hampton Court Palace – Apartment 39
Hampton Court Palace, East Molesey KT8 9AU
■ Sat/Sun 10am-5pm. Regular tours, first come basis. R T B
Open to commemorate the centenary of the Gallipoli campaign, Apartment 39 was Lord Birdwood's living quarters – he lived at the palace from 1943-51 and was Commander-in-Chief at Gallipoli. C19.
Rail: Hampton Court; 111,216,411,R68

Kew House
10 Cambridge Road, Kew TW9 3JB
■ Sat/Sun 10am-5pm. First come basis. Shoes off. Last entry 4.30pm. E R T A P Q d
A contemporary family home formed of two weathering steel volumes inserted behind the retained facade of a C19 brick stables, set within a conservation area on the doorstep of Kew Gardens. Piercy & Company 2013.
Tube/Rail: Kew Gardens; Rail: Kew Bridge; 391,65

Kilmorey Mausoleum
275 St Margaret's Road (opposite Ailsa Tavern) TW1 1NJ
■ Sun 1pm-5pm. Max 5 inside mausoleum. R d
Egyptian-style, pink and grey mausoleum for the second Earl of Kilmorey. The form relates to the shrines at the heart of Egyptian Temples. HE Kendall C19. Entry: mausoleum, main grounds, wildlife garden.
Tube/Rail: Richmond; Rail: St Margaret's; H37

Langdon Down Centre
2a Langdon Park TW11 9PS
■ Sun 11.30am-4pm. Tours at 12.30pm, 1.30pm, and 2.30pm. Displays of community aspect. Last entry 3.45pm. N D R T B P
Grade II* listed Normansfield Theatre and Langdon Down Museum of Learning Disability. Gothic proscenium arch and elaborate stage and scenery. Originally built as part of the Normansfield Hospital for patients/students with learning disabilities. Rowland Plumbe 1877. Entry: theatre, basement.
Rail: Hampton Wick; 281,285 (from Kingston)

Orleans House Gallery, Octagon Room and New Arts Education Centre
Riverside TW1 3DJ
■ Sun 10am-5pm. Max 60 at one time. N R T B P d
Louis Philippe, Duc d'Orleans, lived here 1815-17. Gibbs' Octagon room and adjoining gallery/stable block are remaining parts of Orleans House. Coach house education centre opened 2006. Further developments 2007-8 including café. John James 1710/James Gibbs 1720/Patel Taylor (new centre) 2006. Entry: Octagon Room, main gallery, stables gallery.
Tube/Rail: Richmond, Rail: St Margaret's, Twickenham; 33,490,H22,R68,R70

Parish Church of St Anne
Kew Green TW9 3AA
■ Sat 10am-1pm. N R T P d
Grade II* listed, originally built as a chapel under the patronage of Queen Anne in 1714 and subsequently enlarged. Many notable memorials including to scientist William Jackson Hooker and tombs of Thomas Gainsborough and Johan Zoffany. Joshua Kirby/Robert Browne 1714/1770/1805.
Tube/Rail: Kew Gardens; Rail: Kew Bridge; 65,391

Pope's Grotto and Radnor House School
Radnor House School, Pope's Villa, Cross Deep TW1 4QG
■ Sat tours 10am, 11am, 12noon. Pre-book ONLY via hdolan@radnorhouse.org. Max 25 at one time. R T P
Grotto with mineral decoration is last remaining part of Alexander Pope's villa built 1720, demolished 1808 and replaced and redeveloped many times in following years. Entry: grotto, school.
Rail: Twickenham, Strawberry Hill; 33,R68,R70,H22,267

Richmond Lock Building (Surrey Side)
The Towpath, Richmond TW9 2QJ
■ Sun 10am-5pm. Regular talks by lock keeper. Last entry 3.30pm. Max 30 at one time. N T P d
Example of good-quality late-Victorian functional design. 1894. Entry: lock cottage and lock side.
Tube/Rail: Richmond; Rail: St Margaret's; 33,65,490,H22,R68,R70

Richmond Theatre
The Green, Richmond TW9 1QJ
■ Sun 1pm-5pm. Tours also available, pre-book ONLY via 0844 871 7651. Max 20 per tour. R T C
A typical Matcham design, this beautiful 840 seat theatre was exhaustively researched and then restored in 1989 to a fabulous crimson, cream and gold. All original mouldings restored and renewed. Frank Matcham 1899. Entry: auditorium, backstage, foyers. Architecture-inspired treasure trails and art activities for children aged 4+.
Tube/Rail: Richmond; 65,371,419,493

Richmond, the American International University in London
Richmond Hill Campus, Queen's Road TW10 6JP

Key. A Architect on site **B** Bookshop **C** Childrens' activities **d** Some disabled access **D** Full wheelchair access **E** Engineer on site **G** Green Features
N Normally open to the public **P** Parking **Q** Long queues envisaged **R** Refreshments **T** Toilets

Kew House

Bushy House

■ Sat/Sun 10am-5pm. First come basis. Hourly tours. Last entry 4.30pm. N R T P d
An impressive neo-Gothic building set in 5 acres. Originally home of the Wesley Theological Institution and now Richmond University, built of Bath stone with façade largely unchanged. Grounds contain many rare specimens of plants and trees. Andrew Trimen 1843. Entry: main building, grounds.
Tube/Rail: Richmond; 371

Royal Botanic Gardens, Kew: Herbarium, Library, Art and Archives
Royal Botanic Gardens, Kew TW9 3AE
■ Sat/Sun 10am-5pm. Last entry 4pm. Max 70 at one time. D R B
As well as learning about the architectural design and history of both the historic and contemporary Herbarium, Library, Art and Archives buildings, visitors will be able to meet Kew's scientists and archivists, examine plant and fungi specimens, and learn about Kew's flagship historic collections and current scientific projects. To complement Kew's summer and autumn spice-themed programme, visitors will also be able to learn all about the exotic world of spices through beautiful art, and fascinating artefacts and books. Open House Herbarium visitors entitled to discounted entry to main Kew Gardens on the day. C18/Edward Cullinan Architects (new wing) 2010. Entry: Herbarium, library, art & archives.
Tube/Rail: Kew Gardens; Rail: Kew Bridge; 65,391,237,267
www.kew.org

Sir Richard Burton's Mausoleum
St Mary Magdalen's RC Church, 61 North Worple Way, Mortlake SW14 8PR
■ Sun 1pm-5pm. Last entry 4.30pm. N C P d
Grade II* listed mausoleum in the form of an Arab tent with ripples in the stone imitating canvas. Interior is embellished with oriental lamps, devotional paintings and camel bells. Storyteller present during opening. Isabel Arundell Burton 1890. Entry: exterior only, interior views through panel in roof via step ladder.
Tube/Rail: Richmond; Rail: Mortlake; 209,33,337,493,485

St Leonard's Air Raid Shelter, East Sheen
Palmers Road, East Sheen SW14 7NG
■ Sun 1pm-5pm. Access is only via a staircase however some

aspects can be viewed at ground level where there is an interpretation board. Small groups will be escorted around the shelter due to restricted space. d
An unusual four roomed shelter with day and night rooms, still with some original fittings, underneath a raised central garden area in St Leonards Court. 1938.
Rail: Mortlake; 337,493,33

St Mary Magdalene
Paradise Road, Richmond TW9 1SN
■ Sat 10am-5pm/Sun 8am-7.30pm. Tours of the tower and monuments taking place. Refreshments at 10.30am on Sun with 6.30pm evensong. N D R T C A
A historic living parish church, progressively shaped from the Tudor to the Edwardian period. Newly restored windows recapture the original airiness of the C18 nave. 1506/A.W.Blomfield & G.F. Bodley 1904.
Tube/Rail: Richmond

Style Council
46 Barnes Avenue SW13 9AB
■ Sat 10am-5pm. Half-hourly tours. Last entry 4.30pm. A G Q
'Style Council' is the transformation of a former post WW1 council house into a stylish, modern, energy efficient home. Located on a large south facing corner plot, the house has been extended in every direction possible, with the interiors completely re-planned as light filled open plan spaces for multi-generational family living. Features include bamboo sliding screens, modern 'peek-a-boo' bay windows, a suspended 'musical' staircase, granny lift, dynamic furniture and private courtyard connected to new garden studio. KSKa Architects 2014. Entry: Ground floor, garden.
Tube: Hammersmith; Rail: Barnes Bridge; 33,72
www.kska.co.uk

The Cedars (Span House)
2 The Cedars, Teddington TW11 0AX
■ Sat 10am-5pm. First come basis. Architect talk at 2.30pm. Max 15 at one time. Q A G P d
Example of a T2 house by Span Developments with Eric Lyons, famous for forward-looking housing of the '50s and typified by modernist lines, good internal planning and communal gardens. Recent ground floor extension and

refurbishment with 'Mondrian' primary colour scheme, plus many sustainable features including solar PV cells, solar heating of water, and wood burning stove. Eric Lyons 1958/ KMK Architects 2011.
Rail: Teddington; 33,R68,281,285

The Darke House
25 Montpellier Row TW1 2NQ
■ Sun 10am-5pm. Guided tours, first come basis. Queuing outside if necessary. Last entry 5pm. Max 6 per tour. T Q
Designed by celebrated architect Geoffrey Darke as his own home. Described in Grade II listing as 'the country's finest example of modernist house in a Georgian setting'. Nearly all original features and many fittings remain. Geoffrey Darke (of Darbourne & Darke) 1968. Entry: house, garden.
Tube/Rail: Richmond; Rail: St Margaret's; R68,490,R80,H22,H37

The Old Town Hall, Richmond
Whittaker Avenue, Richmond TW9 1TP. Meet at War Memorial in Riverside Gardens at end of Whittaker Avenue.
■ Sat 9.30am-4pm. Tours at 10am, 11am, 12noon, 1pm, 2pm. Max 10 per tour. N T d
Red brick and Bath stone grand 'Elizabethan Renaissance' style building altered by war, political changes and reflecting Richmond's history. Overlooking the war memorial and the Thames. W J Ancell 1893.
Tube/Rail: Richmond; 65,33,H37,22,R70

York House
Richmond Road TW1 3AA
■ Sat 1pm-5pm/Sun 3pm-5pm. E T P d
Mid-C17 house, a scheduled ancient monument, with fine staircase and C18 additions. Entry: parlour, council chamber, other rooms.
Tube/Rail: Richmond; Rail: Twickenham; 490,33,H22,R68,R70

Supported by

LONDON BOROUGH OF RICHMOND UPON THAMES

Southwark

See openhouselondon.org.uk/southwark
to find out more about this area

4 Carmarthen Place ●
4 Carmarthen Place SE1 3TS
- ■ Sun 1pm-5pm. First come basis. Shoes off. Max 9 at one time. T G

One of two eco wooden houses and artist's studio with sedum roof. New to the UK and prefabricated in Europe to exacting designs, the complete panels were craned into site. Emma Doherty & Amanda Menage/Architects in Residence 2006.
Tube/Rail: London Bridge; 47,188,381,RV1

15 and a half Consort Road
15 and a half Consort Road SE15 2PH
- ■ Sat 10am-5pm. First come basis, queuing if necessary. Queue closes 4pm. Architects available for discussion. Max 20 at one time. E Q A G d

As seen on Grand Designs, the opening roof and sliding bath typify this unique and extraordinary response to various constraints and opportunities for a tight budget on an 'unusable' brownfield site. Shortlisted RIBA Awards 2006. One of six voted as Nation's favourite Grand Designs' houses. Sustainable features include use of wasteland, recycled materials and innovative ideas. Richard Paxton Architects/MOOARC/Flower Michelin 2005. Entry: whole house.
Rail: Peckham Rye, Queen's Road Peckham

80 Great Suffolk Street
80 Great Suffolk Street SE1 0BE
- ■ Sat/Sun 10am-1pm. First come basis. T A d

TDO Architecture studio is a stunning plywood office suspended from a grid of red steelwork in a renovated arch under the railway on Great Suffolk Street. TDO Architecture 2013.
Tube: Southwark, Borough; Tube/Rail: London Bridge, Waterloo; 344,45,63,100,35

142 Bermondsey Street
Flat B, 142 Bermondsey Street SE1 3TX
- ■ Sat 11am-2pm. Half-hourly guided tours, pre-book ONLY via studio@hampsonwilliams.com with Open House in the subject line. Last entry 2pm. Max 4 per tour.

Refurbishment and extension of a post-war steel frame building using cross laminated timber forming a contemporary bookend on a historic street. Hampson Williams 2015.
Tube/Rail: London Bridge; 42,78,188,C10

240 Blackfriars
240 Blackfriars Road SE1 8NV
- ■ Sat 10am-1pm. Architect led talk and tours at 10am, 11am,12noon. Pre-book ONLY via openhouse@ahmm.co.uk. Include 'Blackfriars' in the subject line. Max 25 per tour. D A

New 89m tall, 220,000ft² office and retail building with adjoining residential development at the south end of Blackfriars Bridge. The building's crystalline form is wrapped in a fluid 'pinstripe' glass skin. Allford Hall Monaghan Morris 2014.
Tube: Southwark; 63,59

Al Jazeera Media Network UK
Main Reception, The Shard, 32 London Bridge Street SE1 9SG
- ■ Sat tours led by design team 9.30am,10.15am,11am, 11.45am. Pre-book ONLY via https://goo.gl/OnSafY. Max 10 per tour. D T A

ORTUS

Al Jazeera Media Network's UK headquarters on level 16 of The Shard. Collaboration between Al Jazeera's creative technology team along with John McAslan + Partners (office interior designers), and Veech X Veech (news studio and newsroom). Creates a pre-eminent broadcast production facility, not a traditional 'black box' studio. John McAslan + Partners 2013. Reception and Al Jazeera Media Network studios.
Tube/Rail: London Bridge
www.mcaslan.co.uk

Allies and Morrison
85 Southwark Street SE1 0HX
- ■ Sat 10am-5pm. Regular tours, first come basis. Last tour 4.15pm. Max 8 at one time. D T A

A tour of Allies and Morrison Studios complex – the original RIBA award winning studio, a converted Grade II listed warehouse and a new timber building. Allies and Morrison 2003/2013.
Tube: Southwark; Tube/Rail: London Bridge, Blackfriars; 381,RV1

Anise Gallery / AVR London
13a Shad Thames SE1 2PU
- ■ Sat/Sun 10am-5pm. T N D A

A Victorian spice warehouse, re-invented to house an architectural artwork gallery and an architectural illustrator's studio. The design focuses on flexibility and workspace collaboration. Tate Harmer 2013.
Tube: Bermondsey; Tube/Rail: London Bridge; 47,188,381,RV1

Asylum Road
126a Asylum Road SE15 2LW
- ■ Sat 10am-5pm. Max 10 at one time. Q

Inventive re-working of a mechanics garage into a low budget, two bedroom family house. Located on a constrained site

with no external views at ground level, the design utilises courtyards and roof lights to animate the interior and connect to outside. MOS Architects 2014.
Rail: Queen's Road Peckham; P12,36,136,171,436

Brunel Museum ●
Railway Avenue SE16 4LF
- ■ Sat/Sun 10am-5pm. First come basis, queuing outside if necessary. Guided descents of underground chamber half the size of Shakespeare's Globe. Trains to view Thames Tunnel portico, one time shopping arcade, banquet hall and fairground. Bring travel ticket valid for zone 2. Award winning river gardens. Children's activities including 'Make a Thames Tunnel peep show.' Saturday 5pm- 11pm 'Liquid engineering', cocktails with the Midnight Apothecary in the roof gardens above the Thames Tunnel. R T B C P

The Brunel Museum is housed in the Brunel Engine House, designed to be part of the infrastructure of the Thames Tunnel. Sir Marc Brunel 1842.
Tube/Rail: Canada Water; Rail: Rotherhithe; 1,188,381

Canada Water Library
21 Surrey Quays Road SE16 7AR
- ■ Sat 9am-5pm/Sun 12noon-4pm. Tours Sat 10am, 11am, 3pm/Sun 1pm. Max 20 per tour. N D R T

A civic centrepiece for the regeneration of the area around Canada Water. Its inverted pyramid form is an innovative response to providing an efficient single large library floor on a smaller footprint site. CZWG 2011. Entry: entrance area, main library level, mezzanine level, roof.
Tube/Rail: Canada Water; Rail: South Bermondsey, Surrey Quays; 1,47,188,199,225,381,P12

CGP London Café Gallery
Centre of Southwark Park SE16 2UA
- ■ Sat/Sun 11am-5pm. Last entry 4.40pm. Max 150 at one time. N D R T B

Previously a derelict café, rebuilt in 2001 fit for purpose as an art gallery with allotment garden, for the Bermondsey Artists' Group. SBDS, John Wilder 2001. Entry: lobby and main space.
Tube/Rail: Canada Water; Rail: Surrey Quays; 1,47,188,199,225

City Hall ●
The Queen's Walk, More London (from Tower Hill, walk across Tower Bridge) SE1 2AA
- ■ Sat 9am-6pm. City of a Thousand Architects kids activity 11am-3pm (see p16). Last entry 5.30pm. N D R T Q C G

Home of the Mayor of London and London Assembly, an environmentally-aware building with innovative spiral ramp and fine views across London. Foster + Partners 2002. Entry: London's Living Room, spiral ramp, chamber.
Tube: Tower Hill; Tube/Rail: London Bridge; 47,42,78,381,RV1

Courtyard House
35 Dovedale Road SE22 0NF
- ■ Sun 2pm-6pm. Last entry 5.30pm. Max 8 at one time. A G P Q d

Single-storey courtyard house on constrained site, built out to the perimeter whilst providing light and private views to the habitable rooms and avoiding overlooking of the surrounding properties. Bathrooms are located along the street façade with opaque glass windows to provide a buffer zone between the living space and the pavement. Design-Cubed 2012.
Rail: Honor Oak Park; 63,363

Crystal Palace Subway
Crystal Palace Parade SE19 1LG
- ■ Sat/Sun 10am-4.30pm. Regular tours. Pre-book ONLY via www.cpsubway.org.uk. Under 18s must be accompanied by an adult. No wheelchair access.

Key. A Architect on site **B** Bookshop **C** Childrens' activities **d** Some disabled access **D** Full wheelchair access **E** Engineer on site **G** Green Features
N Normally open to the public **P** Parking **Q** Long queues envisaged **R** Refreshments **T** Toilets

Royal Road

Magnificent subway under Crystal Palace Parade resembling a vaulted crypt. The subway connected the High Level Station (Charles Barry junior 1865; demolished 1960) to the Crystal Palace (Joseph Paxton 1854; burnt down 1936).
Rail: Crystal Palace; 3,202,322,410,450

Dawson's Heights
Bredinghurst, Overhill Road, East Dulwich SE22 0PL
- ■ Sat 10am-5pm. Half-hourly tours, pre-book ONLY via https://dawsonheightsopenhouse2015.eventbrite.co.uk. Last entry 4.30pm. Max 10 per tour. D

Split between 2 blocks consisting of nearly 300 flats, all with private balconies, Dawson's Heights is a fantastic example of beautifully designed social housing with uninterrupted views of the London skyline. Kate Macintosh for Southwark County Council Architects Dept 1966-72.
Rail: Forest Hill, Peckham Rye, East Dulwich; 176,185,197,P13

Dilston Grove
Southwest corner of Southwark Park SE16 2DD
- ■ Sat/Sun 11am-5pm. Max 200 at one time. N D T

A former Clare College mission church, now contemporary art gallery and recently renovated, was the first concrete-poured building in England, now Grade II listed. 2010 renovation by Walter Menteth & Sherry Bates. Sir John Simpson & Maxwell Ayrton 1911/Walter Menteth & Sherry Bates (renovation) 2010. Entry: lobby and main space.
Tube/Rail: Canada Water; Rail: Surrey Quays; 1,47,188,199,225

Employment Academy
29 Peckham Road SE5 8UA
- ■ Sat 10am-5pm. Half-hourly tours, first come basis. R T d

The Employment Academy is a Grade II listed, late Victorian 'Baroque' building that has now become a local asset to the Southwark community. Edwin Thomas Hall 1904/Peter Barber Architects 2013.
Rail: Peckham Rye, Denmark Hill; 171,436,36,12,345

Friern Road, East Dulwich (Pear Tree House)
190a Friern Road SE22 0BA
- ■ Sat 10am-5pm. Hourly tours 11-4pm, first come basis. Last entry 4.30pm. A G P d

Contemporary self-build architect's house designed around a 100-year old pear tree, constructed of board marked concrete and timber cladding featuring onsite crafted joinery and light fittings. Edgley Design 2014. Entry: whole house.
Rail: Peckham Rye; 12,197,176,185,363

Grow Elephant ●
New Kent Road SE17 1SL
- ■ Sat/Sun 12noon-9pm. Talks at 4pm both days in geodesic dome. N D R T A G

Explore London's only mobile community garden, now on its 3rd site in as many years. Find out more about how local residents run the garden and how it has evolved. Disco and soul DJs in onsite café.
Tube/Rail: Elephant & Castle; 1,53,63,168,172,188,363,453

House of Antoni & Alison
80 Southwark Bridge Road SE1 0AS
- ■ Sat 10am-5pm. Access via regular tours only, first come basis, queuing outside if necessary. Max 20 per tour. R Q d

An 1820s mid-terrace house, found derelict and covered in plastic flowers, now fully renovated revealing its hidden gems and history past and present. Reclamation of architectural salvage pieces used throughout. Creative partners Antoni & Alison (MBE) established their fashion and design company in 1987 and continue to work on their fine art photography and fashion projects. Examples will be shown. Pop-up version of olde worlde super modern tearoom will be on site serving charity teas. Entry: all floors.
Tube: Borough; Tube/Rail: London Bridge; 344,381,RV1,35,133

Jerwood Space ●
171 Union Street SE1 0LN
- ■ Sat 10am-5pm. Tour at 3pm, will include information on the Orange Street School. Visitors on tour may see elements of rehearsal process. Jerwood Drawing Prize open until 3pm. Portable loop system available for hard-of-hearing (please pre-book via 0207 654 0171). N R T P d

Former Victorian school converted in contemporary idiom (Paxton Locher Architects 1998) to provide theatre/dance rehearsal facilities, plus striking gallery alongside a café and glazed courtyard (the Glasshouse – Satellite Architects 2003). New studios and meeting rooms (Munkenbeck & Partners/Elliott Wood Partners 2007) on the restored top floor (lost to wartime bombing). Sustainable features include sedum roof.
Tube: Southwark; Tube/Rail: London Bridge; 40,45,63,344,RV1
www.elliottwood.co.uk

London Bridge Station Redevelopment ●
Thameslink Programme Visitor Suite, 30-32 Tooley Street SE1 2SZ
- ■ Sat tours of the London Bridge station construction site. Full PPE will be required to tour the Victorian arches and view construction of the new street-level station concourse. Pre-book ONLY via www.thameslinkprogramme.co.uk/OpenHouse. Tour times confirmed on booking website. Max 15 per tour. E R T G

Tour of Thameslink sites, the iconic new Borough High Street Bridge and early redevelopment works on the station (subject to project activities) and archeology that has recently been unearthed. Various/Grimshaw/Jestico and Whiles 1836-2011.
Tube/Rail: London Bridge; 17,47,133,141,149

London Fire Brigade Museum, Winchester House
94 Southwark Bridge Road SE1 0EG
- ■ Sat 10am-4pm. Tours at 11am, 2pm exploring how the site has evolved. Last entry 3.30pm. Max 150 at one time. T B

Georgian mansion built as two houses in 1820, converted in 1878 into one large residence for the Chief Officer of the LFB. Grade II listed, retaining many original features including an exquisite mosaic entrance.
Tube: Borough, Southwark; Tube/Rail: London Bridge, Blackfriars; 344,40,35,133,343

LSBU Clarence Centre for Enterprise and Innovation
6 St George's Circus SE1 6FE
- ■ Sat 10am-4pm. Regular tours led by the architect or client, first come basis. Last entry 3pm. A G D R T

Office space and support for start-up businesses at London South Bank University, incorporated into two Grade II listed Georgian terraces and a former pub. A careful juxtaposition of new and old. Rivington Street Studio 2013.
Tube/Rail: Elephant & Castle; 1,45,63,68,148,172

Nunhead Cemetery ●
Linden Grove SE15 3LP
- ■ Sat/Sun 1pm-5pm. Tours at 2pm, 3pm of the cemetery and visits to chapel and crypt. N T B G P d

Magnificent Victorian cemetery with Gothic chapel and ruined lodge. One of London's wildest and most overgrown cemeteries. Restored with the help of a lottery grant. Unique in London – 52 acres of woodland, complete with bats, owls, foxes and squirrels. Thomas Little & JJ Bunning 1840. Entry: cemetery, chapel.
Rail: Nunhead; 484, P3, P12

Old Operating Theatre Museum & Herb Garret
9a St Thomas Street SE1 9RY
- ■ Sun 10am-5pm. Access via 32-step bell tower spiral staircase. Last entry 4.45pm. Max 60 at one time. B

St Thomas' Church attic (1703) once part of old St Thomas' Hospital, houses the Herb Garret and Britain's only surviving C19 operating theatre. Thomas Cartwright 1703.
Tube/Rail: London Bridge; 21,35,40,43,47,48,133,149

ORTUS ●
82-96 Grove Lane, Denmark Hill SE5 8SN
- ■ Sat 10am-5pm. Architect led hourly tours, first come basis. Last entry 4.40pm. N D R T A G

A new 1550m² pavilion housing learning and events facilities, café and exhibition spaces. The central focus of this unique project, initially coined 'Project Learning Potential', is to create a totally immersive learning environment generating a series of interconnecting spaces to encourage intuitive learning activities. Duggan Morris Architects/Elliott Wood Partnership/Skelly & Couch 2014.
Rail: Denmark Hill; 40,42,68,176,185,468,484
www.elliottwood.co.uk

Passmore Edwards Library and Bath House
Wells Way SE5 0PX
- ■ Sat/Sun 1pm-5pm. First come basis.

The old library is adjacent to the bathhouse which is used by well known boxing club Lynn AC. Main entrance porch is flanked by 2 Ionic columns, decorative carvings and relief work. On the side of the building the Camberwell Beauty butterfly is rendered in ceramic tiles. Maurice Adams 1902.
Tube/Rail: Elephant and Castle; 42,343,136

Peckham Coal Line

Copeland Park, 133 Rye Lane SE15 4ST

■ Sat 1pm-5pm/Sun 10am-1pm. Tours on the hour. Also self-guided tours. Sat/Sun talk 12noon. Max 25 per tour. C

Grass roots initiative to create an urban park using disused railway sidings between Queens Road Peckham and Rye Lane. Connecting history, nature and communities in Peckham. Children's Activities: scavenger hunt along walk.

Rail: Peckham Rye; 78,12,63,343,P12

Peckham Library

122 Peckham Hill Street SE15 5JR

■ Sat 10am-5pm/Sun 12noon-4pm. Tours Sat 11am, 2pm/Sun 2pm to non-public areas. Max 25 per tour. N D T

A dramatic design resembling an upside-down 'L' of coloured glass and green copper. A pure C21 building. RIBA Award Winner 2000. Alsop and Stormer 2000.

Tube: Elephant and Castle (then bus 12,63,171,343); Rail: Peckham Rye

Perronet House

48 & 79 Perronet House, Princess Street (buzz flat 79) SE1 6JS

■ Sat 1pm-5pm. First come basis. Last entry 4.45pm. R T Q

Purpose-built council block with scissor construction flats with spectacular views of Elephant & Castle. Commended in 1971 Good Design in Housing Awards. Detailed historical notes and images shown. One flat significantly remodelled in 2012. Sir Roger Walters 1970. Entry: 2 homes.

Tube/Rail: Elephant & Castle; 12,176,63,344,188

Raw House

28 Anstey Road SE15 4JY

■ Sat 10am-5pm. Architect-led tours every 30mins. Last entry 4.30pm. A Q

Contemporary refurbishment and extension to an existing Victorian terrace to create a light filled home of industrial elegance. Don't Move, Improve Awards, Third Place 2014. Mustard Architects 2014.

Rail: Peckham Rye; 12,78,37,63,363
www.mustardarchitects.com

Regeneration at Heart of Community – Camberwell Residential

149 Southampton Way, Camberwell SE5 7EW

■ Sat 11am-5pm. Half-hourly tours, first come basis. Queuing in café at ground floor if necessary. Max 4 per tour. R T A G E d

Reconstruction of a building derelict for more than 40 years and transformation into a modern residential property over a community restaurant/bar, including a striking two-storey glass roof extension. Twist In Architecture 2012. Entry: All areas.

Tube: Oval, Kennington; Tube/Rail: Elephant & Castle; Rail: Denmark Hill; 343,136

Royal Road

Enter using courtyard gate on Otto Street SE17 3NR

■ Sat 1pm-5pm. First come basis. Tours taking place. Small exhibition with scale model. Last entry 4.30pm. Max 10 per tour. D A G

A new development with heights varying from four to nine storeys, provides 100% affordable housing. All homes are spacious with two or three aspects focused around a central communal garden. Retaining most of the healthy mature trees, the development blends into the streetscape. Panter Hudspith Architects 2013. Entry: communal areas.

Tube: Kennington, Oval; Tube/Rail; Vauxhall, Elephant & Castle; 133,155,333,415,P5

Sands Films Studios & Rotherhithe Picture Research Library

82 St Marychurch Street SE16 4HZ

■ Sat/Sun 10am-5pm. Hourly tours. Last entry 5pm. R T B P d

Grade II listed riparian granary built with reclaimed timbers felled in 1700s. Converted in 1970s to picture library, film studios, prop and costume workshops. Oscar-winning international costume house for film, TV, theatre, opera, ballet. 1770s-1940s. Entry: picture research library, film studio, cinema, costume and prop workshops, canteen.

Tube: Bermondsey; Tube/Rail: Canada Water; Rail: Rotherhithe; 47,188,381,C10,P12

Siobhan Davies Studios

85 St George's Road SE1 6ER

■ Sat 2pm-6pm. Last entry 5.30pm. Max 150 at one time. N D T G

A landmark home for dance, the daring design with 2-storey atrium and undulating ribbon roof that breathes life into an old school building. RIBA Award Winner 2006. Many sustainable features. Sarah Wigglesworth Architects 2006.

Tube: Lambeth North; Tube/Rail: Elephant & Castle, Waterloo; 12,53,148,344,360,453

Southwark Integrated Waste Management Facility

43 Devon Street, off Old Kent Road SE15 1JR

■ Sat 10am-4pm. Half hourly tours, first come basis. No heels or open toe shoes can be worn on the tours. Standard tours for ages 7 and older; limited special tours for children under 7. Last tour 3.30pm. Max 20 per tour. E R T C G d

One of Europe's most advanced recycling facilities, comprising many sustainable features including grey water, solar panels and green roof. Designed for the purpose of turning waste into a resource. Thorpe Wheatley 2012.

Tube/Rail: Elephant & Castle; Rail: Queen's Road Peckham; 453,53,21,172
www.veolia.co.uk/southwark/wonderday2015

Springbank

81A Grove Park SE5 8LE

■ Sun 1pm-5pm. First come basis, queuing outside if necessary. Last entry 4.30pm. T A G Q d

One of a pair of modern houses on a sensitive site in a conservation area. A staircase atrium runs the full height, and ground floor areas open onto courtyard gardens on three sides. SE5 Architects 2013. Entry: all areas.

Rail: Denmark Hill, Peckham Rye; 176,185,40,63,12

The Exchange – Bermondsey Spa Gardens

17 Spa Road, Bermondsey SE16 3SA

■ Sat/Sun tour at 11am, first come basis. A d

The Exchange is a new mixed-tenure housing development, designed as an urban village for modern living for Notting Hill Housing. PCKO Architects 2014.

Tube: Bermondsey; 1,78,188,42,47

The Old Mortuary

St Marychurch Street SE16 4JE

■ Sat/Sun 10am-5pm. Regular tours and special display of features of local history. Last entry 4pm. Max 10 per tour, max 25 at one time. D R T

Erected in 1895 and situated in Rotherhithe Conservation Area. Retains many original features including a vaulted ceiling in Russell Hall, original doors, lantern skylight and iron girder in Varney Room (formerly post-mortem room), wooden panelling in chapel. Now community centre with local history group (Time and Talents Association). Norman Scorgie 1895. Entry: former mortuary, post-mortem room, chapel.

Tube: Bermondsey; Tube/Rail: London Bridge, Canada Water; Rail: Rotherhithe; 47,188,381,C10,P12

Tower Bridge Magistrates Court

211 Tooley Street SE1 2JY

■ Sat 10am-3pm. Guided tours, first come basis.

Original Grade II listed Tower Bridge Magistrates Court in Tooley Street conservation area. John Dixon Butler 1902-1909. Entry: lobby, court, cells.

Tube/Rail: London Bridge; 47,188,381,42,78

Tuke School

Daniel Gardens SE15 6ER

■ Sat 10am-4pm. Hourly tours, first come basis. Last entry 3.30pm. Max 20 per tour. D T A

Tuke is a new-build Special Educational Needs school. The key concept is 'The Sensory School' – a building that offers a sensory experience throughout rather than only in dedicated locations. Haverstock 2010.

Rail: Peckham Rye; 63,363

Unicorn Theatre

147 Tooley Street SE1 2HZ

■ Sat 10am-4pm. Hourly tours, first come basis. First tour 10am, no tour 1pm. Performances running throughout day. Last tour 4pm. Max 18 per tour. N R T B A d

The first professional, purpose-built theatre for young audiences in UK. Described as an asymmetric pavilion, the building has transparent elevations revealing its core, and was designed in consultation with young people. RIBA Award Winner 2006. Keith Williams Architects 2005. Entry: theatre, foyer, some backstage areas.

Tube/Rail: London Bridge; 47,RV1,381,17,21,35

William Booth College

Champion Park SE5 8BQ

■ Sat 9am-5pm. Half-hourly tours. Entry to tower 9-4pm. Talk on building in assembly hall 10am, 11am 2pm, 3pm. R T d

Monumental Grade II listed college with massive brick tower and commanding views to the City and Docklands. Giles Gilbert Scott 1929. Entry: tower, grounds, assembly hall, International Heritage Centre (Salvation Army Museum), third floor.

Rail: Denmark Hill; 40,42,68,176,185,468,484

WALKS/TOURS

Bankside Urban Forest

■ Meet: Sat 12noon and 3pm at Bankside Community Space, 18 Great Guildford Street SE1 0FD. G

Guided walk of Bankside Urban Forest, a public space partnership and strategy with an ecological approach. Learn about recent and emerging public space and urban greening projects within one of London's oldest neighbourhoods. Witherford Watson Mann, Adams & Sutherland, Gort Scott, VOGT Landscape, Wayward Plants and more 2008-present.

Tube: Southwark, Borough; Tube/Rail: London Bridge, Blackfriars; RV1,381,344

City Hunt Bermondsey

Stall located on Bermondsey Street, part of Bermondsey Street Festival. SE1

■ Sat 10am-5pm. C d

Local treasure hunt which takes you back through Bermondsey's vibrant and historical past. Children's map, prizes to be won.

Tube: Bermondsey; Tube/Rail: London Bridge; 42,78,188,C10

Supported by

Southwark Council

Key. A Architect on site **B** Bookshop **C** Childrens' activities **d** Some disabled access **D** Full wheelchair access **E** Engineer on site **G** Green Features **N** Normally open to the public **P** Parking **Q** Long queues envisaged **R** Refreshments **T** Toilets

Sutton

See **openhouselondon.org.uk/sutton**
to find out more about this area

All Saints Carshalton
High Street, Carshalton SM5 3AQ
■ Sat/Sun 10am-4pm. Regular tours. Max 50 at one time. N D
R T P
C12 south aisle and former chancel. Blomfield nave, chancel,
baptistry. Kempe glass, Bodley reredos and screen, spectacular
Comper decorations, monuments and brasses, award-winning
lighting scheme, fine modern benches. A & R Blomfield C11-19.
Rail: Carshalton

BedZED ●●
24 Helios Road, Wallington SM6 7BZ
■ Sat 10am-1pm. Guided tours on the hour, first come basis.
Max 15 per tour. D T A G
Come explore the UK's first large-scale mixed use eco-village
and sustainable community. Completed in 2002, BedZED
is still an inspiration for low carbon neighbourhoods that
promotes One Planet Living across the world, developed in
partnership with Peabody Trust and Bioregional. Bill Dunster
Zedfactory Architects/Adams & Sutherland 2002.
Rail: Hackbridge; Rail/Tram: Mitcham Junction; 127,151

Carshalton Water Tower and Historic Gardens
West Street, Carshalton SM5 2QG
■ Sat/Sun 1pm-5pm. First come basis. If disabled access
required, call 020 8647 0984 in advance. Last entry 4.30pm.
R T B C d
Early C18 Grade II listed building incorporating plunge bath
with Delft tiles, orangery, saloon and pump chamber with
part-restored water wheel. Hermitage and sham bridge in
grounds. Entry: orangery, saloon, bathroom, pump chamber,
roof. Quiz sheets for children.
Tube: Morden; Rail: Carshalton; 157,127,407,X26,154

Honeywood
Honeywood Walk, Carshalton SM5 3NX
■ Sat/Sun 10am-5pm. Last entry 4.45pm. N R T B C d
Chalk and flint house dating to C17 with many later additions
including major extensions of 1896 and 1903 when owned by
John Pattinson Kirk, a London merchant. Rich in period detail
and the interior recently restored and back stairs opened up
with funding from the Heritage Lottery Fund. Now a local
museum.
Rail: Carshalton; 127,157,407,X26

Little Holland House
40 Beeches Avenue, Carshalton SM5 3LW
■ Sat 1pm-5pm. First come basis. Max 25 at one time. N T B d
Grade II listed building whose interior was created entirely by
Dickinson, inspired by the ideals of John Ruskin and William
Morris and contains Dickinson's paintings, hand-made
furniture, furnishings, metalwork and friezes, in Arts & Crafts
style. Frank Dickinson 1902-4. Entry: ground floor, master
bedroom, back bedroom, bathroom, garden.
Tube: Morden, then 154 bus; Rail: Carshalton Beeches

Lumley Chapel
St Dunstan's Churchyard, Church Road, Cheam SM3 8QH
■ Sat/Sun 2pm-4.30pm.
Medieval former chancel of parish church after remainder

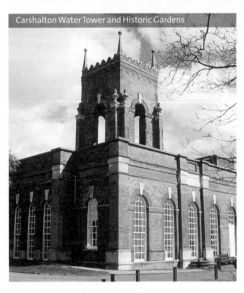
Carshalton Water Tower and Historic Gardens

was demolished in 1864. Part C11, with many important post-
Reformation monuments including to the family of John, Lord
Lumley of Nonsuch Palace. St Dunstan's Parish Church (1864)
open on Saturday. Local historian present on Sunday.
Rail: Cheam; 151,213,293,X26

Nonsuch Gallery and Service Wing at Nonsuch Mansion
Nonsuch Park, Ewell Road, Cheam SM3 8AP
■ Sun 2pm-5pm. Regular tours. Last entry 4.30pm. D R T B P
Georgian mansion, designed in Tudor Gothic style, later
used at Windsor Castle. Built for wealthy merchant Samuel
Farmer. Restored Service Wing includes dairy, kitchen, scullery,
larders and laundries, loose-box. Gallery has timeline and first
ever model of Henry VIII's Nonsuch Palace, scale drawings,
archaeological dig artifacts, and restoration of Georgian
mansion stained glass. Jeffrey Wyatt 1806. Entry: service wing
museum, gallery (not inside mansion itself).
Rail: Cheam; 213,151,293,X26

Russettings
25 Worcester Road, Sutton SM2 6PR
■ Sun 10am-1pm. First come basis. Last entry 12.45pm. Max 25
at one time. N D T P
A double-fronted red brick upper-middle class house,
Russettings is one of a few Victorian villas to survive in Sutton.
The well-preserved interior includes an entrance hall with
a mosaic tiled floor and an oak galleried staircase. Frederick
Wheeler 1899.
Rail: Sutton; 470,S4

The Circle Library ●●
Green Wrythe Lane, Carshalton SM5 1JJ
■ Sat 10am-5pm. N D T P G
An inviting, accessible contemporary social space. Full of
air and natural light with spacious free-flowing areas, the
building incorporates a range of environmental features
designed to keep carbon footprint to a minimum including
ground-source heating, sedum roof and rainwater harvesting.
Curl la Tourelle Architects 2010. Entry: library, courtyard garden,
multi-purpose room, heritage meeting space. 'The Making of
an Estate' St Helier 1935-50 exhibition.
Tube: Morden; Rail: Carshalton; S1,151

The Sutton Life Centre

The Sutton Life Centre ●
24 Alcorn Close SM3 9PX
■ Sat 10am-5pm. Tours at 11am, 3pm, first come basis. Max 25
per tour. D R T C G P
Multi-purpose community building awarded BREEAM
Excellent for its use of sustainable energy. Key features include
a unique learning facility for children aged 10-13, library,
eco-garden, sports pitch and climbing wall. Curl La Tourelle
Architects/Elliott Wood Partnership 2010. Entry: library, eco-
garden, life skills zone, media lab. Arts and crafts for kids.
Tube: Morden; Rail: Sutton Common; S3,80,470
www.elliottwood.co.uk

Whitehall
1 Malden Road, Cheam SM3 8QD
■ Sat/Sun 10am-5pm. N R T B C d
Originally a farmer's house dating to 1500, with jettied upper
storey. Later additions through the centuries reflect the
changing lifestyles of the owners, including the Killicks for
over two centuries. Now houses scale model of Henry VIII's
Nonsuch Palace. Restored by John West & Partners 1974-76.
House model-making for children.
Rail: Cheam; X26,151,213

Supported by

Sutton

**Navigate your way
around Open House
in your area with the
app. See p14**

●AJ Library Building   ●Green Exemplar   ●Landscape/Public realm   ●Infrastructure/Engineering   ■Open Saturday   ■Open Sunday   ■Open Saturday and Sunday

Tower Hamlets

See **openhouselondon.org.uk/towerhamlets** to find out more about this area

Concrete House

20 Winkley Street
20 Winkley Street E2 6PY
- Sat 10am-1pm. Regular tours, first come basis. Max 6 per tour. A G Q

A contemporary open plan house is hidden behind a traditional brick façade. Three small storeys are connected by vast glazing, open voids, folded metal stairs and the vertical garden. The internal interplay of space, light and materials creates a voluminous residence in a dense mews setting. Kirkwood McCarthy 2014. Entry: house, garden.
Tube: Bethnal Green; Rail: Hoxton; 48,55,388,254,8

Boundary
2-4 Boundary Street E2 7DD
- Sat/Sun 10am-5pm. N D T

The original building, a late Victorian warehouse, was carefully converted over a period of 3 years. Special attention was given to preserving attractive industrial features, from the double-height basement to the original brickwork and sash windows. Prescott & Conran Ltd 2009.
Tube: Old Street; Tube/Rail: Liverpool Street; Rail: Shoreditch High Street

Bow Arts
183 Bow Road E3 2SJ
- Sat 11am-4pm. Max 15 per tour. D R T A

In collaboration with Delvendahl Martin Architects, Bhajan Hunjan presents her latest work, an installation comprising re-used materials entitled 'Transient Matters'. The piece will be the first in a series of interventions in the courtyard at Bow Arts, a flexible event space that forms part of the development. The project consolidates the charity's activities at the heart of its Bow Road studio complex. Located in a set of historic warehouse buildings grouped around the courtyard, the scheme provides offices, meeting facilities and a flexible event space. Delvendahl Martin Architects 2014. Entry: Offices and private courtyard.
Tube: Bow Road; Tube/DLR: Bow Church; Tube/DLR/Rail: Stratford; 8,25,108,276,425,D8

Bow School
Bow School, Gillender Street E3 3QW
- Sat tours at 10.15am, 11.15am, 12.15pm, pre-book ONLY via kate@vhh.co.uk, giving preferred tour time. Max 15 per tour. Visitors should arrive 15 minutes before tour start. D R T A G

Completing LBTH's Building Schools for the Future programme, the new school provides great facilities for 1600 pupils, in 3 blocks around a landscaped playground facing the Limehouse Cut. van Heyningen and Haward Architects 2014. Entry: whole site including 3 buildings, interior, roof and external landscaped areas.
Tube: Bow Road; Tube/DLR: Bow Church; Tube/DLR/Rail: Stratford; 108,488,323,309

Chrisp Street Market
The Clocktower, Chrisp Street Market E14 6AQ
- Sat/Sun 10am-5pm. Regular tours to Clocktower, in association with the National Trust. Sat 12noon tour of Festival area and related points of interest.

A beautiful Modernist 'practical folly' designed as part of the

site for the 1951 Festival of Britain live architecture exhibition. Sir Frederick Gibberd 1951.
DLR: All Saints; D8,15,115,D6,108,309

Concrete House ⦿
40 Roman Road E3 5QJ
- Sat 10am-5pm. Closed 1pm to 2pm. Hourly tours. Max 4 per tour. A Q

The remodelling of a Victorian terraced house to include a new rear extension and garden design. Concrete, steel and Iroko timber used as a palette of materials internally that bleed externally into the garden. Studio Gil 2014.
Tube: Mile End; Tube/Rail: Bethnal Green; 8,277,D6,309
http://www.studio-gil.com/

Crossrail - Mile End Shaft ⦿
Burdett Road E3 4HL
- Sat/Sun 10am-1pm. Hourly tours. Pre-book ONLY via www.crossrail.co.uk/openhouse. Max 10 per tour. E

Crossrail's Mile End Shaft is 30m deep. Once complete, the shaft will house emergency stairs, lifts and ventilation from the tunnels to street level for the new Crossrail route from Reading and Heathrow in the West to Shenfield and Abbey Wood in the East. Due 2017.
Tube: Mile End, Bow Road; DLR: Bow Church; 277,D6,D7
www.crossrail.co.uk/openhouse

Darbishire Place (Peabody Whitechapel Estate)
John Fisher Street E1 8HA
- Sat 10am-1pm. N E G d

A new block of 13 homes which completes an ensemble of six housing blocks surrounding an internal courtyard. The façade complements the characteristics of the existing Victorian buildings designed by Henry Astley Darbishire. RIBA Award Winner 2015. Niall McLaughlin Architects 2014.
Tube: Tower Hill; 100,78,42,RV1

Four Corners ⦿
121 Roman Road E2 0QN
- Sat 10am-5pm. Half-hourly tours and presentations on the history of the project. R T G

Refurbished building now a centre for film and photography. Extension and a clear circulation route form spine of building,

central courtyard or integrated 'hub' allows light and air to filter through. New loft conversion to create studio and work space. Sustainable features include natural light and ventilation, sedum roof to reduce rainwater run-off and provide heat saving and summer cooling. JaK Studio (refurb) 2007/2011. Entry: gallery, darkrooms, offices, garden, green roof.
Tube/Rail: Bethnal Green; 106,8,277

Hermitage Community Moorings
16 Wapping High Street E1W 1NG
- Sat/Sun 10am-4pm. First come basis. Information regarding history of the vessels. Special visiting boats open to the public. Last entry 3pm. R T A P d

An exciting development of residential and recreational moorings for historic vessels on the Thames. The architectural scheme has been designed as a model for river dwelling that takes into account its tidal location. The unique Pier House, built to a high specification, provides a floating community centre just downstream from Tower Bridge. Anna Versteeg & Ollie Price 2010. Entry: The Pier House, possible access to some historic vessels.
Tube: Tower Hill; 100,RV1

Hult International Business School ⦿
35 Commercial Road E1 1LD
- Sat/Sun 10am-5pm. T G d

Transformation of a listed brewery and recent extension into a new undergraduate campus for the Hult International Business School. Sergison Bates Architects 2014.
Tube: Aldgate East, Aldgate; 15,115,135,25,205

Kingsley Hall
Powis Road, off Bruce Road E3 3HJ
- Sat 11am-6pm. Hourly tours from 12noon. Last tour 5pm. Max 18 per tour. R T P d

Grade II listed, pioneer East End community centre founded by peace campaigners Muriel and Doris Lester. Includes main hall and 5 rooftop cells for community volunteers. Links with Gandhi, George Lansbury, R D Laing's Philadelphia Association 1965-1970. Set for Attenborough's Gandhi 1983. Charles Cowles Voysey 1928. Entry: Gandhi's cell, Peace Garden, history and archives exhibition.
Tube: Bromley-by-Bow; DLR: Bow Church; 8,25,108,488

Lawdale Primary School Community House
Mansford Street E2 6LS

■ Sat 10am-1pm. First come basis. Last entry 12.50pm. N D A

Extension to Lawdale Primary School Community House, which takes direct reference from local context through materials, details, patterned design and considered use of daylight. LB Tower Hamlets 2015.
Tube/Rail: Bethnal Green; 8,388,D3

Limehouse Town Hall
646 Commercial Road E14 7HA

■ Sat/Sun 1pm-5pm. Information on history of building and plans for future developments, and audio tour. Last entry 4.45pm. R T

Palazzo-style former town hall with stone dressings, vast arched moulded windows and grand Portland stone staircase. A & C Harston 1881. Entry: lobby, main staircase, main hall (former council chamber), side stairs, workshop spaces.
Tube/DLR: Canary Wharf; DLR/Rail: Limehouse; 15,115,D6,D7,277,D3

London Buddhist Centre
51 Roman Road E2 0HU

■ Sun 10am-5pm. First come basis. Tours at 11am, 4pm to section of normally inaccessible 1st floor. Last entry 4.45pm. Max 20 per tour. N R T B P d

Ornate vernacular red brick Victorian former fire station. Grade II listed. Now a Buddhist Centre with 3 beautiful shrine rooms with Buddha figures and paintings. Robert Pearsall 1888.
Tube/Rail: Bethnal Green; Rail: Cambridge Heath; D6,8,309,106,388

London Dock - Pennington Street Warehouses
Pennington Street Warehouse, Pennington Street E1W 2AD

■ Sat 10am-1pm/Sun 1pm-5pm. Last entry 15mins before close. D N

Grade II listed early C19 brick vaults designed for storage of imported goods brought into the London Docks. Daniel Asher Alexander 1805. Entry: section of historic warehouse vault.
Tube: Tower Hill, Aldgate East; 100,D3

Mint Street ⊙
Meeting point: corner of Coventry Road and Witan Street E2 6JL

■ Sat 10am-1pm. Tours every 45 mins. Places available on the day on first come basis but places can also be pre-booked on admin@pitmantozer.com. Last tour 12.15pm. A G

A new housing development of 67 flats for Peabody, close to the railway creating a new pedestrian public street. An example of how to combine affordable, shared ownership and market sale homes on a noisy urban site creating a pleasant environment. RIBA Award Winner 2015. Pitman Tozer Architects 2014.
Tube/Rail: Bethnal Green; 8,254,106,205,388

One Bishops Square ⊙
One Bishops Square E1 6AD

■ Sun 10am-5pm. Last entry 4.30pm. Max 150 at one time. D R T G

An efficient, flexible, user-friendly and supportive working environment. 'Intelligent' building with many sustainable features, including London's largest office-based solar installation and inbuilt computer system aimed at efficiency and energy conservation. Lights and air conditioning operate only when area is populated. Triple glazing and blinds reduce solar gain on all south-facing windows. Foster + Partners 2006. Entry: 6th floor coffee bar, office area, terrace, lobby.
Tube/Rail: Liverpool Street; 8,11,26,35,42

Hult International Business School

One Canada Square, Canary Wharf Group Marketing Suite and Level 39
Meet: South Lobby, One Canada Square E14 5AB

■ Sat 10am-5pm. Tours/talks on the hour around architectural models of marketing suite and Level 39, Europe's largest technology accelerator space. Pre-book ONLY via openhouse@canarywharf.com with names and preferred time. Last entry 4pm. Max 20 per tour. D R T

In the last 25 years, Canary Wharf Group plc has achieved a feat of civic transformation – an iconic urban regeneration – designing and constructing 37 office buildings and 5 retail malls across a 97 acre business and shopping district, with a workforce of 105,000 people. Level 39 is a sophisticated accelerator, social and event space, designed in 'tech industry' style by Gensler. Cesar Pelli 1991.
Tube/DLR: Canary Wharf; DLR: Heron Quays; D3,D7,D8,135,277

Oxford House in Bethnal Green
Derbyshire Street E2 6HG

■ Sat 10am-5pm. Regular tours. Max 15 per tour. D R T

First 'University Settlement', now an arts and community space. New Pocket Park opened 2014. Sir Arthur Blomfield 1891/ All Clear Designs (extension) 2003. Entry: all areas, Victorian chapel will be open.
Tube/Rail: Bethnal Green; 8,254,106,388

Providence Row Arts and Activity Building at the Dellow Day Centre
82 Wentworth Street E1 7SA

■ Sat 1pm-5pm. Hourly tours. Last entry 4pm. Max 8 per tour. T d

The new building sits opposite the original centre providing improved facilities for the homeless charity Providence Row. The charity offers an integrated service of crisis support, advice, recovery and learning programmes from this site, helping homeless and vulnerably housed people. The new building strengthens connections with the courtyard and the main centre, providing light and views in and out through a faceted façade. RIBA Award winnner 2012. Featherstone Young Architects 2011.
Tube: Aldgate East; Tube/Rail: Liverpool Street; 149,67,25,253,205

Roominaroom ⊙
1 Narrow Street E14 8DP (raised ground floor flat at far western end of Narrow Street). Doorbell in alleyway facing Limehouse Link tunnel entrance.

■ Sat architect-led tours at 10am, 10.45am, 11.30am and 12.30pm. First come basis, queuing outside if necessary. Max 8 per tour. T A Q

A digitally fabricated gem – a highly sculptural and bespoke installation to create an extra bedroom within its host house, that magically swells from the walls to create a beautiful nook. atmos 2012.
DLR/Rail: Limehouse; 135,277,D3,D7

Society for the Protection of Ancient Buildings (SPAB)
37 Spital Square E1 6DY

■ Sat 10am-5pm. First come basis, activities available throughout the day. Last entry 4.30pm. T B C

Take this rare opportunity to visit the only Georgian building left on Spital Square, see some of the archives on display and chat with the gardener. Technical team on hand to answer queries, archive and craft displays. 1740s. Entry: ground floor, first floor rooms, courtyard garden.
Tube: Moorgate; Tube/Rail: Liverpool Street; 8,26,35,47,48,78,149,242,344

St Matthias Old Church – Community Centre
113 Poplar High Street E14 0AE

■ Sun 10am-5pm. Regular tours, first come basis. N D R T P

Oldest building in Docklands built in the Gothic and Classical styles, with original C17 stonework and fine mosaics. One of only three churches built during the Civil War, it was originally the East India Company Chapel. John Tanner 1649.
DLR: Poplar, All Saints; 15,115,D6,D7,D8

St Paul's Bow Common
Cnr Burdett Rd/ St Paul's Way E3 4AR

■ Sat 10am-5pm/Sun 12noon-5pm. N D T P

Described as 'the most significant church built after the 2nd World War in Britain' – Brutalist, inclusive and influential signpost for future church design. Robert McGuire & Keith Murray 1960s.
Tube: Mile End; DLR: Westferry; DLR/Rail: Limehouse; 277,D6,D7,205,15

St Paul's Old Ford

St Paul's Church, St Stephen's Road E3 5JL
■ Sat 10am-4pm. Regular tours, first come basis. Pictorial treasure hunt for children. Last entry 3.45pm. N D R T C
Victorian church, rehabilitated to include 'a building within a building' – a stunning Ark or Pod of tulipwood situated in the nave. "Stylish...thrilling..." Jay Merrick in The Independent. Winner of RICS Community Benefit Award, London Region 2005. Matthew Lloyd Architects LLP 2004.
Tube: Bow Road; Tube/Rail: Bethnal Green; DLR: Bow Church; 8,276,488

Swanlea School – Sixth Form Expansion

31 Brady Street E1 4SD
■ Sat 10am-4pm. Regular tours, first come basis. Last entry 3.30pm Max 15 per tour. N D A
The project extends and unifies with the existing Sixth Form building through careful use of timber cladding and highly detailed internal material choices. London Borough of Tower Hamlets 2015. Entry: all teaching rooms.
Tube/Rail: Liverpool Street, Whitechapel; 25,205,254

Thames River Police

98 Wapping High Street E1W 2NE
■ Sat/Sun 10am-5pm. Regular tours, first come basis. Last entry 4pm. Max 25 at one time. N E T d
A unique ex-carpenters' workshop contained within a working police station. The workshop space now displays a history of Thames River Police. 1910. Entry: museum.
Rail: Wapping; 100

The Grim House

16 Underwood Road E1 5AW
■ Sat/Sun 10am-1pm. Regular tours. A Q
The Grim House has emerged from its 1980s cocoon, reimagining space and light, transforming precious London real estate into an innovative solution for a growing family. Checa Romero Architects 2015.
Tube: Aldgate East; Tube/Rail: Whitechapel; 25,205

The Tree House

200 Jubilee Street E1 3BP
■ Sat tours at 11am, 12noon, 2pm, 3pm, 4pm. Pre-book ONLY via https://goo.gl/3cmbh2. D A G
The tree house is a timber framed and reclaimed timber clad addition to two 1830s terraced cottages. Its ramped interior reframes the activities of the house around the garden, absorbing the storey level differences. The mother of a busy family remains central to activity whether in her wheelchair or resting. RIBA London Small Project Award 2014. RIBA Stephen Lawrence Prize 2014. RIBA London Award 2014. 6a Architects 2013. Entry: 6a extension.
Tube/Rail: Whitechapel, Bethnal Green; 25

Tower Bridge House

St Katharine's Way (entry at level 1, not Quay level) E1W 1AA
■ Sat 10am-4pm. First come basis, queuing outside if necessary. Last entry 3.45pm. D T
Inspired by the great warehouses of St Katherine's Dock, this office building is characterised by a giant 'window' that overlooks the Tower of London, with a public piazza fronting onto the dock basin. Richard Rogers Partnership 2005. Entry: common areas only.
Tube: Tower Hill; Rail: Tower Gateway, Fenchurch Street

Tower Hamlets Cemetery Park

Tower Hamlets Cemetery Park, Southern Grove E3 4PX
■ Sun 10am-5pm. Guided history walks at 10.30am, 12.30pm, 2.30pm; nature walk at 2pm. N T P d

One Bishops Square

One of the 'magnificent seven' cemeteries, opened 1841. Burials ceased 1966, now 33 acres of mature woodland, glades, meadows and ponds including the Soanes Centre educational facility (Robson Kelly 1993). It is of outstanding importance for plant and animal biodiversity, set amongst a wealth of funereal monuments, some listed. Thomas Wyatt & David Brandon.
Tube: Mile End; DLR: Bow Church; DLR/Rail: Limehouse; 25,277,D6,D7,425,339,323

Toynbee Hall

28 Commercial Street E1 6LS
■ Sat 10am-5pm. Tours on the hour, first come basis. Archive display on history and future development. Max 20 per tour. R T d
Built to provide educational and social meeting spaces for East Londoners – a model for later university settlements. Arts & Crafts Grade II listed building with notable room decorated by CR Ashbee. Elijah Hoole 1884/Alister McDonald 1938.
Tube: Aldgate East; Tube/Rail: Liverpool Street; Rail: Shoreditch High Street; 25,115,253,15,67

Trevelyan House

7 Trevelyan House, Morpeth Street E2 0PY
■ Sun 11am-5pm. Guided tours on first come basis. Max 7 per tour. A
An opportunity to visit a modern re-design of a maisonette located in a classic 1950s Grade II listed Brutalist building designed by Denys Lasdun. Sir Denys Lasdun c1950/Bradley Van der Straeten Architects (refurb) 2015.
Tube: Stepney Green; Tube/Rail: Bethnal Green; Rail: Cambridge Heath; 8,D6

Darbishire Place (Peabody Whitechapel Estate)

Trinity Buoy Wharf/Container City

64 Orchard Place E14 0JY
■ Sat/Sun 10am-5pm. Sat 12noon, history/art and regeneration tour. First come basis, meet at lighthouse. Last entry 4.30pm. N T d
Home to London's only lighthouse, fine stock buildings and examples of the innovative Container City buildings including the Olympic Legacy, Clipper House. This former buoy manufacturing site is now a centre for the creative industries with various sculptures and installations. 1822-75/James Douglass (Lighthouse)1864/Eric Reynolds/Buschow Henley/ABK Architects/Lacey and Partners (Container City) 2001-14. Entry: Trinity Buoy Wharf, Container City, lighthouse, historic buildings, pier, lightship.
DLR: East India; DLR/Tube: Canning Town; 277

Supported by

TOWER HAMLETS

Key. **A** Architect on site **B** Bookshop **C** Childrens' activities **d** Some disabled access **D** Full wheelchair access **E** Engineer on site **G** Green Features **N** Normally open to the public **P** Parking **Q** Long queues envisaged **R** Refreshments **T** Toilets

Waltham Forest

See openhouselondon.org.uk/walthamforest to find out more about this area

Highams Park Signal Box ●
Level Crossing, Hale End Road, Higham E4 9PT
- Sat/Sun 10am-5pm. First come basis. N B P

The Signal Box dates from 1925. It is one of the few boxes remaining in London and has recently been refurbished and converted into an office space (signaling equipment removed) by a local builder, Dendales. There is a small exhibition and views from the signal box windows.
Rail: Highams Park; 212,275,W16

Kelmscott School
245 Markhouse Road E17 8DN
- Sat 10am-4pm/Sun 10am-3pm. First come basis. Last entry half hour before close. R T P

One of the first schools refurbished under the government's Building Schools for the Future programme. Includes new outdoor amphitheatre and 'green' play spaces. BSF Best Design for Remodelled School Award Winner 2008. architecture plb 2008. Entry: amphitheatre, school hall, ground floor main building. Display of construction drawings and photos.
Tube/Rail: Walthamstow Central; Rail: St James Street; 158,58,97,212,69

Leytonstone Library
6 Church Lane Leytonstone E11 1HG
- Sat 9am-6pm/Sun 12noon-4pm. First come basis. Sun 2.15pm-3.30pm architectural tour 'Drinkwater to Jacobi – The People and Places of Leytonstone', pre-book via www. wfculture.eventbrite.com. N E D T

A prominent, purpose-built library with a classical exterior and Art Deco interior. Renovation work reinstated original lighting and exposed the eclectic spirit of the orginal design. James Ambrose 1934.
Tube: Leytonstone; Rail: Leytonstone High Road; W15,257,66,W16,W13

Queen Elizabeth's Hunting Lodge
Rangers Road, Chingford E4 7QH
- Sun 10.30am-5pm. Illustrated talks on Epping Forest history at 11am, 3pm. BSL interpreter available 2-5pm. Last entry 4.45pm. N T B P d

Unique Grade II* listed atmospheric timber-framed hunt-standing, commissioned by Henry VIII, set amongst ancient pollards of Epping Forest. 1589 fireplace and Tudor food displays. 1543. Entry: three floors.
Rail: Chingford; 97,179,212,313,379,444

Sir George Monoux College
190 Chingford Road E17 5AA
- Sat/Sun 10am-5pm. Regular tours. Last entry 12.30pm. Max 20 per tour. D T G P

Original school buildings (1927) have been extended and modified to meet changing needs. Pyramidal dining room by van Heyningen & Haward (1990); Brockman Building including Music suite (2002); £4.5m Drapers Building including modern Learning Resource Centre (2004). Entry: original and new buildings, grounds.
Tube/Rail: Walthamstow Central; 34,97,215,357,505

The Arcade
Fontaine House, 196 Hoe Street E17 4BF
- Sat 10am-1pm.

New development of private sale affordable rental and shared ownership homes surrounding a communal garden, built on top of new cinema and restaurants to help regenerate centre of Walthamstow. PTEa 2015.
Tube/Rail: Walthamstow Central; Rail: Walthamstow Queens Road; 34,69,97,230,W15

The Walthamstow Pumphouse Museum
10 South Access Road E17 8AX
- Sat/Sun 10am-5pm. First come basis. Displays on industrial heritage of Lea Valley. Last entry 3.30pm. N R T B P d

Grade II listed Victorian engine house (1885) remodelled in 1897 to take a pair of Marshall steam engines, still in working order. Entry: pump house, Victorian workshop, café, fire station.
Tube/Rail: Blackhorse Road; Rail: St James Street (Walthamstow); 58,158,230,W19

Walthamstow Assembly Hall
Waltham Forest Town Hall Complex, Forest Road E17 4JF
- Sun 10am-1pm. First come basis. Last entry 12.45pm. T d

Grade II listed subsidiary building of the Town Hall built in a restrained style in Portland stone. Art Deco interior. P D Hepworth 1942. Entry: main hall, foyer, balcony.
Tube/Rail: Walthamstow Central; Rail: Wood Street; 123,34,97,212,357,W11

Walthamstow Library
206 High Street E17 7JN
- Sat 9am-6pm/Sun 10am-4pm. Sat tour 11am-12.15pm 'The Walthamstow Walk', pre-book via www.wfculture. eventbrite.com. A chance to explore the restored Edwardian splendour of Walthamstow library and a look around the local area to see important post-war buildings by FW Southgate and some important survivals of the earliest phases of the town's transformation from elite rural idyll to Victorian suburb. N D T C

The 1903 Reading Room and 1909 Wren-style red brick building with stone dressings, were refurbished in 2006 creating a new 8m high glass foyer with terracotta cladding and new children's library. JW Dunford 1909/FaulknerBrowns 2006.
Tube/Rail: Walthamstow Central; 20,212,215,230,257,34,357,48

Walthamstow School for Girls
58-60 Church Hill E17 9RZ
- Sat 1pm-5pm. Half-hourly tours. Last entry 4.30pm. Max 20 per tour. d

Founded in 1890 and moved to the site of the vicarage glebe in 1913, retaining St Mary's Vicarage (1902). The Grade II listed frontage was built by CJ Dawson in a red brick English Baroque style. The most recent rebuilding won a BCSE Design Award in 2011. Within the grounds there is a Greek Theatre, built in the 1920s. CJ Dawson 1911-13/ArchitecturePLB 2010. Entry: grounds, Greek theatre, ground floor, hall.
Tube/Rail: Walthamstow Central; Rail: Walthamstow Queens Road; 212,20,257,48,275,97

Walthamstow Stadium
Chingford Rd E4 8SL
- Sat 10am-5pm. Guided tours every 20 minutes, first come basis. Max 10 per tour. E R T A G P d

Sensitive restoration and refurbishment of the Stadium's Grade II listed Tote building and former dog kennels, which will be brought into long-term use for the whole community as part of the wider development. 1931/HTA due 2016. Entry: tote room and kennels.
Tube/Rail: Walthamstow Central; 215,97,357,158,W11

The Arcade

Walthamstow Town Hall
Waltham Forest Town Hall Complex, Forest Road E17 4JF
- Sat 10am-12.30pm. Last entry 12noon. Max 15-20 at one time. D T P

Impressive civic centre, built in Portland stone with a classical layout in Swedish influenced popular inter-war style. Art Deco internal design. PD Hepworth 1937-42.
Tube/Rail: Walthamstow Central; Rail: Wood Street Walthamstow; 123,275

William Morris Gallery ●
Lloyd Park, Forest Road E17 4PP
- Sat/Sun 10am-5pm. Sun 11am tour 'The Water House and Edward Lloyd', limited places, first come basis. N D R T B

Handsome 1740s Georgian Grade II* listed former Water House with original features including oak-panelled and marble-flagged entrance hall with fine plasterwork, with new extension by Pringle Richard Sharratt Architects. As well as exploring the history of the buiding, the tour introduces Edward Lloyd, the Victorian newspaper proprietor, publisher and entrepreneur. 1740s. Entry: all public areas.
Tube/Rail: Walthamstow Central (then 34,97,215,275,357 to Bell Corner); Blackhorse Road (123 to Lloyd Park)

WALKS/TOURS

Walthamstow Wetlands ● ●
Meeting point to be provided on booking.
- Sat tours 1pm, 3pm, led by London Wildlife Trust and Stirling Prize winning architects Witherford, Watson, Mann. Tours will explore historical heritage of the site and its importance as a nature reserve, and give access to the construction site prior to opening in 2017. Pre-book ONLY via wetlands@wildlondon.org.uk. T A P d

Walthamstow Wetlands will be the most significant urban nature reserve development in Britain for many years. This largely hidden working landscape, where Victorian engineering once supplied London's water, has evolved into a distinctive wild space and is now designated as a Site of Special Scientific Interest, internationally renowned for wildfowl. Historic buildings and structures include the Grade II listed Coppermill and Old Marine Engine House (1850s).
Tube/Rail: Tottenham Hale, Blackhorse Road; 41,192,123,230

Supported by

Waltham Forest

Wandsworth

See openhouselondon.org.uk/wandsworth
to find out more about this area

BAC (Battersea Arts Centre)
Lavender Hill SW11 5TN
- ■ Sat tours at 11am, 2pm, first come basis. Max 30 per tour. N R T P d

Designed and built as Battersea's Town Hall and home to BAC for the last 30 years. Striking features include a glass bee mosaic floor, marble staircase and stained glass dome. Discover plans to rebuild the Grand Hall after the fire in March earlier this year. E W Mountford 1893.
Tube: Clapham Common; Rail: Clapham Junction; 87,77,156

Brandlehow Primary School
Brandlehow Road SW15 2ED
- ■ Sat 10am-5pm. Regular tours. Last entry 3.30pm. Max 25 at one time. T A G d

Series of extensions to a listed modern school by Ernö Goldfinger formed from prefabricated timber elements clad with cedar boards. Ernö Goldfinger 1952-63/team51.5° architects 2006. Entry: all three buildings.
Tube: East Putney; Rail: Putney; 270,220,337,14,74

Burntwood School
Burntwood Lane SW17 0AQ
- ■ Sat/Sun tours 10am, 11.30am. Pre-book ONLY via openhouse@ahmm.co.uk. Include 'Burntwood' in the subject line. Max 25 per tour. D T A

Striking precast concrete-clad buildings, refurbishment of Leslie Martin-designed pool and assembly hall, and a new landscape plan for the school's original 1950s Modernist educational campus. Allford Hall Monaghan Morris 2013.
Tube: Tooting Bec, Tooting Broadway; Rail: Earlsfield; G1

Emanuel School
Battersea Rise SW11 1HS. New entrance via bridge over the railway on Spencer Park.
- ■ Sat 2pm-5pm. Regular short tours from 2pm to 4pm or longer historical walking tours of the school and grounds at 2.15pm and 3.45pm. Access to school's archives. T P d

Former Royal Patriotic orphanage, converted to school 1883, with 1896 additions. High Victorian style with stained glass by Moira Forsyth. Set in 12 acres. Henry Saxon Snell 1871. Entry: main building, chapel, library, concert hall.
Tube: Clapham South; Rail: Clapham Junction; 77,219,319,337

Foster + Partners Studio ◉
Riverside, 22 Hester Road SW11 4AN
- ■ Sat 10am-5pm. Regular tours. Last entry 4.30pm. D R T A

Single-space, double-height purpose-built architects' studio 60 metres long – part of a larger riverside building that has 30 apartments. Foster + Partners 1990. Entry: entrance and mezzanine (with view over whole studio). Display of projects.
Tube: Sloane Square, South Kensington; Rail: Clapham Junction; 19,49,170,319,345

Gala Bingo Hall (former Granada Cinema)
Mitcham Road SW17 9NA
- ■ Sun 9.30am-11.30am. Regular guided tours. Last entry 11am. R T P

Exceptional example of the 'super cinema style' of the 1930s with outstanding Gothic interior by Theodore Komisarjevsky.

Roehampton University

The first Grade I listed cinema. Cecil Masey 1931. Entry: main auditorium.
Tube: Tooting Broadway; Rail: Tooting, Earlsfield; 44,57,77,127,133 264,270,280,355

Graveney School Sixth Form Block (Bradford Building)
Graveney School, Welham Road SW17 9BU
- ■ Sat/Sun 10am-5pm. Last entry 4.30pm. A C T P d

Specialist Sixth Form Block that sets a template for new school buildings. Innovative, sustainable and economical, the cross-laminated timber and polycarbonate building achieves maximum architectural output using minimal means. Urban Projects Bureau 2015.
Tube: Tooting Broadway; Rail: Tooting; 333,127,57
www.urbanprojectsbureau.com

National Tennis Centre Sports Canopy ◉
100 Priory Lane, Roehampton SW15 5JQ
- ■ Sat 10am-5pm. Regular architect-led tours of canopy and exterior of National Tennis Centre. Last tour 4.30pm. Max 10 per tour. D T A G

The world's first composite demountable air-beam canopy, spanning 42m, to support player training and development on the Centre's clay courts. Timeless nature of the arched form provides an inspirational and 'clutter free' playing environment attuned to players' needs. ICE London Award Winner and British Construction Industry UK Small Project of the Year 2011. George Stowell 2010. **ICE**
Rail: Barnes; 72,33,337,493

Nightingale Lane
131 Nightingale Lane SW12 8NE
- ■ Sun 10am-5pm. Tours every 20 minutes. Last entry 4.30pm. Max 8 per tour. A Q d

Burntwood School

A dramatic refurbishment of a typical 1930s semi. A carefully selected palette of materials is used throughout. The new sculptural staircase twists up through the centre of the house; its design pares back elements of the traditional domestic stair. Daykin Marshall Studio 2013.
Tube: Clapham South; Rail: Wandsworth Common; 319, G1

Pump House Gallery
Battersea Park SW11 4NJ
- ■ Sun 11am-5pm. N R T C d

Beautiful Grade II listed Victorian ex-water tower overlooking Battersea Park lake. Now houses a contemporary art gallery. Visit website for more information on architectural tours and children's activities. James and William Simpson 1861.
Tube: Sloane Square; Rail: Battersea Park, Queenstown Road; 137,19,44,49,239,344,345,452

Roehampton University – Parkstead House, Whitelands College
Holybourne Avenue SW15 4JD
- ■ Sun 11.30am-4.30pm. Tours at 12noon, 2.30pm, first come basis. T P d

Beautifully sited Grade I listed neo-classical Palladian villa built for the 2nd Earl of Bessborough by the royal architect William Chambers, to house the Earl's celebrated collection of classical artefacts. Sir William Chambers 1762.
Tube: East Putney, Hammersmith; Rail: Barnes; 72,85,265,493

Skinner-Trevino House
67 Santos Road SW18 1NT
- ■ Sat 10am-4.30pm. NB. Closed between 1-2pm. First come basis, queuing outside if necessary. Top floor unsuitable for small children or those with vertigo. Last entry 4pm. Max 13 at one time. Q A G d

Key. A Architect on site **B** Bookshop **C** Childrens' activities **d** Some disabled access **D** Full wheelchair access **E** Engineer on site **G** Green Features **N** Normally open to the public **P** Parking **Q** Long queues envisaged **R** Refreshments **T** Toilets

Graveney School Sixth Form Block (Bradford Building)

Skinner-Trevino House

Spiral House

A late Victorian house which has been almost completely gutted; the house is flooded with light by a new glass extension opening onto the semi-open plan ground level and a glass box extension into the roof. This new level constructed of structural glass is accessed by glass stairs and includes a master bedroom suite with balcony and a sun deck. Luis Trevino 2009.
Tube: East Putney; Rail: Putney, Wandsworth Town; 37,170,337
www.luistrevino.co.uk

Spiral House
19b Culverden Road, Balham, SW12 9LT
■ Sun 10am-1pm. Last entry 12.30pm. A G
A single storey house conceived as one wall, which wraps the boundary before spiralling into the centre of the site to form habitable space. Jack Woolley Architects 2015.
Tube/Rail: Balham; 315

St Mary's Church, Battersea
Battersea Church Road SW11 3NA
■ Sat 12noon-5pm/Sun 1pm-5pm. Regular tours. Fair on Saturday in churchyard. D R T
Classic Grade I listed Georgian church with outstanding interior and monuments. New engraved glass doors by Sally Scott. Joseph Dixon 1775-7.
Tube: South Kensington, Sloane Square; Rail: Clapham Junction; 19,49,170,319,345

The Garden House
163a Trinity Road SW17 7HL
■ Sat 10am-10pm/Sun 10am-5pm. Hourly tours. Evening garden lounge and refreshments, weather permitting. Project illustrated through various phases. Max 8 per tour.
1970s bungalow converted into a wide and spacious modern house, with a landscaped garden in a secluded area. Alpex Architecture Ltd 2014.
Tube: Tooting Bec; Rail: Wandsworth Common; 219,319,G1

Thrive, Battersea Park
East Carriage Drive, adjacent to Millennium Arena building, Battersea Park
■ Sat 10am-5pm. Last entry 4.45pm. D R T A G N
A training building and garden for charity teaching gardening and life skills to local residents with a wide range of physical and mental health disabilities. Pedder & Scampton 2014.
Tube: Sloane Square; Rail: Battersea Park, Queenstown Road; 137,44,156,344,452
www.pedderscampton.com

Tooting Bec Lido
Tooting Bec Road SW16 1RU
■ Sat/Sun 6am-5pm. Regular tours with club members 10am-3pm. Illustrated boards showing history of the Lido on display. N D R T P
The pool measures 100 x 33 yards and contains one million gallons of unheated water. Modernised in the 1930s hence the iconic, multi-coloured changing room doors. A new Art Deco style entrance was added in 2001 by WM Architects and the deep end area is being refurbished in 2015 with a new pavilion and sunbathing area (David Gibson Architects). H J Marten 1906/LCC Parks Dept (remodelled) 1936. Entry: all areas normally open to public.
Tube: Tooting Bec; Tube/Rail: Balham; 249,319

WALKS/TOURS

New Covent Garden Flower Market Tour
■ Meet: Sat 7.30am New Covent Garden Market, Nine Elms Lane SW8 5NA. Pre-book ONLY via info@cgma.co.uk or 020 7501 3495. Further details provided upon booking. Max 25 per tour. R T
Tour of London's wholesale flower market during market hours, covering its history and future plans for the site. 1974. Entry: market hall, mezzanine and market floor.
Tube/Rail: Vauxhall; 156,344,77,87

Nine Elms Walk ●
■ Meet: Sat/Sun 1pm at Tea House Theatre, 139 Vauxhall Walk, Vauxhall Pleasure Gardens SE11 5HL for refreshments and introductory talk. Tour will begin at 2pm. Pre-book ONLY via www.vauxhallone.co.uk/news. Duration approx 2 hours. Max 50 on walk. A
Nine Elms on South Bank is the largest regeneration zone in central London. Walk includes talk on history of Vauxhall and provides an insider look at progress on new landmark developments at Embassy Gardens, a Ballymore development designed through an exemplary collaboration between world class architectural practices: Terry Farrell and Partners, Feilden Clegg Bradley Studios and Allford Hall Monaghan Morris. Riverlight, a St James development, has been designed by world-renowned architects Rogers Stirk Harbour + Partners.
Tube/Rail: Vauxhall; 185,2,36,436

Supported by

Westminster

See **openhouselondon.org.uk/westminster** to find out more about this area

10 Downing Street
10 Downing Street SW1A 2AA
- ■ Sat tours at 11am & 2pm, by ballot ONLY, see p17 for more details. Background checks will be carried out on winning entries. Bring valid photo ID for entry. Max 20 per tour. D T

10 Downing Street has been the residence of British Prime Ministers since 1735. Behind its black door have been the most important decisions affecting Britain for the last 275 years. It functions as the official residence of the Prime Minister, their office and also where the PM entertains guests including Her Majesty the Queen. Every single room, every staircase and corridor has witnessed events that have shaped our nation. Sir Christopher Wren 1684/William Kent 1735. Entry: State rooms.
Tube: Westminster; Tube/Rail: Charing Cross, Waterloo; 12,24,53,88,253

10 New Burlington Street
10 New Burlington Street W1S 3BF
- ■ Sat 10am-4pm. Architect-led tours and talks at 10am, 12noon, 2pm. D T A

New office and retail accommodation that sensitively balances preservation of the characters of Regent Street and New Burlington Street with the insertion of contemporary buildings, forming a distinctive new contribution to the neighbourhood's built heritage. Regent Street and RIBA windows collaboration taking place on the street. Allford Hall Monaghan Morris 2014.
Tube: Oxford Circus, Piccadilly Circus; 3,6,12,13,88,94,159,453

22 Whitehall – DFID (formerly 26 Whitehall)
Whitehall SW1A 2EG
- ■ Sat/Sun 10am-4pm. First come basis. Q

Grade I listed former Old Admiralty Building, behind Robert Adam's Admiralty Screen on Whitehall. Now owned by Department for International Development. S P Cockerell 1788. Entry: Old Admiralty Boardroom.
Tube: Embankment, Westminster; Tube/Rail: Charing Cross; 11,12,24,88,159,453,53,87

37a Leamington Road Villas
37a Leamington Road Villas W11 1HT
- ■ Sat/Sun 10am-5pm. Q A

The use of exposed brickwork, concrete floors, skylights, exposed shuttered underpinning from which floating oak steps project, all give rise to this unique and stunning 3 bed home converted from a 1 bedroom Victorian flat. 3x3m glass doors give a seamless transition into the rear multi-levelled landscaped garden oasis with a cedar batten clad outbuilding. Studio 1 Architects 2013.
Tube: Westbourne Park; 27,31,7,328,70

55 Baker Street ●
55 Baker Street W1U 8EW
- ■ Sat/Sun 10am-5pm. Regular tours, first come basis, queuing outside if necessary. Max 20 at one time. D T A

This radical renovation of a 1950s office building transforms the site into an important new urban amenity. The scheme enhances activity and interest at street level by offering an enriched mix of uses and introducing a substantial new public space to the streetscape. Three glass infills or 'masks' span the voids between existing blocks to create a new façade for the building, with the central glazed section enclosing a 7-storey atrium which is open to the public. make 2007. Entry: ground floor and atria only.
Tube: Baker Street; Tube/Rail: Marylebone; 2,74,13,139,82,189,113,274,30

55 Broadway (London Underground Head Office)
55 Broadway SW1H 0BD
- ■ Sat/Sun tours 10.30am, 11.30am, 12.30pm, 2.30pm, 3.30pm, 4.30pm, pre-book ONLY via http://www.cvent.com/d/ rrqwvf Max 20 at one time, minimum age 10 years. T d

Headquarters of London Underground described on its 1929 opening as 'the cathedral of modernity'. Its exterior features sculptures by eminent artists of the day, including Henry Moore, Jacob Epstein and Eric Gill. Charles Holden 1927-9. Entry: ground floor, office, roof terrace.
Tube: St James's Park; 11,24,148

68 Dean Street
68 Dean Street W1D 4QJ
- ■ Sat 10am-5pm. Tours on the hour (not 1pm), first come basis. Last tour 4pm. Max 15 per tour. T Q d

Fine example of early C18 London domestic architecture by local carpenter/builder, with separate cesspits for the Meards and servants, largely panelled and with hidden rooms. John Meard Jnr 1732.
Tube: Piccadilly Circus, Leicester Square, Tottenham Court Road; Tube/Rail: Charing Cross

Admiralty House
Ripley Courtyard, Whitehall SW1A 2DY
- ■ Sat/Sun 10am-5pm. Queuing outside if necessary. Last entry 4pm. D Q

Grade I listed former Admiralty Building, behind Robert Adam's Admiralty Screen on Whitehall. Now owned by Cabinet Office; works of art and antiques from Ministry of Defence Art Collection. Samuel Pepys Cockerell 1785. Entry: state rooms in Admiralty House.
Tube: Embankment, Westminster; Tube/Rail: Charing Cross; 11,12,24,53,87,88,159,453

Argentine Ambassador's Residence
49 Belgrave Square SW1X 8QZ
- ■ Sat/Sun 12noon-5pm. First come basis, queuing outside if necessary. Max 80-100 at one time. D Q

Known as the 'Independent North Mansion' and christened by Sydney Herbert as 'Belgrave Villa' and then simply 'The Villa' by his successor the 6th Duke of Richmond. Owned by Argentina since 1936 and with sumptuous interiors still intact. Thomas Cubitt 1851. Entry: all main rooms and art exhibition.
Tube: Hyde Park Corner; Tube/Rail: Victoria; 19,22,14,38,10

Asia House
63 New Cavendish Street W1G 7LP
- ■ Sun 10am-5pm. Regular tours. Max 50 per tour. N T d

Grade II* listed town house originally planned by Robert and James Adam. Library book shelves designed by Sir John Soane for Philip Yorke in 1781. Interior of the rooms is Adamesque with filigree plasterwork, inset classical paintings and elaborate marble chimney pieces. Former Institute of Psychoanalysis (1951-99). John Johnson 1775. Entry: library, café, fine rooms 1, 2 and 3.
Tube: Oxford Circus, Great Portland Street

Banqueting House
Whitehall SW1A 2ER
- ■ Sat/Sun 10am-5pm. Scaffold tours of current conservation work 10am-3.30pm, pre-book ONLY via Hannah.

37a Leamington Road Villas

Matthews@hrp.org.uk by Friday 4 September 2015. Last entry 4.15pm. Max 500 at one time. R T d

Stunning regal building originally part of Whitehall Palace, one of the first examples of the principles of Palladianism being applied to an English building. Ceiling paintings by Rubens. Inigo Jones 1619. Entry: main hall, undercroft.
Tube: Westminster, Embankment; Tube/Rail: Charing Cross; 3,11,12,24,53,87,88,159

Benjamin Franklin House
36 Craven Street WC2N 5NF
- ■ Sat/Sun 10.30am-4pm. Half-hourly tours, first come basis. First tour 10.30am. Last tour 4pm. Max 15 per tour. T B

Grade I listed Georgian house, the only surviving home of Benjamin Franklin, retaining many original features including central staircase, lathing, C18 panelling, stoves, windows, fittings and beams. 1732/Patrick Dillon Architect (refurb) 2006.
Tube: Embankment; Tube/Rail: Charing Cross; 6,9,11,13,15,23,87,91,139,176

Burlington House
Burlington House, Piccadilly W1J 0BF
- ■ Linnean Society of London Sat 10am-5pm. Last entry 4.30pm. Royal Astronomical Society Sat 10am-5pm. Half-hourly tours (no tours 1-2pm). Tours include Society's library. Royal Society of Chemistry Sat 10am-5pm. Last entry 4.30pm. Society of Antiquaries of London Sat 10am-5pm. Regular 30minute tours, first-come basis. The Geological Society of London Sat 10am-5pm. Hourly guided tours 10am-4pm, early booking advised via receptionist@ geolsoc.org.uk providing name and preferred tour time. Max 20 per tour. D T B C d
- ■ Royal Academy of Arts Sat/Sun 10am-6pm. Talks, tours, family activities (including drawing in the historic RA Schools Life Room) over the weekend. N D R T B C

1660s town-palace, remodelled in Palladian style by Colen Campbell and William Kent for Lord Burlington. The main building is at the northern end of the courtyard and houses the Royal Academy, while five learned societies occupy the two wings on the east and west sides of the courtyard and the Piccadilly wing at the southern end.
Linnean Society of London - Part of the extension to Burlington House to provide accommodation for learned societies. Banks & Barry 1873. Entry: meeting room, 'double cube' library, entrance hall.
Tube: Piccadilly Circus, Green Park; 14,19,22,38
www.linnean.org/openhouse
Royal Academy of Arts - Main Galleries by Sidney Smirke RA and also RA Schools Cast Corridor and studios, the latter added to by Norman Shaw RA. The Sackler Wing of Galleries, with glass stair and lift, by Foster + Partners opened in 1991. Entry:

Key. A Architect on site **B** Bookshop **C** Childrens' activities **d** Some disabled access **D** Full wheelchair access **E** Engineer on site **G** Green Features
N Normally open to the public **P** Parking **Q** Long queues envisaged **R** Refreshments **T** Toilets

Burlington House

Royal Academy Schools, The John Madejski Fine Rooms and all public areas.
Tube: Green Park, Piccadilly Circus; Tube/Rail: Victoria; 9,14,19,22,38
www.royalacademy.org.uk

Royal Astronomical Society - Part of the extension to Burlington House to provide accommodation for learned societies, the home of the Royal Astronomical Society since 1874 with recent refurbishment. Children's science activities am and pm, check website for booking details. Banks & Barry 1874/Peregrine Bryant Associates 2007.
Tube: Piccadilly, Green Park; Tube/Rail: Victoria; 9,14,19,22,38
www.ras.org.uk

Royal Society of Chemistry - Enjoy a fascinating and historical tour around the East Wing of Burlington House, home to the Royal Society of Chemistry. Part of the quadrangle building extension to Burlington House, purpose built for the learned societies. Ground floor restoration by Hugh Broughton Architects. Banks & Barry 1873. Entry: reception, ground floor rooms, first floor rooms including Council Room and Library.
Tube: Green Park, Piccadilly Circus; Tube/Rail: Victoria; 9,14,22,19,38
www.rsc.org

Society of Antiquaries of London - Part of New Burlington House, purpose built in 1875 for learned societies. Historic apartments with highlights from the collection on display. Imposing top-lit library with double galleries and marbled columns. Banks & Barry 1875. Entry: Entrance hall, meeting room, council room, main stairway and library apartments.
Tube: Piccadilly Circus, Green Park; Tube/Rail: Victoria; 9,14,19,22,38
https://www.sal.org.uk/open-house-london/

The Geological Society of London - Part of the extension to Burlington House built to provide accommodation for learned societies. Recent refurbishment by Julian Harrap Architects in 2007. Banks & Barry 1873. Entry: entrance hall, meeting room, galleried libraries, council room.
Tube: Green Park, Piccadilly Circus; Tube/Rail: Victoria; 9,14,19,22,38
www.geolsoc.org.uk

Caledonian Club
9 Halkin Street SW1X 7DR
■ Sun 10am-5pm. Hourly tours. Pre-book ONLY via 020 7333 8712. Last tour 4pm. Max 12 per tour. T d
Built 1908 in Neoclassical style by Detmar Blow for Hugh Morrison (1868-1931), was the last mansion house of its kind to be built in London. The club, founded in 1891, moved to the premises in 1946. Detmar Blow 1908.
Tube: Hyde Park Corner; 38,22,C2,19,73

Canada House
Canadian High Comission, Canada House, Trafalgar Square SW1Y 5BJ
■ Sat/Sun 10am-4pm. Pre-book ONLY via www. unitedkingdom.gc.ca - click 'Visit Canada House' on the right hand side. Security checks will take place before entry. Last tour 3pm. Max 25 per tour.
Canada's diplomatic home in the United Kingdom, the revitalised Canada House serves as a showcase for the very best of Canada in the 21st century. Sir Robert Smirke1823-7/Septimus Warwick(1925 renovations)/Stantec(2014 revitalisation).
Tube: Leicester Square, Embankment; Tube/Rail: Charing Cross; 453,13,15,11,9

Channel Four Television ◉
124 Horseferry Road SW1P 2TX
■ Sat/Sun 10am-1pm. Pre-book ONLY via openhouse@ channel4.co.uk. No studios included in this building. Max 25 per tour. T d
Headquarters building with curving high glass and steel entry atrium. RIBA Award Winner. Richard Rogers Partnership 1994. Entry: reception, walkway, restaurant, drum.
Tube: St James's Park; Tube/Rail: Victoria; 11,24,211

Chelsea College of Arts
16 John Islip Street SW1P 4JU
■ Sat 10am-5pm. N T G d
Located on the site of the former Royal Army Medical College overlooking both the river Thames and Tate Britain. The Grade II listed building was sensitively renovated as a purpose-built art college in 2005. Sustainability features include grass roofs on several buildings. John Henry Townsend Woodd & Wilfred Ainslie 1907/Allies and Morrison (refurb) 2005.
Tube: Pimlico; Tube/Rail: Vauxhall, Victoria; 2,36,88,185,436
http://www.arts.ac.uk/chelsea/

City of Westminster Archives Centre
10 St Ann's Street SW1P 2DE
■ Sat 10am-5pm. Hourly tours from 11am. Last tour 4pm. Max 15 per tour. N D R T B
Modern red brick building purpose-built to house City of Westminster's historic records. Opportunity to visit the conservation studio and strongrooms. Tim Drewitt 1995. Entry: ground floor public library facilities.
Tube: St James's Park; Tube/Rail: Victoria; 11,24,88,211,148

Dazzle Ship
HMS President (1918), Victoria Embankment EC4Y 0HJ
■ Sat/Sun 10am-5pm. Hourly talks and tours with Captain. T
The London Dazzle Ship, HMS President (1918) has been dazzled by German artist Tobias Rehberger as part of 14-18 NOW: the First World War Centenary Art Commissions. This temporary art work takes as its inspiration a style of optical distortion used extensively during the First World War called 'dazzle painting'. Learn more about one of the only three surviving war ships in "below decks" tours and talks.
Tube: Temple; Tube/Rail: Blackfriars; 4,11,15,17,23
www.1418NOW.org.uk

Dover House, Office of the Secretary of State for Scotland
66 Whitehall SW1A 2AU
■ Sun 10am-5pm. Pre-book ONLY via david.mott@scotland office.gsi.gov.uk. Last entry 4pm. Max 25 at one time. D
Elegant Whitehall façade and domed entrance commissioned by the Duke of York. Interesting original interiors. J Paine 1754-8/H Holland 1787. Entry: ministerial rooms.
Tube: Embankment, Westminster; Tube/Rail: Charing Cross; 3,11,12,24,53,87,88,159

Fitzrovia Chapel

Fitzrovia Chapel
Fitzrovia Chapel, Fitzrovia Place, Pearson Square W1T 3JE
■ Sat/Sun 1pm-5pm. T D
The Fitzrovia Chapel is located within the Fitzroy Place development on the site of the former Middlesex Hospital. Open House will provide the first opportunity for the public to view the beautifully restored chapel. John Loughborough Pearson/Frank Pearson 1891/1929.
Tube: Tottenham Court Road, Oxford Circus, Goodge Street
www.fitzroviachapel.co.uk

Foreign & Commonwealth Office
King Charles Street SW1A 2AH
■ Sat/Sun 10am-5pm. Last entry 4.30pm. R T B Q d
Grade I listed Victorian government office buildings. Route includes the magnificent and richly decorated Durbar Court, India Office council chamber, Locarno suite and the Foreign Office grand staircase. Find out more at www.gov. uk/openhousefco. Sir George Gilbert Scott & Matthew Digby Wyatt 1861-1868.
Tube: Westminster; Tube/Rail: Charing Cross, Victoria; 3,11,12,24,53,87,88,159,453

Former Conservative Club (HSBC offices)
78 St James's Street SW1A 1JB
■ Sat 10am-1pm. Timed entry every half hour, pre-book ONLY via 020 7024 1255. Last entry 12.30pm. Max 40 at one time. E T d
Grand and monumental building with rich carvings and spectacular decorated saloon at its heart. Conserved and refurbished to replace 2 wings and provide new glazing to atrium at junction of new and old sites. Grade II* listed. Sidney Smirke & George Basevi 1844/Squire & Partners 2004. Entry: Grade II* listed areas.
Tube: Green Park; Tube/Rail: Charing Cross, Victoria

Gap House ◉◉
28D Monmouth Road W2 4UT
■ Sun 10am-12noon. Half-hourly tours, pre-book ONLY via admin@pitmantozer.com. Last tour 11.30am. Max 10 per tour. A G
Family home with a minimal carbon footprint on a very narrow site (8ft wide), once the side alley and garden of adjacent house. Each room has good natural light whilst fitting in between two listed buildings. Cost effective design methods achieved an environmentally friendly house, utilising amongst many eco-friendly devices ground source heat pump heating and rainwater harvesting. RIBA Manser Medal Winner 2009. Pitman Tozer Architects 2007.
Tube: Bayswater, Queensway; 70,23,7,27,52

10 New Burlington Street

Hallfield Primary School ⊙
Hallfield Estate W2 6HF
■ Sun 2pm-4.30pm. First come basis. School governors and architects on hand to answer questions. A d
1950s masterpiece by the architect of the National Theatre. Richly imaginative, with its sinuous shape defining a precinct. The scale relates to a child's world with curved corridors, dappled by light and surrounded by trees. Two new carefully-scaled classroom buildings were added contributing to the intimate atmosphere of pavilions and gardens. RIBA Award Winner 2006. Drake and Lasdun 1953-4/Caruso St John 2006.
Tube: Bayswater, Queensway, Royal Oak; Tube/Rail: Paddington; 7,23,27,36,70

HM Treasury
1 Horse Guards Road SW1A 2HQ
■ Sat/Sun 10am-5pm. Last entry 4pm. D R T Q
Grade II* listed Government offices, Great George Street constructed 1900-17 in two phases. Refurbishment completed 2002, now occupied by HM Treasury. John Brydon & Sir Henry Tanner 1917/Foster + Partners 2002. Entry: reception, inner courtyard garden, drum.
Tube: Westminster, St James's Park; Tube/Rail: Charing Cross, Victoria; 3,11,12,24,53,87,88,159,211

Home House
19, 20 & 21 Portman Square W1H 6LW
■ Sun 1pm-5pm. Sun tours at 3pm, 4pm, 5pm, pre-book ONLY via openhouse@homehouse.co.uk, confirmation sent by email. Max 12 per tour. D T
Built in 1776 by Wyatt with very fine interiors by Adam. Was the London base of the Countess of Home and is probably the greatest surviving Georgian town house. James Wyatt & Robert Adam 1776. Entry: drawing rooms.
Tube: Marble Arch; Tube/Rail: Paddington; 2,13,82,139,159,390

Hopkins Architects' Office
27 Broadley Terrace NW1 6LG
■ Sat 10am-1pm. First come basis. Current work on display. Last entry 12.45pm. D T A G
The practice's main campus includes two office buildings constructed using its own Patera pre-fabricated system, and linked by a glass reception area and covered walkway. Hopkins Architects 1982. Entry: north building, courtyard.
Tube/Rail: Marylebone; 139,189,205,18,27

Horse Guards
Whitehall SW1A 2AX
■ Sat/Sun 10am-3.30pm. Access only by half hourly tours. Duration 45 mins. Approx waiting time 1.5-2hrs at peak. Last tour 3.30pm. Open House volunteer priority entry not valid. Max 20 at one time. Q

Grade I listed beautifully-detailed Palladian composition at the heart of Whitehall, for a hundred years HQ of the British Army. Duke of Wellington's office as it was c.1842. William Kent 1745-55. Entry: Horse Guards Arch, south side.
Tube: Westminster; Tube/Rail: Charing Cross; 3,11,12,24,53,87,88,91,139,159

Isis Education Centre at The LookOut
Hyde Park (north of the Serpentine, south-west of Speaker's Corner) W2 2UH
■ Sat/Sun 10am-3pm. Hourly tours 12noon-3pm. Max 20 per tour. Nature-based play and crafts. D T C A G
Old meets new at this award-winning eco-friendly building. Sitting proudly on top of a re-instated Victorian reservoir with an Edwardian Reservoir at its entrance, this building emulates the canopy of a tree, blending into its listed surroundings of Hyde Park. Sustainable features include living roof. David Morley Architects 2012. Entry: grounds, main building area.
Tube: Marble Arch, Hyde Park Corner; Tube/Rail: Victoria, Paddington; 10,137,148,16,2,36,414,436,73,74,82,452,52,9

Italian Cultural Institute
39 Belgrave Square SW1X 8NX
■ Sat 10am-5pm. First come basis. N T d
Grade I listed stucco-fronted Belgravia town house. Library extension built 1960s. George Basevi c1825. Entry: reception area, conference room, library, reading room, reception rooms.
Tube: Hyde Park Corner; Tube/Rail: Victoria; 9,16,36,38,52,82

King's College London, Strand Campus
The Strand WC2R 2LS
■ Sat/Sun 1pm-4pm. N D T
King's College London's Grade I listed Strand Campus includes: the Chapel (George Gilbert Scott, 1864); the Archaeology Room, displaying some of the foundations of the original Tudor Somerset House visible through a glass floor; and the Inigo Rooms, Somerset House East Wing, currently exhibiting 'Out of Chaos; Ben Uri: 100 Years in London'. Sir Robert Smirke 1829/Building Design Partnership (BDP) 2004.
Tube: Temple; Tube/Rail: Charing Cross, Waterloo; 1,59,341,243,15

London School of Economics: Saw Swee Hock Student Centre ⊙ ⊗
1 Sheffield Street WC2A 2AP
■ Sat 10am-5pm. Regular tours. Max 12 per tour. T E D R G Q
Home to the LSE Students' Union, this award winning building, shortlisted for the Stirling Prize, has dramatic sculptural form and unusual perforated brick façade achieving BREEAM Outstanding status. O'Donnell + Tuomey 2014.
Tube: Holborn, Temple; Tube/Rail: Charing Cross; 1,168,15,23,26

Marlborough House
Pall Mall SW1Y 5HX
■ Sat 10am-5pm. Last entry 4.30pm. Max 150 at one time. R T d
Originally home of the Dukes of Marlborough, and later of Edward VII and Queen Mary. Now HQ of the Commonwealth Secretariat and Commonwealth Foundation. Sir Christopher Wren 1709-11/Sir James Pennethorne 1861-3. Entry: all fine rooms on ground floor.
Tube: St James's Park, Green Park, Piccadilly; Tube/Rail: Victoria, Charing Cross; 23,12,9,15,159,88,6,38,14,24

Merchant Square Footbridge ⊙
Harbet Road W2 1JS
■ Sat 1pm-5pm. Specific bridge opening times 2pm, 3.30pm, 5pm. N E D T A
The moveable footbridge is raised using hydraulic jacks with an action similar to a traditional Japanese hand fan, forming a unique kinetic sculpture. Knight Architects/AKT II 2014.
Tube: Edgware Road; Tube/Rail: Paddington; 18,332

Methodist Central Hall Westminster
Storey's Gate SW1H 9NH
■ Sun 1.30pm-5pm. Regular tours, first come basis. Music recital 3pm-4pm, historical footage. N D R T B
A masterpiece of Edwardian neo-baroque architecture opposite Westminster Abbey. Great Hall was the venue for the Inaugural General Assembly of the United Nations in 1946. Lanchester & Rickards 1906-1912. Entry: Great Hall, roof balcony, dome, café.
Tube: St James's Park, Westminster; Tube/Rail: Victoria, Waterloo; 11,24,88,159,87,453,148

National Liberal Club
1 Whitehall Place SW1A 2HE
■ Sat/Sun 11am-5pm. Guided tours, pre-book ONLY via secretary@nlc.org.uk. Max 12 per tour. T d
The club's impressive neo-Classical building over the Embankment of the river Thames is the second-largest clubhouse ever built. It was the first London building to incorporate a lift, and the first to be entirely lit throughout by electric lighting. Alfred Waterhouse 1886.
Tube: Embankment; Tube/Rail: Charing Cross

Peabody Avenue ⊙ ⊗
Peabody Avenue SW1V 4AT
■ Sat 10am-1pm. First come basis. D T Q
Victorian social housing estate with striking 200m long avenue. Designated Conservation area. 55 new homes created in 2011 with landscaping and community facility. New design seeks to draw on the scale and material texture of the historic estate. Haworth Tompkins 2011. Entry: community centre, external areas, no entry to flats.
Tube: Victoria, Sloane Square, Pimlico; 360,C10,24,44,452

Pimlico District Heating Undertaking (PDHU) ⊙ ⊗
The Pumphouse, Churchill Gardens Road SW1V 3JF
■ Sat/Sun 10am-5pm. Regular tours, first come basis. Last entry 4.30pm. Max 25 at one time. R T Q d
Churchill Gardens Estate used energy from waste heat from Battersea Power Station when it was functional. The Pumphouse still provides low carbon heating to Pimlico from combined heat and power engines and has the UK's largest thermal store. Powell and Moya 1950.
Tube: Pimlico; Tube/Rail: Victoria; 24,36,137,360,C10
http://www.cwh.org.uk/locations/churchill-gardens/the-pimlico-district-heating-undertaking-pdhu-/

Portcullis House
Victoria Embankment SW1A 0AA
■ Sat 10am-5pm. Last admission to the queue 4pm. Last entry 4.30pm. Max 300 at one time. D R T B Q A
Portcullis House contrasts its imposing façade with a generous light-filled courtyard covered by a glass roof at second level and surrounded by a 2-storey cloister. Extensive collection of parliamentary portraiture from Gilray to Scarfe. RIBA Award Winner. Hopkins Architects 2001. Entry: ground floor courtyard and 1st floor. Entry to Portcullis House only via main entrance on Victoria Embankment.
Tube: Westminster; Tube/Rail: Charing Cross; 3,11,12,24,53,87,88,159,211

Reform Club
104 Pall Mall SW1Y 5EW
■ Sat 10am-5pm/Sun 10am-3pm. Pre-book ONLY via paul.austin@reformclub.com. NB. Regret no children under 12 admitted. Max 15 per tour. N E G d
Built as a Whig gentleman's club and inspired by Italian Renaissance palaces. Lobby leads to an enclosed colonnaded courtyard with complementary glazed roof and tessellated

Key. A Architect on site **B** Bookshop **C** Children's activities **d** Some disabled access **D** Full wheelchair access **E** Engineer on site **G** Green Features
N Normally open to the public **P** Parking **Q** Long queues envisaged **R** Refreshments **T** Toilets

floor. Tunnelled staircase leads to upper floor. Sir Charles Barry 1841. Entry: ground & 1st floor principal public rooms.
Tube: Piccadilly Circus; Tube/Rail: Charing Cross

Regent Street Cinema
309 Regent Street W1B 2UW
■ Sun 10am-1pm. Guided tours, first come basis.
Built as a theatre for optical demonstrations as part of the Royal Polytechnic, the Lumière brothers showed the first film to a British Audience here. Now part of University of Westminster, it has been re-opened as a 250-seat public cinema and heritage destination which connects its rich history with current cinema production. Tim Ronalds Architects 2015.
Tube: Oxford Circus

RIBA
66 Portland Place W1B 1AD
■ Sun 10am-5pm. Guided tours of RIBA's stunning art deco headquarters 11.30am, 3.30pm (first come basis, max 20 per tour). Free entry to Palladian exhibition all day with curator-led tours 12.30pm, 2.30pm (first come basis, max 20 per tour). Original drawings, models and photographs from unrivalled collection of architectural objects, including Open House favourites (drop in 11am-4pm). Max 20 per tour. N R T B C d
Fine example of Grade II* listed 1930s architecture with many original features and fittings. Grey Wornum 1932-4. Entry: council chamber, Aston Webb room, Jarvis hall, Lutyens room, Christopher Wren room, British Architectural Library and all public areas. Children's activities: design your own city scape, make your own London Skyline hat, create a button badge and scale up the city! Drop in 11am-4pm.
Tube: Great Portland Street, Oxford Circus, Regent's Park; 88, C2, 453

Romanian Cultural Institute
1 Belgrave Square SW1X 8PH
■ Sat/Sun 10am-5pm. Last entry 4.30pm. N D T
Situated in one of the grandest and largest C19 squares in London, 1 Belgrave Square was acquired by Romania in 1936 and is now home to the Romanian Cultural Institute. Thomas Cubitt 1828. Entry: ground and first floors.
Tube/Rail: Victoria; Tube: Hyde Park Corner; C2, 2, 9, 14, 82, 137, 148, 73, 436

'Roman' Bath
5 Strand Lane (access via Surrey Street steps) WC2R 2NA
■ Sat/Sun 10am-5pm. First come basis, queuing outside if necessary. Last entry 4.30pm. N E G d
A plunge bath, popularly known as the 'Roman' bath, originally a C17 feeder cistern for a grotto-fountain at the old Somerset House. The brick-lined, spring-fed pool is located in a vault below a C19 building. Literary associations with Dickens, whose character David Copperfield takes regular plunges there. 1612.
Tube: Temple; Tube/Rail: Charing Cross; Rail: Blackfriars; 4, 9, 15, 91, 168

ROOM by Antony Gormley
The Beaumont, Brown Hart Gardens W1K 6TF
■ Sat 1pm-5pm. Tours every 30mins, pre-book ONLY via https://goo.gl/3d4oFl. Last entry 4.30pm. Max 6 per tour. R T d
ROOM is a monumental, inhabitable sculpture by Antony Gormley on the listed façade of The Beaumont Hotel. The interior is as important as its exterior: a giant crouching cuboid figure based on the artist's body. Antony Gormley/Reardon Smith 2014.
Tube: Bond Street; 6, 10, 15, 23, 73

Royal Albert Hall
Kensington Gore SW7 2AP (Entry via door 12)
■ Sat 10am-3pm. First come basis, self-guided tours. Entrance times may be staggered when demand is high. N D R T G d
One of Britain's most iconic buildings, the Royal Albert Hall was designed by Royal Engineers Captain Francis Fowkes & General Henry Scott. Completed in 1871 and now a Grade I listed building, it hosts over 370 main events every year including a full range of music, sport and films. Captain Fowkes & General Scott 1871.
Tube: South Kensington, Gloucester Road, High St Kensington; Tube/Rail: Victoria; 9, 10, 52, 360, 452

Royal College of Nursing
20 Cavendish Square W1G 0RN
■ Sat 10am-5pm. First come basis, queuing outside if necessary. Regular tours of period rooms. Last tour 4pm. N D R T B
A cleverly integrated mixture of architectural styles and periods, incorporating a late 1720s house with rare and Baroque painted staircase and the purpose-built College of Nursing (1926). George Greaves 1729/Sir Edwin Cooper 1921/EPR Architects 2001/Bisset Adams Architects 2013. Entry: Library and Heritage Centre, painted staircase, 1720s rooms, Cowdray Hall, glass walkways only accessible on guided tours.
Tube: Oxford Circus; 3, 12, 25, 55, 73

Royal Courts of Justice
Strand WC2A 2LL
■ Sat 10am-4pm. Activities and displays until 3.30pm, doors close promptly at 4pm. NB. Any knives brought in will be confiscated. N R T C d
Street's masterpiece and one of Victorian London's great public buildings. C13 Gothic given a Victorian interpretation. G E Street 1874-82. Entry: main hall, selected courts, cells and areas of interest. Children's tours.
Tube: Temple, Holborn, Chancery Lane; Tube/Rail: Waterloo, Charing Cross; 4, 11, 15, 23, 26, 76, 172, 341

Royal Geographical Society (with IBG)
1 Kensington Gore (Exhibition Road entrance) SW7 2AR
■ Sat 10am-5pm. Pavilion exhibition and self-guided tours. N R T B d
Originally a private home in R Norman Shaw's Queen Anne style, with later additions for the Society. Richard Norman Shaw 1874/Kennedy and Nightingale 1930/Studio Downie 2001-4. Entry: pavilion, Stanfords travel bookshop, Ondaatje Theatre, Council room, Map room, education centre, Lowther room, Members' Room, terrace and garden.
Tube: South Kensington; Tube/Rail: Paddington, Victoria; 9, 10, 52, 452

Royal Institution of Chartered Surveyors
12 Great George Street, Parliament Square SW1 3AD
■ Sat 10am-5pm. Regular tours covering building highlights. Max 25 at any one time. R T
Historic grade II listed gabled Victorian building purpose built for the RICS in Franco-Flemish style. Only surviving Victorian building in the street. Alfred Waterhouse 1899. Entry: ground, 1st floor, 5th floor suite & terrace.
Tube: Westminster; Tube/Rail: Victoria, Waterloo; 11, 12, 24, 148, 211

Royal Over-Seas League
Park Place, St James's Street SW1A 1LR
■ Sat/Sun 10.30am-2.30pm. Sat/Sun tours 10.30am, 12noon, 2.30pm, pre-book ONLY via gmatthews@rosl.org.uk or 0207 408 0214 ext 204. Max 20 per tour. T
Over-Seas House is an amalgamation of two Grade I listed houses – Rutland House (James Gibbs, 1736) and Vernon House

Two Temple Place

(1835 rebuilt 1905). It is now the International Headquarters of the Royal Over-Seas League. James Gibbs 1736/1905. Entry: period style function rooms.
Tube: Green Park; Tube/Rail: Victoria; C2, 9, 14, 19, 22, 38
www.rosl.org.uk

Serpentine Gallery Pavilion ⊙
Kensington Gardens W2 3XA
■ Sat/Sun 10am-6pm. Last entry 5.45pm. Max 200 at one time. N D R T B
Amorphous, double-skinned, polygonal structure consisting of translucent, multi-coloured fabric membrane (EFTE), woven through and wrapped in webbing. With 'secret corridor' and a brilliant, stained glass-effect interior. SelgasCano 2015.
Tube: South Kensington, Lancaster Gate; 9, 10, 52, 94, 148

Soho Green – Art Loo
St Anne's Churchyard, Wardour Street W1D 6BA
■ Sat 11am-3pm. First come basis. A G d
A treasure trove of a toilet – an egg shaped capsule in oak with etched glass hinting at the bodies buried below; an homage to the history of Soho within. Steven Johnson 2007.
Tube: Piccadilly Circus; Tube/Rail: Charing Cross; 38, 19, 23, 6, 14

Somerset House
Strand WC2R 1LA
■ Sat/Sun 12.15pm, 1.15pm, 2.15pm, 3.15pm various behind the scenes tours exploring the recently opened New Wing and other areas of the building not usually accessible to the public. Max 20 per tour. N D R T B
Grade I listed restored building of five wings, four of which surround large courtyard. Construction began in 1775. New Wing, overlooking Waterloo Bridge, dates from 1850 by Sir James Pennethorne. Sir William Chambers 1775-86/Dixon Jones 2001. Entry: tours will visit a selection from Nelson Stair, Seamen's Waiting Hall, King's Barge House, Dead House, New Wing and West Wing.
Tube: Embankment, Covent Garden, Temple; Tube/Rail: Charing Cross, Waterloo; 6, 9, 11, 13, 15, 23, 87, 91, 176

St Barnabas Church
St Barnabas Street SW1W 8PF
■ Sat 10am-5pm/Sun 1pm-5pm. Regular tours, first come basis. Last entry 4.45pm. N R T d
Church in Early English style, full of Pre-Raphaelite decoration. Important works by Bodley, Comper and Cundy and windows by Kempe and Tower. First Oxford Movement church. Recently restored 10 bell peal; bell ringing quarter peal Sat 2pm-3pm. Thomas Cundy 1850. Entry: church, crypt.
Tube: Sloane Square; Tube/Rail: Victoria; 11, 211, 170, C10

St John's Smith Square
Smith Square SW1P 3HA
- Sat 10am-5pm/Sun 10am-1pm. N D R T P

Rare example of Thomas Archer's work and a masterpiece of English Baroque style, this was originally dubbed Queen Anne's Footstool. Following extensive bombing damage to original building, restoration by Marshall Sisson took place in 1965. Now a concert venue. Thomas Archer 1714-28/Marshall Sisson 1965-68. Entry: church, crypt.
Tube: Westminster; Tube/Rail: Victoria, Charing Cross, Waterloo; 3,87,88

Studio McLeod
320 Kilburn Lane W9 3EF
- Sat/Sun 10am-5pm. Regular tours. Last entry 4.50pm. T A

Architect's studio and family home with curved oak panelled walls, grass terrace and a sliding staircase hiding a motorcycle. Exhibiting selected projects. Studio McLeod 2015. Entry: studio, first floor, terrace.
Tube/Rail: Queens Park; 6,36,187,316,206

The British Academy
10-11 Carlton House Terrace SW1Y 5AH
- Sun 10am-5pm. Hourly tours, first come basis. Last tour 4pm. Max 15 per tour. D T

Grade I listed Nash-designed terraced houses described as one of London's finest Georgian treasures. Interiors in No.10 by Bonomi later altered by Billery and Blow in 1905-07; No.11 interiors by Pennethorne, Nash's pupil. The British Academy, the UK's national body for the promotion of the humanities and social sciences moved to the building in 1998. 2010 refurbishment includes state of the art auditorium. John Nash 1833/Feilden & Mawson 2010. Entry: ground, first floor rooms.
Tube: Piccadilly Circus; Tube/Rail: Charing Cross; 11,24,29,87,91

The College of Optometrists
42 Craven Street WC2N 5NG
- Sun 1pm-5pm. Last entry 4.45pm. Max 50 at one time. T B d

HQ of professional and examining body for UK optometrists occupying two terraced houses, no. 41 (Flitcroft c1730 with later additions) and no. 42 (rebuilt by Tarmac plc, c1989). Henry Flitcroft c1730. Entry: Council room, Panelled room, Sutcliffe room, Print room, Giles room, Library.
Tube: Embankment; Tube/Rail: Charing Cross; 3,6,11,12,24

The House of St Barnabas
1 Greek Street, Soho Square W1D 4NQ
- Sun 10am-5pm. Hourly tours. Pre-book ONLY via www. hosb.org.uk. Questions to mary@hosb.org.uk. Last tour 4pm. R T

Soho's grandest Grade I listed Georgian townhouse. Fine Roccoco plasterwork commissioned 1754. Victorian Oxford Movement Chapel built 1862 by Joseph Clarke. Owned by charity supporting the homeless back into the workplace. House: Joseph Pearce 1746. Entry: house, private members club, chapel, gardens.
Tube: Tottenham Court Road, Leicester Square; Tube/Rail: Charing Cross; 14,19,24,29,38,176

The London Library
14 St James's Square SW1Y 4LG
- Sat 10am-5pm. Hourly tours. Pre-book ONLY via 020 7766 4704. Last tour 4pm. Max 20 per tour. T d

The world's largest independent lending library, housing 1 million books in atmospheric Victorian cast-iron bookstacks. Elegant reading room that has been home to generations of literary London. A labyrinth of disparate buildings have been recently remodelled and restored. Features include an award-winning lightwell over a newly created reading room and

contemporary but sensitive finishes. James Osborne Smith 1896-8/Haworth Tompkins 2010. Entry: bookstacks, reading room, art room, main hall. NB. Many stairs. Please wear flat shoes due to grille flooring.
Tube: Piccadilly Circus, Green Park; Tube/Rail: Charing Cross; 9,14,19,22,38

The Queen's Chapel (St James's Palace)
St James's Palace, Marlborough Road, SW1A 1BG
- Sat/Sun 10am-5pm. Pre-book ONLY via tickets. royalcollection.org.uk/queens-chapel. Last entry 4pm. D

The first Palladian style post-Reformation Church in England and private Chapel of Charles I's bride Henrietta Maria; later extensively refurbished by Sir Christopher Wren in 1682-3. It is one of the facilities of the British monarch's personal religious establishment, the Chapel Royal. Inigo Jones 1623.
Tube: Green Park, St James's Park; Rail: Victoria; 9,14,19,22,38,C2

The Royal Society
6-9 Carlton House Terrace SW1Y 5AG
- Sat 10am-6pm/Sun 12pm-5pm. Tours every 20 mins, first come basis. Max 15 per tour. D T

Grade I listed Nash-designed town houses, refurbished in the 1890s before conversion into the German Embassy. 2004 refurbishment provided additional facilities for the home of the UK's national science academy. Nash 1828/Speer 1930s/ William Holford & Partners 1960s/Burrell Foley Fischer 2004. Entry: lecture theatres, reception rooms, library.
Tube: Piccadilly Circus; Tube/Rail: Charing Cross; 29,91,24,9,6,13

The UK Supreme Court (formerly the Middlesex Guildhall)
Parliament Square SW1P 3BD
- Sat/Sun 9.30am-4.30pm. Queue likely to close at 4pm. Last entry strictly 4.30pm. N D R T Q C

Sensitive refurbishment of this neo-gothic Grade II* listed building enhances the historic fabric whilst reversing more recent adaptations that had left it feeling gloomy. The north and south light wells were cleared bringing light back into the building, improved orientation, and greatly enhanced the appearance of original features such as stained glass windows, wood panelling and ornate ceilings. J S Gibson 1913/ Feilden + Mawson 2009. Entry: courts, library, reception area, lobbies, exhibition, café.
Tube: Westminster, St James's Park; Tube/Rail: Victoria, Charing Cross; 11,24,29,88,159

Two Temple Place
2 Temple Place WC2R 3BD
- Sun 10am-5pm. Call in advance for disabled access. T B d

Finished in 1895 for the first Viscount Astor, William Waldorf Astor, to the elaborate architectural specifications of John Loughborough Pearson. The house sits on reclaimed land overlooking the River Thames, it embodies much of the outstanding workmanship and architecture of the late Victorian period. J L Pearson 1895. Entry: main part of house.
Tube: Temple; Tube/Rail: Charing Cross, Waterloo; 6,9,13,87,139

Western Pumping Station
124 Grosvenor Road SW1V 4BE
- Sat/Sun tours at 10am, 11am, 12noon, 2pm, 3pm. Pre-book ONLY via londonopenhouse@thameswater.co.uk, clearly marking the subject 'WESTERN'. Please do not turn up without pre-booking. Max 20 per tour. E

View the 52m high Italianate chimney and 22m high pump house with ornate mansard roof, built to house 4 beam engines. The steam engines were replaced by diesel in 1936. Charles Driver (attrib.) 1873.
Tube: Sloane Square; Rail: Battersea Park; 44,137,360,452

Westminster Hall
House of Commons (Cromwell Green entrance) SW1A 0AA
- Sun 10am-5pm. Last admission to the queue 4.00pm. Last entry 4.30pm. Max 300 at one time. R T Q d

One of the finest and largest Medieval halls in Europe with a magnificent hammerbeam ceiling. Work began in 1097. The architect for the C14 rebuilding was Henry Yevele, with Hugh Herland who designed the roof. Henry Yevele C14.
Tube: Westminster; Tube/Rail: Victoria, Charing Cross, Waterloo; 11,87,12,53,24,109,159

Wigmore Hall
36 Wigmore Street W1U 2BP
- Sat 10.30am-3pm. Live music from the stage and the chance to explore backstage. Creative music workshops for children and families at 10.45am, 11.45am, 1pm, 2pm. R T C

Refurbished in 2004, sumptuous auditorium with famous Art Nouveau mural. Thomas E Collcutt 1901. Entry: auditorium, Bechstein room, Green Room, backstage.
Tube: Bond Street, Oxford Circus

WALKS/TOURS

Creative Church Street
The Cockpit, Gateforth Street, NW8 8EH
- Sat 10am-5pm. Regular 15-20 minute tours, first come basis. Talks and displays at Alfie's Antique Market, Showroom Gallery, Penfold Community Hub, Cockpit Theatre and more. Last entry 4pm. R T C G d

Discover this vibrant global crossroads and the communities that shape the neighbourhood. Includes six listed buildings, notable C19-21 architecture, public art and community garden.
Tube: Edgware Road; Tube/Rail: Marylebone, Paddington; 6,18,27,139,205

Leicester Square
- Meet: Sun 11am at Leicester Square Gardens WC2H 7NA Tour duration 1 hour. N D T A

The design is based on the creation of a coherent city block and includes intrinsic landscape qualities of a London square with contemporary and unique design features found nowhere else in the UK. Burns + Nice 2012.
Tube: Leicester Square; Tube/Rail: Charing Cross; 24,12,38,29,176

PRE-EVENT

One Great George Street – Institution of Civil Engineers
One Great George Street SW1P 3AA
Friday 18th Sept tours at 2pm, 3pm and 4pm led by ICE archivist, pre-book ONLY via www.ice.org.uk/london. Duration 1 hour. Max 30 per tour. E D R T
Grade II* listed HQ building of the world's premier engineering institution, the first of its kind. Fine example of Edwardian architecture. James Miller 1913.
Tube: Westminster, St James's Park; Tube/Rail: Charing Cross; 3,11,12,24,53,87,88,91,139,159

Supported by

City of Westminster

Key. A Architect on site **B** Bookshop **C** Childrens' activities **d** Some disabled access **D** Full wheelchair access **E** Engineer on site **G** Green Features
N Normally open to the public **P** Parking **Q** Long queues envisaged **R** Refreshments **T** Toilets

Programme index

Listed here are special events, and buildings by type. The website search facility at openhouselondon.org.uk/london enables you to use different criteria such as location, architect and period, as well as additional special activities taking place.

Get the app

Use the **app** to store your favourites in advance, find 'buildings nearby me' and get what's new this year

Please help keep Open House weekend free for all Text CITY23 £3 to 70070

Come and see where the champions stayed, the former Athletes' Village

Sunday 20th Sept

Book your place on the
Open House London tour of East Village
GetLivingLondon.com/openhouse

east village
london E20

Brought to you by

GET
LIVING
LONDON

Take part in our event survey and be in with a chance to win tea for two at the Gherkin

About the event:
Did Open House London make you think differently about the architecture of your local area? **Yes / No** If yes, how?

_____

Have you learned more about the role of engineers, landscape architects and housing associations from the weekend?

☐ Engineers ☐ Landscape architects ☐ Housing associations

How important is Open House London in engaging you with the city's architecture?

☐ Essential ☐ Very important ☐ Important ☐ Not important ☐ Don't know

Tell us what your priorities are for the future shape of London to inform the upcoming mayoral election at **open-city.org.uk/futurelondon**

Please tell us about you:
Where did you originally see or hear about Open House London this year?
Please circle all that apply:
OHL website   Open-City/Open House newsletter   Open House flyer   other website/newsletter   magazine/newspaper   local library   Radio/TV   Robert Elms Show   Leaflet/poster   Transport advertising   word of mouth   Facebook   Twitter   Instagram

How many times have you taken part in Open House London?

☐ 1 ☐ 2–5 ☐ more than 5

What were your reasons for taking part? **Leisure / Professional / Both**

Where did you obtain this guide?

_____

Are you willing to be contacted by us in future for a more detailed research exercise?
Yes / No

Do you want to receive our free enewsletter. If yes, please tick here ☐
DETAILS (please complete for survey, enewsletter and purchases):

Name:

Address:

London Borough or County: Postcode:

E-mail:

Tel:

Nationality   Occupation

Age   Gender

Order next year's Open House London guide

I would like to order the following: Cost

1 **Annual Open House London Event Programme**
17 & 18 September 2016 Event (published August 2016).   £8.50 (incl p&p)

2 **Open House London: An Exclusive Insight into 100 Architecturally Inspiring Buildings in London (2012)**
The first hardback illustrated book on Open House London, celebrating its 20th anniversary.
Published by Ebury Press.   £23.30 (incl p&p)

3 **Mapguide to Contemporary Architecture (2014 edition)**
A map of 270 contemporary London buildings with details of address, architect & year.   £3.95 (incl p&p)

4 **London's Contemporary Architecture: A Visitor's Guide** Ken Allinson & Victoria Thornton – full colour, 6th edition, 2014. Map-based guide to London's new buildings.   £23.95 (incl p&p)
£

Sub Total

Donation to support and sustain Open-City's education programmes for young Londoners   £

TOTAL

GIFT AID Please tick here ☐   **Signature**
(Gift Aid is a simple scheme that enables charities to reclaim the tax you pay on your donations at no extra cost to you. **Please provide address below left and sign above.** You must pay tax at least equal to the tax that we will reclaim on your donation.)

The charity's education initiatives are funded solely through individuals, companies, grants and trusts donations
Registered Charity No.1072104

METHOD OF PAYMENT (if making a purchase above):

Cheque: £_____   (made payable to Open-City)

Credit card details:

I authorise Open-City to charge £_____ to my *VISA/MASTERCARD/SWITCH/DELTA (*delete as appropriate) SORRY NO AMEX

No. ☐☐☐☐ ☐☐☐☐ ☐☐☐☐ ☐☐☐☐

Expiry date_____ Issue date_____

Issue Number (Switch/Delta only) _____

Date: _____

Visit open-city.org.uk/shop for more books and products
Find us on Facebook and Twitter @openhouselondon

Tear out page and send to:
FREEPOST RRXR-UBCB-ZKYC, Open House, 18 Ensign Street, London E1 8JD